NEUTRON DETECTION

NEUTRON
DETECTION

by

W. D. ALLEN, B.Sc., D.Phil.

**Atomic Energy Research Establishment,
Harwell, England**

PHILOSOPHICAL LIBRARY INC.
15 EAST FORTIETH STREET
NEW YORK 16, N.Y.

© W. D. ALLEN Great Britain 1960

Published 1960 by Philosophical Library, Inc.
15 East 40th Street, New York 16, N.Y.

MADE AND PRINTED IN GREAT BRITAIN FOR PHILOSOPHICAL LIBRARY BY
WILLIAM CLOWES AND SONS, LIMITED, LONDON AND BECCLES

PREFACE

This book is addressed to those who, with some background knowledge of nuclear physics and particle detectors, require a more detailed knowledge of the main methods of neutron detection. The chief difficulty in writing the book has been to know what background knowledge can reasonably be assumed. If one assumes too little, then the book becomes unbalanced by the inclusion of lengthy and detailed accounts of nuclear physics and detection methods which are adequately dealt with elsewhere. If, however, an extensive knowledge is assumed, the less experienced reader is left behind at the beginning, while for the expert the scope of the book does not permit sufficient detail in any one of the particular fields of neutron detection. I have, therefore, attempted a middle course. For the less experienced reader, I have in Chapter 1 and parts of Chapter 3 briefly summarised the necessary elements of nuclear physics and particle detection: and, in general, I have described in detail those methods and techniques which I consider important, and have mentioned only in passing or in the bibliography many others. For the expert, the scope of the book is not sufficient to permit detailed discussion of every aspect of neutron detection: the bibliography and the appendices may perhaps prove useful.

The neutron energy range above 20 MeV is barely touched on, except by occasional illustration of extension of techniques established for neutrons of energy less than 20 MeV. The subject matter covers material available up to the end of 1957 : a limited attempt has been made to include in the bibliography references up to the end of 1959.

I am much indebted to Professor H. H. Barschall for a reprint of his article on the subject in the *Encyclopaedia of Physics*, Vol. XLV; I have retained his general outline, while differing in emphasis and detail. I am also indebted to Professor O. R. Frisch, Dr. E. Bretscher, Mr. F. D. Brooks and Mr. G. W. K. Ford for individual comments : and in particular to Dr. J. F. Raffle for extensive comment and criticism.

W. D. ALLEN

v

CONTENTS

Chapter 1 INTRODUCTION

1.1 Historical   1

1.2 The elementary principles of neutron detection   5
    1.2.1 Nuclear constitution
    1.2.2 Interactions of neutrons with nuclei
    1.2.3 Particle detection

1.3 Neutron sources and neutron detectors   11
    1.3.1 The neutron energy range 10 keV to 20 MeV
    1.3.2 Slow neutrons
    1.3.3 Radioactive neutron sources

Chapter 2 REACTIONS USED IN NEUTRON DETECTION

2.1 The (n,p) and similar reactions   17
    2.1.1 Kinematics
    2.1.2 Cross sections
    2.1.3 Range-energy relation

2.2 The $B^{10}(n,\alpha)Li^7$ reaction   24

2.3 Other neutron-induced reactions: exoergic reactions   26
    2.3.1 Charged particle reactions
    2.3.2 Fission
    2.3.3 Radiative capture
    2.3.4 The Szilard-Chalmers process

2.4 Other neutron-induced reactions: endoergic reactions: threshold detectors   36

Chapter 3 THE CHIEF INSTRUMENTS OF NEUTRON DETECTION

3.1 The ionisation chamber   41
    3.1.1 (a) The behaviour of free ions and electrons in gases
       (b) Saturation
    3.1.2 The induction effect
    3.1.3 Some practical ionisation chambers

3.2 Proportional counters   62
    The BF_3 counter: time delays

3.3 The scintillation counter   72
    3.3.1 The principles of scintillator detection
    3.3.2 Organic scintillators as neutron detectors

3.3.3   Inorganic scintillators
3.3.4   Miscellaneous scintillation techniques

3.4   Neutron detection by nuclear emulsions
3.4.1   Photographic plates
3.4.2   Neutron radiography

3.5   Miscellaneous other methods
Cloud chambers: neutron thermopiles

Chapter 4   APPLICATIONS OF NEUTRON DETECTORS

4.1   Measurement of relative intensity: shielding and
collimation   107

4.2   Measurement of fast neutron flux   113

4.3   Neutron spectrometry   127

4.4   Time of flight spectrometry   136

4.5   Slow neutron flux measurements   145
4.5.1   Introduction
4.5.2   Relative measurements
4.5.3   Absolute determination of thermal flux
4.5.4   Flux distortion and depression

4.6   Neutron detectors in health monitoring   159

Chapter 5   NEUTRON STANDARDS

5.1   Radioactive neutron sources   166

5.2   Source calibration   170
5.2.1   Relative source calibrations
5.2.2   Absolute source calibration
5.2.3   Intercomparison of source strength measurements

5.3   Fundamental neutron cross sections   185
5.3.1   Neutron-proton cross sections
5.3.2   Other thermal cross sections: B, Au, U^{235}

Appendices   I to XII   191

Bibliography   226

Index   253

References and Bibliography
(Author's note)

References are given as footnotes and numbered. They are also collected together at the end, in the reference index and bibliography, under chapter and section headings, with the number as in the text. Also under the same headings are other relevant references not specifically alluded to in the text. Each section, therefore, has its own collection of references, which, although not exhaustive, should serve as a guide to the main articles on the subject.

LIST OF PLATES

(Between pages 96 and 97)

I. INTERIOR OF THE PARTIALLY ASSEMBLED DETECTOR TANK OF A LARGE LIQUID SCINTILLATOR.

II. VIEW OF A TUBE BANK OF 55 MULTIPLIERS ON ONE END OF A LARGE LIQUID SCINTILLATOR.

III. NEUTRON RADIOGRAPH OF A WAXED STRING IN A BLOCK OF LEAD 2 IN. THICK.

IV. NEUTRON RADIOGRAPH OF PLANT TISSUES.

I

INTRODUCTION

I.I. Historical

The remarkable developments during the war and in the post-war decade in nuclear energy, for both civil and military purposes, have focused attention on the neutron, not only as a fundamental particle of pure physics but as an important element in modern engineering technology. In this book we shall give an account of the main methods by which neutrons are detected. Many books have been written on nuclear physics, on neutron physics and on particle detectors, in all of which neutron detection is referred to in passing. Here neutron detection is the main theme, and aspects of nuclear physics, neutron physics and particle detection will be briefly summarised where relevant. In this chapter we shall concern ourselves with a brief account of the basic nuclear physics involved in neutron detection and of the main types of neutron source with which experiments and measurements are made.

It may be of interest if we begin with an account of some of the early experiments in neutron physics and neutron detection, since many of the properties of neutrons, now taken for granted, were originally established by experiments which were both simple and elegant. Before 1930, the only penetrating radiation known was gamma radiation, and it was assumed that the harder the gamma rays the greater the penetration. In 1930, Bothe and Becker[1] reported that when light elements such as lithium, beryllium or boron were bombarded with alpha particles from polonium, a very penetrating radiation was obtained, i.e. the absorption in lead was very small. Their

---

(1) *Zeit. für Phys.* **66**, 289 (1930).

original explanation was that this was due to gamma rays of 7–15 MeV energy, a conclusion which was reinforced by their failure to observe cloud chamber tracks corresponding to the radiation.

The problem was further attacked by Curie and Joliot[2] (1932), who used ionisation chambers as detectors. In particular, they found that when the chamber wall nearest the source had an inner lining of hydrogenous material, a large increase in current was observed. Both ionisation chamber and cloud chamber studies showed that this increase was due to protons recoiling from the hydrogenous material. The cloud chamber investigation showed that the maximum proton energy was 5 MeV.

Curie and Joliot explained these phenomena by postulating that the assumed gamma rays had energies of 50 MeV. Soon after, Chadwick[3] measured carefully the recoil energies observed when an ionisation chamber, as in the Curie-Joliot experiment, had an inner wax lining. By using aluminium absorbers, he showed that the maximum recoil energy was 5·7 MeV. In a companion paper, Feather showed that tracks in a nitrogen-filled cloud chamber corresponded to nuclei recoiling with a maximum energy of 1·2 MeV. Chadwick showed that there were many reasons for rejecting the gamma ray hypothesis. Thus, gamma rays of energy as far apart as 55 MeV and 90 MeV would be required; the cross sections involved in the reaction, and the very high energies required for the gamma rays, were improbable, and so on. By assuming that the penetrating radiation was due to a neutral particle, of mass nearly equal to the proton, Chadwick showed that these difficulties were avoided and that all the facts fell neatly into place. Thus, as is shown in Chapter 2, a neutron can in a head-on collision deliver its full energy to the proton, but only a fraction of its energy to the heavier nitrogen nucleus. A first approximation to the mass of the neutron came from a comparison of the maximum recoil energies in hydrogen and nitrogen. A more accurate figure came from a study of the energy balance in the $B^{11}(\alpha,n)N^{14}$ reaction, which gave a mass

(2). *Comptes Rendus*, **194**, 273 (1932).
(3). *Proc. Roy. Soc.* **A.-136**, 692 (1932).

of 1·0067 for the neutron, which is impressively close to the modern figure of 1·00897.

The first evidence of nuclear disintegration by neutrons was given in 1932 by Feather,[4] whose cloud chamber photographs demonstrated the disintegration of nitrogen. The photo-disintegration of beryllium was discovered by Szilard and Chalmers[5] in 1934, and of the deuteron by Chadwick and Goldhaber.[6] The field of slow neutrons was explored by Fermi[7] and his collaborators, who showed in 1934 that many materials became radioactive when bombarded with neutrons. This radioactivity was greatly enhanced in the case of some elements when the neutron source was surrounded with paraffin wax, a fact that suggested that absorption was much more marked for slow neutrons, probably those which had reached thermal equilibrium with the protons in the paraffin wax. This was confirmed by Moon and Tillman,[8] who showed that the temperature of the wax had a marked influence on the capture of slow neutrons by various elements. The elements showing high absorption were not confined to any particular section of the periodic table. Using counters containing boron, rather than radioactive detectors, Dunning[9] and his collaborators showed that the very large cross sections occurring in particular elements were due to absorption, not scattering. In 1936, Amaldi and Fermi[10] in Rome, and Szilard[11] in Oxford, showed that the differences between elements as regards slow neutron absorption became much more pronounced if the neutrons were filtered through cadmium. It was concluded that part of the slow neutron energy spectrum was absorbed by all elements (and particularly strongly by cadmium), while in addition particular elements strongly absorbed different parts of the spectrum. Since cadmium absorption was unaffected by changing the tempera-

(4). *Proc. Roy. Soc.* **A.-136,** 709 (1933).
(5). *Nature,* **134,** 494 (1934).
(6). *Nature,* **134,** 237 (1934).
(7). *Nuov. Cim.* **12,** 201 (1935).
(8). *Proc. Roy. Soc.* **A.-153,** 475 (1936).
(9). *Phys. Rev.* **48,** 265 (1935).
(10). *Phys. Rev.* **50,** 899 (1936).
(11). *Nature,* **136,** 950 (1936).

ture of the slow neutron source, it was concluded that the absorption band of cadmium must cover the thermal region of velocities. It was also shown that the absorption shown by particular elements for particular neutron groups was unexpectedly large. For example, when the slow neutron source was cadmium filtered, and silver was used as a detector, the absorption curve for silver was very high.

By comparing the absorption of different elements with different detectors, these "resonance" absorption bands were divided into groups. The first classification of these groups in order of increasing energy was carried out by Amaldi and Fermi, who studied the spatial distribution of neutrons round a Ra-α-Be source immersed in water, using different detectors. If the resonance energy of one detector was low, many neutron-proton collisions were required to reduce the initial energy to the resonance energy, and the peak of the distribution would be (relatively) far from the source. If the resonance energy were high, the peak would be nearer the source. The classification of Amaldi and Fermi was confirmed by the determination of the absorption in boron or lithium of these neutron groups. The absorption in these elements was expected to vary with neutron velocity as $1/v$, and the experiment confirmed the classification of Amaldi and Fermi. By comparing the absorption with the absorption of neutrons of the cadmium group, a specific energy to the resonances concerned was assigned.

From the point of view of neutron detection, the detectors in vogue from 1932 to 1938 differed considerably from their modern counterparts. The scintillation counter and the photographic plate were virtually unknown. Fast neutrons were detected with ionisation chambers or cloud chambers, although threshold detectors such as phosphorus were sometimes used. For slow neutrons, much of the early work was done, as the above account suggests, with radioactive detectors, although the advantages in using the $B^{10}(n,\alpha)Li^7$ reaction in ionisation chambers lined with boron, or counters filled with BF_3 gas, were early recognised. The first mechanical chopper to be used as a spectrometer was reported in 1935, but it was not till 1938 that a pulsed accelerator was described as a time-of-flight spectrometer.

Many of the crucial experiments were conducted using radioactive sources, although machines accelerating deuterons (especially cyclotrons) were increasingly used as more powerful neutron sources. When one considers the problems facing the early experimenters, with low source strengths on the one hand and low detector efficiencies on the other, it is interesting to reflect that nearly all the basic properties of the neutron and of its interaction with the nucleus had been settled by about 1939, the year of the discovery of fission.

I.2. The elementary principles of neutron detection

It is not profitable to enter into an extensive discussion of the elements of nuclear and atomic physics, but we shall be describing many phenomena for which some background knowledge is required, and it is convenient to summarise here some of the concepts which are essential to an understanding of neutron detection.

I.2.I. Nuclear constitution.
The two constituents of the nucleus are the proton (the positive nucleus of the hydrogen atom) and its neutral counterpart, the neutron. The force between any pair of these particles is strong, attractive, of very short range (10^{-13} cm) and is approximately the same whichever pair we choose. Thus, two protons at a distance of say 10^{-11} cm will repel each other because of the electrostatic or Coulomb repulsion: at close quarters, within a nucleus, the attractive nuclear force overcomes this repulsion. When a neutron enters a nucleus, the new or compound nucleus gains an energy called the *binding energy* of the neutron. For most elements, this energy is about 8 million electron volts (MeV). The fact that the binding energy is nearly constant for all elements is evidence that the nuclear particles interact only with their nearest neighbours in the nucleus, i.e. nuclear forces are very short range. The corresponding analogy in atomic physics is the liquid drop, in which the binding energy is the latent heat released when a molecule or atom condenses into the drop.

All nuclei consist of roughly equal numbers of protons and

neutrons. In heavy elements, the Coulomb repulsion of the protons is not negligible, and a neutron excess is necessary to maintain stability. A chemical element has chemical properties which are characterised by the number of electrons in the atom, i.e. by the charge, which in turn depends on the number of protons in the nucleus. For a given number of protons, there is often a varying number of neutrons. Nuclei with a common number of protons and different numbers of neutrons are called *isotopes*. A nucleus with neutron number N can be transmuted to an isotope with neutron number $N + 1$ by the absorption of a neutron. There are various ways in which this transmutation may further develop. The new isotope may be stable (e.g. $Cd^{113} + n \rightarrow Cd^{114}$) and beyond the emission of 9 MeV in gamma radiation, there are no further developments. The new isotope may be unstable to beta emission (e.g. $Au^{197} + n \rightarrow Au^{198} \rightarrow Hg^{198} + \epsilon^-$) so that, while most of the binding energy is released promptly as gamma radiation, some of the energy is later released in negative (sometimes positive) electron emission, and often in further gamma radiation. This process is familiar through the production of radioisotopes in reactors.

For light nuclei (e.g. $Li^6 + n \rightarrow He^4 + H^3$) the emission of charged particles (protons or alphas) is possible. We have mentioned the Coulomb repulsion between pairs of protons. When a positive particle approaches a nucleus, it is repelled unless it has sufficient energy to approach within the range of the nuclear forces, i.e. it must have sufficient energy to surmount the Coulomb barrier. The heavier the nucleus, the higher the barrier. The Coulomb barrier is of the order of 1 MeV for protons on lithium, but is of the order of 10 MeV for protons on lead. Conversely, a charged particle escaping from a nucleus requires sufficient energy to surmount the Coulomb barrier. We therefore find that charged particle emission following slow neutron absorption is limited to the light elements.

I.2.2. Interactions of neutrons with nuclei. We can summarise the interaction of neutrons with nuclei as follows:

(1) **Scattering.** The most important example of elastic scattering is that of scattering of neutrons by protons. As in the collision between two billiard balls, all events are equally

probable between a glancing blow and a head-on collision (this is no longer true if the neutron energy is greater than 10 MeV). In the case of a head-on collision, the full neutron energy is transferred to the proton. Most methods of fast neutron detection depend on detecting the proton recoiling from a neutron-proton collision.

To some extent, neutrons are elastically scattered by all nuclei, but, with the exception of hydrogen, elastic scattering is rarely employed in neutron detection. An allied process, inelastic scattering of fast neutrons (in which part of the neutron energy is emitted as gamma radiation) is also rarely used.

(2) **Absorption.** The following processes can occur:

(a) With heavy elements, most of the binding energy is released in gamma emission. The resulting isotope may be stable (Cd^{114}) or unstable (Au^{198}), in which latter case it will decay by positive or negative electron emission and perhaps by the release of further gamma rays.

(b) With light elements, proton ($He^3 + n \rightarrow T + p$) or alpha ($Li^6 + n \rightarrow He^4 + H^3$) emission can occur. With fast neutrons, many secondary reactions are possible. For example, with incident neutrons of about 3 MeV, sulphur and phosphorus will emit protons, while with neutrons of higher energy (10–15 MeV) a second neutron can be emitted, the process being known as (n,2n).

(c) With very heavy nuclei, we have the important process of fission. These nuclei absorb neutrons and split into two unequal fragments. In the liquid drop analogy, the drop distorts into a dumb-bell shape and breaks in two. We have said that the Coulomb repulsion between protons, at short range, is small compared with the attraction of nuclear forces. When, however, there are sufficient protons in the nucleus, the Coulomb repulsion is considerable, and, for elements heavier than thorium, the addition of a further neutron with its binding energy is sufficient to cause instability leading to fission. Some of the heavy elements, notably U^{233}, U^{235} and Pu^{239} ($Z \geqslant 90$) undergo fission when they capture a thermal neutron. All these heavy elements undergo fission when they capture a neutron of a few MeV energy.

The energy release of the fission fragments (about 160 MeV)

is far greater than in any of the processes described above.   It is in part responsible for the great importance of nuclear energy. In neutron detection, it is important because the high energy release makes the detection of fission fragments in a counter relatively easy in the face of competition from gamma ray backgrounds, since the pulses from gamma-induced electrons are relatively small.

1.2.3. Particle detection: interaction of alphas, protons, electrons and gamma particles with matter.

Since the neutron has no charge, its interaction with atomic electrons is negligibly small.   It interacts strongly only with the nucleus at the centre of an atom, and it is by the observation of the products of this interaction that neutrons are detected.   We now summarise the interaction of these reaction products with matter.

(1) **Protons and alpha particles.**   Because of their charge, these particles exert a strong electrostatic force on the electrons of the atoms of the material through which they pass.   Thus, if a fast proton passes sufficiently close to an atom, it exerts a powerful attractive force on the planetary electrons for a very short time.   If the force is sufficient, i.e. if the proton path is sufficiently close to the atom, the electron is torn from its orbit and escapes, while the residual atom, formerly neutral, has a net positive charge and is called a *positive ion*.   All methods of particle detection depend, one way or another, on the detection of broken atoms.   Thus, the charges can be collected in sensitive electrical detectors (ion chambers or electroscopes), they can form centres on to which water drops can condense (cloud chambers) or centres in photographic plates to which silver ions can migrate, and so on.

The force exerted on an atomic electron by a fast charged particle will depend on the charge of the particle and on its velocity.   Calculation shows that the rate of ionisation varies as the square of the charge, so that the specific ionisation (number of ion pairs per unit length of track) of an α-particle is four times as great as that of a proton moving with the same velocity.   For this reason, the range of an α-particle is much less than the range of a proton of the same initial energy.

As regards particle velocity, we observe that the slower the particle, the greater the time during which it exerts a force on the atomic electron and the greater the probability of the electron being torn from its orbit. This means that the ionisation is most intense towards the end of the range, a phenomenon first noted by W. H. Bragg. Also, if we compare an electron and a proton of the same energy (say 1 MeV) the electron, very much lighter, is travelling much faster. Hence for an energetic electron the specific ionisation is much less than that of a proton of the same energy, and the range of the fast electron is correspondingly greater than that of the proton. Typical values for range in air are:

Energy	1 MeV	10 MeV
Protons	2·0 cm (2·6 mg/cm²)	115 cm (0·15 g/cm²)
Alphas	0·53 cm (0·7 mg/cm²)	10 cm (13 mg/cm²)
Electrons	0·4 g/cm² (in aluminium)	5 g/cm²

The minimum energy required to remove an electron from the atoms we are considering is 10 to 15 eV. The average energy for forming an ion pair when a fast particle traverses a medium is, however, considerably higher, because more than half its energy is converted into heat directly or in excitation without ionisation. For most practical purposes, it is independent of the energy of the fast particle, but varies slightly with the medium. A figure of 32 volts per ion pair is a reasonable average for most media. In practical terms, this means that a 3·2 MeV proton will form 100,000 positive ions and electrons in its career of destruction.

(2) **Electrons.** In some respects, the passage of electrons through matter closely resembles that of positive particles. Thus, the expenditure of energy in forming an ion pair is much the same. The range, as we have said, is much higher because for a given energy the electron travels much faster. There is, however, one important difference. A fast heavy particle travels through the electron cloud of atomic matter much as a bullet might travel through a cloud of gnats; it proceeds almost in a straight line until, its energy expended, it stops. Thus, the *range of a proton of energy 1 MeV in air at N.T.P.* is an accurately defined quantity. For the electron, this is not so.

2—N.D.

Its mass is (for the purposes of this discussion) the same as that of the electrons of the atoms through which it passes, and elastic scattering both by these electrons and by the nuclei is considerable. Consequently, the fast electron pursues a random tortuous path through matter. By *range* is meant the thickness of matter required to reduce the intensity of fast electrons penetrating the thickness effectively to zero. It is an approximate, not an accurately defined, quantity, and the total path length of the electron in the absorber may be up to four times the thickness of the absorber defined as the range.

(3) Fission fragments. For fission fragments the variation in ionisation along the track is very different from that of protons or alpha particles. Although the energy is large (about 80 MeV) the mass is also large (about 100), so that the velocity is about the same as a 1 MeV proton. Initially, the charge (about twenty times that of a proton) is very high, so that the rate of energy loss is very high. However, in addition to ejecting electrons from the atoms of the medium through which it moves, the fission fragment quickly picks up electrons to neutralise its high charge, so that, as the fragment slows down, the rate of energy loss falls off. Thus, the variation of energy loss with fragment velocity is just the opposite of the situation with protons and alpha particles. The range of a typical fission fragment in air is about 2 cm, i.e. the same as a 1 MeV proton.

(4) Gamma rays. The number of neutron detectors which depend on the detection of the gamma ray following nuclear interaction is relatively small. Most neutron detectors, however, are also gamma ray detectors, and the elimination of gamma-induced effects is often a considerable problem. We need to consider the ways in which electrons are ejected from gamma rays by atoms:

(*a*) *Photoelectric effect.* The emission of electrons by a photosensitive cathode irradiated by light is well known. Gamma rays are, like radio and light waves, electromagnetic in origin, so that gamma rays also can liberate photoelectrons from an atom. The whole of the gamma ray energy is absorbed in the process, so that the ejected electrons will in general have considerable energy. The gamma ray interacts with the atom as a whole, and most of the electrons come from the innermost shells. Roughly speaking, the probability of interaction varies as Z^4, i.e. it is negligible for hydrogen but important for lead.

(b) *Compton scattering.* Gamma rays can be thought of as photons, with properties like particles, as well as radiation with properties like waves. In Compton scattering, photons collide with electrons in rough analogy with the way in which neutrons collide with protons. Electrons of all energies from zero to a maximum are emitted, as well as a scattered photon of energy less than the incident photon. The effect of collision between gamma rays and electrons was discovered by A. H. Compton in 1924, and is universally known by his name. In the Compton effect, then, the gamma ray interacts with the individual electron, and the cross section varies as Z. By contrast, in the photoelectric effect, the gamma ray interacts with the atom as a whole, and the cross section varies as Z^4.

(c) *Pair production.* In the electromagnetic field in the neighbourhood of a nucleus, the gamma ray may become absorbed in the production of an electron and positron, of total energy equal to that of the incident photon. This effect is not of major importance in neutron detection.

1.3. Neutron sources and neutron detectors

We have surveyed briefly the main principles of neutron detection: the interaction of neutrons with nuclei, the principal particles or radiations emitted as a result of such interaction and the manner of their passage through matter. We now summarise the main sources of neutrons, the types of experiment and the methods of detection used with them.

1.3.1. The neutron energy range 10 keV to 20 MeV. Some

fast neutron experiments have been conducted with a fission spectrum, which is a continuous spectrum with a peak at 0·8 MeV and a mean energy of about 1·6 MeV. For these experiments, a "converter" of fissile material (usually U^{235}) is placed in a high flux beam of thermal neutrons from a reactor.

The slow neutrons are converted into neutrons by capture in U^{235}, and the emerging fission neutrons are filtered from scattered thermal neutrons by cadmium foil. Source strengths up to 10^{11} neutrons per second can be obtained. This high source strength, and the shielding it requires, can conveniently be attained only by placing the converter within the reactor shield. Since the response of most fast neutron detectors varies considerably over the range of neutron energies involved, the type of experiment which may be performed with such a source (capture cross sections, fission cross sections) is limited.

Of more general application are the monoenergetic neutron sources obtained by bombarding suitable targets by positive ions accelerated in machines.[12] Common to all these reactions is the fact that there are only two particles initially (the positive ion and the target nucleus) and two particles finally (the neutron and the final product particle). Elementary calculations then show that in a given direction with respect to the incident beam the neutrons have a unique energy. For example, in the reaction

$$D + D \rightarrow n + He^3 + 3{\cdot}28 \text{ MeV},$$

the neutrons will have, for very low energy incident deuterons, an energy of $2{\cdot}46$ MeV. As the deuteron energy increases, the neutron energy will depend on the angle of observation. The energy in the forward direction increases with increasing energy, while the energy in the backward direction has rather a flat minimum of $1{\cdot}64$ MeV.

Cockcroft-Walton generators, with voltages in the range 100–1000 keV, are frequently used as sources of D-D and D-T neutrons, with deuteron currents of about 500 microamperes. Targets used are heavy ice or titanium deuteride (tritide, in the case of the D-T reaction). For the D-D reaction, the total source strength is often of the order of 10^8 to 10^9 neutrons per second. For the D-T reaction, the neutron energy for low incident deuteron energy is $14{\cdot}1$ MeV. The cross section at 120 keV is exceptionally large (5 barns) so that, with thick targets and deuteron energies of 300–400 keV, high neutron yields of the order of 10^{10} to 10^{11} neutrons per second can be obtained.

(12). Hanson et al., Rev. Mod. Phys. **21**, 635 (1949).

Van de Graaff machines can deliver currents of protons or deuterons up to 100 microamperes with energies between 1 MeV and 6 MeV. As with other machines, the neutron source strength varies with the type of target, the direction of observation, the thickness of target and the (proton) current, but the normal yield is of the order of 10^8 to 10^9 n/cm² sec. The chief reactions are Li(p,n) (threshold 1·882 MeV) and T(p,n) (threshold 1·02 MeV) so that either reaction can be used to provide neutrons of energy between 10 keV and 5 MeV (neutrons from the Li(p,n) reaction are not accurately monoenergetic for a proton energy greater than 2·3 MeV). Neutrons with energy up to 10 MeV can be obtained by using the D-D reaction with high energy (7 MeV) incident deuterons, although deuteron break-up (i.e. $D + D \rightarrow D + p + n$) is appreciable at 6 MeV, so that above this energy the neutrons are not reliably monoenergetic. The use of high currents in gas targets, such as deuterium or tritium, has enabled total neutron source strengths to be increased to 10^{11} n/sec.[13]

Most detectors used with fast neutrons detect the protons recoiling from the impact of a fast neutron. The recoiling proton may either cause ionisation detected in an ion chamber, a flash of light in a scintillation counter, or a track in a photographic emulsion or cloud chamber. We shall discuss these processes in greater detail in Chapters 3 and 4. As the (n,p) cross section falls off roughly as $1/E^{\frac{1}{2}}$ (Appendix I) measures must be taken at high neutron energies to maintain reasonable efficiency. The recent development of millimicrosecond time-of-flight spectrometry combines the advantage of the high efficiency of the scintillation detector with good resolution. Other methods of detection (photographic plates, cloud chambers, He³ proportional counters) are useful in special applications.

I.3.2. Slow neutrons. (1) **Reactors.** There are many types of reactor, and the literature describing their properties is voluminous. As neutron sources, the range can be briefly illustrated as follows: With natural uranium as fuel, the

(13). Hobles, *Rev. Sci. Inst.* **28**, 962 (1957).

principal moderators are graphite e.g. (Harwell BEPO, Brook-haven) or heavy water e.g. (Chalk River NRX).   The heavy-water pile is compact, so that the thermal flux is high, but the volume available for experiment is small as compared with the graphite pile.   With enriched uranium as fuel, the choice of moderator is less limited.   Several heavy-water moderated piles e.g. (Harwell DIDO, Argonne CP-5) have been built, but light-water moderated piles such as the swimming-pool reactor are coming into extensive use, while the Material Testing Reactor has at present the distinction of the highest thermal flux.   A feature of the light-water moderated reactors is the compara-tively high ratio of fast to thermal flux.

A rough indication of the orders of magnitude of the flux available in these reactors is as follows:

Graphite and natural uranium
　　Harwell BEPO　　10^{12} n/cm^2 sec.
　　Brookhaven　　5×10^{12} n/cm^2 sec.

Heavy water and natural uranium (light-water cooling)
　　NRX　　7×10^{13} n/cm^2 sec.

Swimming-pool reactor, at 100 *kW*
　　3×10^{12} n/cm^2 sec. inside core.
　　Fast flux　　3×10^{11} n/cm^2 sec. at core face.

Light-water moderated and cooled enriched uranium (M.T.R.)
　　Average slow flux available　　2×10^{14} n/cm^2 sec.
　　Maximum slow flux in reflector　　4×10^{14} n/cm^2 sec.
　　Average fast flux available　　10^{14} n/cm^2 sec.

External to the reactor, experiments are normally conducted with neutron beams emerging from holes in the reactor shield. Since the normal working distance is several metres from the core, the effective flux in the experimental area is roughly the reactor flux $\times 10^{-6} \times$ the cross-sectional area of the hole through the shield.   The neutrons emerging in the beam are effectively divided into three groups: the slow or *thermal* neutrons; the *resonance* or *epithermal* neutrons; and the fast, unmoderated neutrons.   The slow neutrons are characterised by a Max-wellian distribution corresponding to a temperature of roughly 400°K, i.e. their velocity spectrum is the same as that of the velocity spectrum of hydrogen atoms in a hypothetical gas of hydrogen atoms heated to about 130°C. To obtain a beam which is almost entirely composed of neutrons in this group, a *thermal column* is used, which is merely an extension of the reflector, about 5 ft square, through the shield. Thermal neutrons in this column are little attenuated by scattering, while fast and resonance neutrons are moderated to thermal energies.

The spectrum of the resonance group is such that, over a wide range of energy, the flux falls off as $1/E$. The intensity of this group, relative to the intensity of thermal neutrons, varies appreciably with the type of moderator employed in the reactor. Similarly, the intensity of the third group, the fast unmoderated neutron group, depends on the type of moderator employed in the reactor. The total intensity of this group is normally appreciably less than the slow flux.

(2) Neutron detection. In addition to the high neutron flux inside a reactor, there is an intense gamma ray flux, so that detectors using proton recoil are precluded. The normal type of monitoring and control instrument is an ionisation chamber filled with BF_3, or filled with argon and lined with boron or fissile material. When the reactor is operating at low power, the neutron flux will be considerably reduced, but the gamma ray level, due to fission products, is still very high. Hence such ion chambers are frequently *gamma ray compensated*, i.e. they are matched with a second chamber filled without boron but without the neutron-sensitive lining. The difference in current between the two chambers then gives the next current due to neutrons. In both the $B^{10}(n,\alpha)$ reaction and in fission, the cross section falls off fairly rapidly with increasing neutron energy, so that both reactions preferentially measure thermal neutron flux.

In addition to these means of measuring neutron flux directly, various neutron measurements are made by activation. A wide range of radioisotopes are made by irradiation of elements in piles, and in theory any one of these can be used for determination of neutron intensity. For example, the flux in a reactor, integrated over a considerable period, can be measured by determining the radioactivity of metallic cobalt (cobalt 60 has a half-life of 5·2 years).

External to a reactor, experiments with thermal neutrons very often employ the $B^{10}(n,\alpha)Li^7$ reaction. The counters most frequently used are the BF_3 filled proportional counter and a scintillator made of B_2O_3 and ZnS. Fission chambers, while less sensitive to neutrons, are more robust and less sensitive to gamma rays. Since the beams from a reactor are not mono-energetic, various means of selecting single neutron energies, such as choppers and crystal spectrometers, are extensively used. In the higher neutron energy range (1 eV to 10 keV) detection presents more of a problem, chiefly because the efficiency is falling off rapidly owing to the falling off of the $B^{10}(n,\alpha)$ cross section with increasing neutron energy. Of several alternatives, the BF_3 proportional counter and the $ZnS:B_2O_3$ glass scintillator are also to be preferred.

1.3.3. Radioactive neutron sources.

Finally, several types of experiment employ sources which do not depend on machines or reactors. Common among such sources are the (Ra-α-Be) source, in which neutrons produced by alpha particle bombardment of Be have a mean energy of about 5 MeV, and (Sb-γ-Be), where neutrons produced by gamma irradiation of Be have an energy of 25 keV. Source strengths range between about 10^6 and 10^7 n/sec per curie of radioactive material. These sources are described in detail in Chapter 5. Measurements made with them are usually made with BF_3 counters or radioactive detectors, in which the activity induced in foils such as indium or gold is determined. These measurements also are described in greater detail in Chapters 4 and 5.

The above is a very cursory survey of the types of sources employed in neutron physics, and of the types of detector used. The remainder of this book will be concerned with a more detailed explanation and amplification of the methods of neutron detection.

2

REACTIONS
USED
IN
NEUTRON
DETECTION

Of the many reactions employed in neutron detection, the two chief are the elastic scattering of fast neutrons by protons, and the capture of slow neutrons by boron 10.   In this chapter, we shall first discuss these reactions in detail.   Other reactions will be more briefly discussed.

2.1. The (n,p) and similar reactions

2.1.1. Kinematics.   We have said that the neutron-proton interaction, at energies below 10 MeV, resembles the collision of two billiard balls.   Let us consider the elastic scattering of a neutron, mass unity, by a nucleus of mass A.   For neutron-proton scattering, A will also be unity.   In Fig. 2.1 (a), we show the state of affairs in the laboratory system of reference: the incident neutron (white circle) has velocity u, and is scattered with velocity v_2 at an angle θ to the incident direction, while the recoil nucleus (black circle) is scattered with velocity v_1 at an angle α.

Now, the total momentum of the system is u, and the total

mass is $(1 + A)$, so that the centre of mass moves with a velocity $\dfrac{u}{1+A}$. In the centre of mass system, therefore, the neutron moves with velocity $\dfrac{Au}{1+A}$, and the recoil nucleus with velocity $\dfrac{u}{1+A}$ and both have momentum $\dfrac{Au}{1+A}$. Figure 2.1 (b) represents the momentum diagram in the centre of mass system. In this system the momentum of the two particles remains

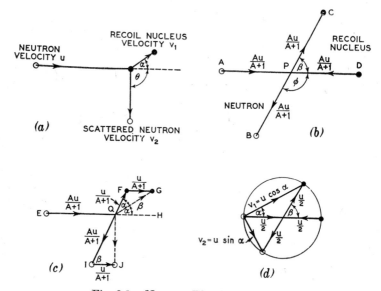

Fig. 2.1.   Neutron Elastic Scattering

(a) Laboratory System
(b) Momentum Diagram, Centre of Mass System
(c) Velocity Diagram, Centre of Mass System
(d) Proton-neutron Scattering

unaltered as a result of the collision; all that is changed is the direction of motion of the particles relative to the incident direction. We call ϕ and β the angles through which neutron and nucleus are scattered. To obtain the velocities and energies of the two particles, we must translate the momentum diagram of Fig. 2.1 (b) into the velocity diagram of Fig. 2.1 (c).

Thus, the vector QF, representing the velocity of the recoiling nucleus in the centre of mass system, is still at an angle β to the incident direction, but its magnitude is $\frac{u}{A+1}$. Finally, to obtain velocities in the laboratory system, we add vectorially to the vectors QI and QF the velocity of the centre of mass in the laboratory system, namely $\frac{u}{A+1}$ in the incident direction.

Considering first the recoil nucleus, we observe that the triangle QFG is isosceles, so that $\beta = 2\alpha$. The velocity of the recoil nucleus in the laboratory system is

$$QG = 2QF \cos \alpha = 2\left(\frac{u}{A+1}\right)\cos \alpha \tag{1}$$

so that the energy of the recoil nucleus is

$$E_{recoil} = \tfrac{1}{2}A\left(\frac{2u}{A+1}\right)^2 \cos^2 \alpha = \frac{2Au^2}{(A+1)^2}\cos^2 \alpha$$

$$= E_n \frac{2A}{(A+1)^2}(1+\cos \beta) \tag{2}$$

where $E_n = \tfrac{1}{2}u^2$ is the energy of the incident neutron. Similarly the energy of the scattered neutron is

$$\tfrac{1}{2}(QJ)^2 = E_n \frac{1+A^2-2A\cos \beta}{(1+A)^2} \tag{3}$$

We observe from (2) that the maximum energy of the recoiling nucleus occurs in a head-on collision for which $\beta = 0$, and for which the nucleus receives energy

$$E_{max} = \frac{4A}{(A+1)^2}E_n \tag{4}$$

This means, for example, that for a proton ($A = 1$) the entire neutron energy is taken up by the recoiling proton in a head-on collision, while, for a carbon nucleus ($A = 12$), E_{max} is roughly $\tfrac{1}{3}E_n$. For this, among other reasons, only light nuclei are of concern as regards neutron detection by elastic scattering. We observe also that for protons, (2) takes the form

$$E_p = E_n \cos^2 \alpha \tag{5}$$

For the neutron-proton scattering, the momentum diagram is the same as the velocity diagram, and takes the simple form of Fig. 2.1 (d). We now derive a simple relation, first given by Barschall and Kanner,[1] which shows that the energy distribution of recoil particles in the laboratory system is the same as the angular distribution of neutrons scattered in the centre of mass system. Let us call σ_s the total scattering cross section and $\sigma(\phi)$ the differential cross section in the centre of mass system. By this we mean that $\dfrac{\sigma(\phi)}{\sigma_s}\,\mathrm{d}\omega$ is the probability that in a collision the neutron is scattered through an angle ϕ into an element of solid angle $\mathrm{d}\omega$, both ϕ and ω being measured in the centre of mass systems. The probability, $p(E)\mathrm{d}E$, of the recoil nucleus having a recoil energy E is the same as the probability of a neutron having an angle of deflection ϕ, namely

$$p(E)\mathrm{d}E = \frac{\sigma(\phi)}{\sigma_s}\,\mathrm{d}\omega = \frac{\sigma(\phi)}{\sigma_s}\cdot 2\pi \sin \phi\, \mathrm{d}\phi \tag{6}$$

But the relation between E and ϕ is that of equation (2), which can by differentiation be rewritten

$$\mathrm{d}E = -\frac{2A}{(1+A)^2}\, E_{\mathrm{n}} \sin \beta\, \mathrm{d}\beta$$

$$= \frac{2A}{(1+A)^2}\, E_{\mathrm{n}} \sin \phi\, \mathrm{d}\phi \tag{7}$$

since from Fig. 2.1 (b), $\phi + \beta = \pi$.

Hence from (6) and (7),

$$p(E) = \frac{\sigma(\phi)}{\sigma_s}\cdot\frac{\pi}{E_{\mathrm{n}}}\cdot\frac{(1+A)^2}{A} \tag{8}$$

i.e. $p(E)$ is proportional to $\sigma(\phi)$.

For neutron-proton collisions below 10 MeV, all angles of recoil are equally probable in the centre of mass system. As shown by equation (8), this means that all energies of recoil protons are equally probable between zero and maximum. At higher energies, however, this is no longer the case. Fig. 2.2

(1). *Phys. Rev.* **58**, 590 (1940).

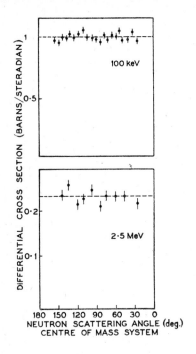

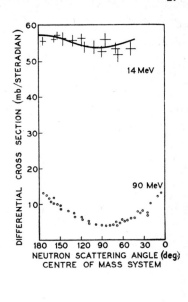

Fig. 2.2.   Differential Cross Section in centre of mass system of neutron-proton scattering

100 keV.   Allen *et al.*, *Proc. Phys. Soc.* **68**, 650 (1955).
2·5 MeV.   Caplehorn and Rundle, *Pro. Phys. Soc.* **A.-64**, 546 (1951).
14 and 90 MeV.   Brolley and Fowler, *Rev. Mod. Phys.* **28**, 103 (1956).

shows experimental results on (n,p) scattering at four representative energies. It is clear that at 100 keV and at 2·5 MeV the pulse height distribution is effectively flat, so that the scattering is isotropic in the centre of mass system. At 14 MeV there is appreciable anisotropy while in the region of 100 MeV the distribution, though approximately symmetrical about 90°, is very far from isotropic.

For deuterium, the angular distribution of scattered neutrons is observably anisotropic for neutron energies as low as 100 keV, while at energies above 1 MeV the distribution resembles Fig. 2.1 (d). Similarly, (n,α) scattering in helium is markedly anisotropic at low energies.

For the detection of neutrons elastically scattered from various substances in the region of 1 MeV, a helium-filled detector has several advantages :

(a) the total cross section of helium has a maximum of 7 barns in the region of 1 MeV ;

(b) the high probability of recoiling alphas having energies near E_{max} means that, by using a detector biased near maximum, one has high sensitivity for neutrons under investigation and low sensitivity for background neutrons of low energy ;

(c) the recoiling alphas, with their high ionisation, have short ranges, so that end and wall effects in the counter are minimised.

Such a counter was successfully used in the study of angular distributions of elastically scattered neutrons by Walt and Barschall.[2] However, neutron scattering in deuterium and helium has not been widely used in neutron detection.

2.1.2. Cross sections. There is one drawback to the use of hydrogen as a detector of fast neutrons, and that is the continuous distribution of recoils from a single energy E_n of incident neutrons. This means, for example, that in a simple system employing a biased detector, the number of pulses above a given bias varies fairly sensitively with the bias, and also that neutron spectrometry, for a spectrum of energies E_n, is difficult. On the other hand, (n,p) elastic scattering has, in comparison with other reactions, many major advantages. Protons struck by slow neutrons will have negligible energy, and detected recoils can refer only to fast neutrons. It has no competing reactions. Hydrogenous gases and stable hydrogenous compounds are readily available. Finally, the total cross section for the (n,p) reaction is known with good accuracy (1 per cent at certain energies) and has been the subject of extensive theoretical analysis. Consequently, if the amount of hydrogen is known, and the number of recoils counted, the neutron flux can be determined.

Experimentally, the (n,p) cross-section is determined by finding the total cross section of a hydrocarbon, preferably

(2). *Phys. Rev.* **93**, 1062 (1954).

one whose chemical composition is accurately known, in good geometry. The measurement, being an attenuation measurement, is capable of considerable accuracy (in the most accurate experiments the difficulties lie mainly in establishing the physical and chemical composition of the material). The total cross section of carbon is then determined, and that of hydrogen is determined by subtraction of the effect due to carbon. Theoretically the cross section is given by a formula which covers the range from epithermal energies up to 10 MeV, and whose constants can be intercompared with those derived from other neutron-proton interactions, such as the binding energy of the deuteron and the capture cross section of neutrons by hydrogen. The agreement of the theoretical with the mean of the experimental results is of the order of 1 to 2 per cent. The (n,p) cross section from 0·01 eV to 100 MeV is shown in Appendix I(a).

2.1.3. Range-energy relation.

If the rate of energy loss of a fast particle in matter were independent of velocity, then the range would be proportional to energy. As we have seen in Chapter 1, however, this is not the case, and the slower the particle, the greater the rate of energy loss. Roughly speaking, if the rate of energy loss is inversely proportional to the velocity, we have

$$-\frac{dE}{dx} = \frac{a}{v} = \frac{b}{E^{\frac{1}{2}}}$$

where a and b are constants, so that

$$-\frac{dx}{dE} = \frac{1}{b} \cdot E^{\frac{1}{2}}$$

and the range is given by

$$R = -\int_{E_{max}}^{0} \frac{dx}{dE}\,dE = \frac{2}{3b}E_{max}^{\frac{3}{2}}$$

i.e. the range varies as $E^{\frac{3}{2}}$. Over quite a wide range of energy this is the case. Towards the end of its range, however, the velocity is sufficiently small to allow electron capture from neutral atoms to take place, so that the fast proton becomes a fast neutral hydrogen atom, while the fast alpha (He^{++}) becomes a fast helium ion (He^{+}) or a neutral He atom. The range under these circumstances becomes more nearly linear with energy. Also, for alpha particles, the energy expended per ion pair is rather greater than it is at high velocities. For protons in hydrogen, however, the energy expended per ion pair remains constant down to energies of 10 keV or less.

Range-energy relations have been the subject of extensive experimental and theoretical investigations in nuclear physics. Detailed discussions will be found in the classic paper of Bethe and Livingstone[3] and in the more recent review of Bethe and Ashkin[4] and of Allison and Warshaw.[5] For the purposes of this book, the data are summarised in Appendix II(a) and (b). These give the range of protons and alphas in air over the relevant range of energies, the range of protons in hydrogen and the stopping power of several media in common use relative to air. Stopping powers of materials not listed can be estimated by determining the stopping power of the constituent elements by interpolation from Appendix II(c). The stopping power per atom, and the range in mg/cm², vary with Z very approximately as $Z^{\frac{1}{2}}$.

2.2. The $B^{10}(n,\alpha)Li^7$ reaction

We now turn to the reaction

$$B^{10} + n \begin{cases} \nearrow Li^7 + \alpha + 2\cdot792 \text{ MeV} & (a) \\ \searrow Li^{7x} + \alpha + 2\cdot31 \text{ MeV} & (b) \end{cases}$$

$$Li^{7x} \rightarrow Li^7 + \gamma + 480 \text{ keV} \qquad (c)$$

For thermal neutrons, only 6·3 per cent of the disintegrations pass through (a) i.e. a 480 keV gamma ray is liberated in 94 per cent of the capture events. It has been shown[6] that the lifetime for the decay of Li^{7x} is $7\cdot7 \times 10^{-14}$ seconds so that, for practical purposes, alpha and gamma rays are prompt coincident.

This reaction is very widely used in neutron detection, particularly for slow neutrons. The reasons for this are that

(3). *Rev. Mod. Phys.* **9**, 246 (1937).
(4). *Experimental Nuclear Physics*, Vol. 1. (Ed. E. Segre), John Wiley & Sons, New York (1953).
(5). *Rev. Mod. Phys.* **25**, 779 (1953).
(6). Bunbury *et al.*, *Proc. Phys. Soc.* **A-69**, 165 (1956).

the boron capture reaction has nearly all the properties required for a slow neutron detector:

(i) it has a high cross section (4010* barns at 2200 m/s for pure boron 10) which varies with neutron velocity as $1/v$ up to an energy of several hundred volts:

(ii) in the reaction, alphas and lithium nuclei are emitted, so that the range of the reaction products is short as compared with, say, protons of the same energy. The energy release is such that the pulses due to gamma-induced electrons are relatively small:

(iii) the fact that in nearly all the capture events a 480 keV gamma ray is released is frequently of value, since neutron capture can be indicated by gamma ray, as well as by alpha particle detection:

(iv) boron occurs, in neutron detectors, in a wide variety of forms. As a gas, it is used extensively as boron trifluoride and sometimes as diborane. As a solid (it occurs normally as an amorphous powder), it can be painted, evaporated, or deposited by electromagnetic separation. As an oxide, it can be fused with zinc sulphide in scintillators, or dissolved as methyl borate in organic scintillators. The total list of neutron detectors employing boron compounds is very extensive.

Against these advantages, there is the minor disadvantage that B^{10} constitutes only 18 per cent of the natural element. However, the relative mass difference between B^{10} and B^{11} is appreciable as compared with, for example, the relative mass difference between U^{235} and U^{238}, and boron 10 has been enriched to high concentrations (96 per cent) in considerable quantity.

It is to be noted that the reaction energies are shared between the reaction products, viz. 7/11 of the total energy for the alpha particle and 4/11 for the Li⁷ nuclei. Since, however, the ionising powers of the two particles are nearly the same, the net pulse height is nearly equal to the pulse height due to alpha particles of energy 2·79 or 2·31 MeV.

---

* Appendix XII gives definitions of various terms used in neutron detection. Under *Cross section* we discuss the relation between the effective cross section of a $1/v$ absorber in a thermal beam to the 2200 m/sec value.

3—N.D.

Cross section. Since the earliest days of neutron studies, the importance of the $B^{10}(n,\alpha)$ reaction in slow neutron measurement has been recognised, and it is surprising to find that it is only comparatively recently that its thermal cross section has been established with reasonable accuracy. For many years after the war, the accepted figure was 707 barns for the natural element, and many cross sections were determined relative to this figure. However, in the period 1952 to 1955, there was considerable discussion as to the true value of the boron cross section, and the present accepted value is 755 barns, which is an appreciable increase on the previous figure. Part of this discrepancy between the results of various groups arose from the fact that the isotopic constitution of the boron used varied slightly. At the present time the extreme discrepancy between the best measurements is some $2\frac{1}{2}$ per cent, which is almost within the limits of experimental error. The question of the accuracy of the boron measurements is discussed in further detail in Chapter 5.

At higher energies, of course, the reaction changes considerably. In the first place, the branching ratio (i.e. the fraction of reactions which go to the ground and the first excited state) varies with energy, and at 2 MeV the fraction of events leading to gamma emission is only one third as compared with 94 per cent at thermal energies.[7,8] Also in the region of neutron energy of, say, 5 to 10 MeV there is complication from the emission of further reaction products; protons, deuterons and tritons can be emitted and have been observed at 14 MeV.[9] There is finally the possibility of alpha emission to higher states of Li^7. These reactions, however, are of little concern in neutron detection, since all the cross sections concerned are quite small, and the reaction has not been used directly in fast neutron detection.

2.3. Other neutron-induced reactions: Exoergic reactions

2.3.1. Charged particle reactions.
Besides the $B^{10}(n,\alpha)Li^7$ reaction, there are a few other exoergic reactions, i.e. reactions

(7). Bischel *et al.*, *Phys. Rev.* **81**, 456 (1951).
(8). Petree *et al.*, *Phys. Rev.* **83**, 1148 (1951).
(9). Frye and Gammel, *Phys. Rev.* **103**, 328 (1956).

in which energy is liberated, which are of interest in neutron detection. These include:

A. $He^3 + n \rightarrow T + p + 765$ keV.

This has an interesting converse reaction, since $T(p,n)He^3$ is widely used as a neutron source in the MeV range. The cross section of the $He^3(n,p)T$ reaction for 2200 m/s neutrons is 5400 barns. If it were not for its cost, He^3 would be a competitor with B^{10} in gas-filled counters, although the higher range of the proton, as compared with the alphas from $B^{10}(n,\alpha)Li^7$, would necessitate higher filling pressures. The main virtue of He^3 is the possibility of its use in a neutron spectrometer in the MeV range. For this purpose it has several advantages:

(i) The cross section varies smoothly from 1·7 barns at 100 keV to 0·75 barns on 1 MeV (see Appendix III) and shows no strong resonances.

(ii) There are no excited states of the daughter nucleus, so that to each neutron energy there corresponds a single reaction energy, i.e. a monoenergetic neutron source will be represented by a line spectrum in the output from the spectrometer.

(iii) It is an exoergic reaction of moderately low energy. The reaction energy from the capture of thermal neutrons is 0·765 MeV, so that the total reaction energy from the capture of an incident neutron of 1 MeV, for example, is 1·765 MeV. This energy is not so high that proton range becomes a serious problem (although fairly high counter pressures are required), while at the same time electrons induced by gamma rays will expend energy in the counter considerably less than 0·765 MeV, so that their pulses will not distort the spectrum.

There are, however, some disadvantages:

(i) Recoiling He^3 nuclei from elastic scattering will have energy greater than 0·765 MeV when the incident neutron energy is greater than about 1 MeV (see equation (2) p. 19). Above this energy, therefore, He^3 recoils will appear above the peak due to the capture of thermal neutrons which are almost always to some extent present.

(ii) While He^3 can be obtained from atmospheric helium by thermal diffusion, it is now usually obtained from tritium decay. For a spectrometer, therefore, the He³ requires high purification to ensure that the decay of the residual tritium does not constitute an unwanted background.

(iii) He³ is relatively rare and expensive.

B. $Li^6 + n \rightarrow T + \alpha + 4 \cdot 78$ MeV.

The cross section at 2200 m/s for this reaction is 945 barns for the pure isotope, i.e. 71 barns for natural lithium. In the thermal region, the cross section varies as $1/v$. For high neutron energies the cross section has a peak of 2·75 barns at 265 keV and thereafter the cross section drops to 0·28 barns at 1·2 MeV and to 0·05 barns at 8 MeV.[10, 11] As with the $B^{10}(n,\alpha)Li^7$ reaction, other reaction products are emitted when the incident neutron energy is sufficiently high.

The main advantage of this reaction is the high reaction energy. Scintillation counters using Li I or Li⁶ I have been developed, especially for detection of thermal neutrons. It has also been used in photographic plates, for example for slow neutron flux measurements in health monitoring and cosmic rays, and in fast neutron spectrum measurement. In general, however, it has not been widely used in neutron detection. Lithium has no usable gaseous compound.

C. $N^{14} + n \rightarrow C^{14} + p + 0 \cdot 625$ MeV.

This reaction was proposed many years ago for fast neutron spectrometry. There are, however, many drawbacks; the cross section is small (the slow neutron cross section at 2200 m/s is only 1·9 barns), there is the competing reaction $N^{14}(n,\alpha)B^{11}$, and the fast neutron cross section varies rapidly owing to compound nucleus formation. However, the reaction has occasionally been of use in neutron detection: for example, the nitrogen occurring naturally in photographic plates has been used to determine the dosage of neutrons in the thermal flux from reactors; at higher energies, a small contamination of nitrogen in a counter gas is sometimes convenient, since it gives an energy calibration point of 625 keV with a thermal neutron beam.

(10). Bame and Cubitt, *Phys. Rev.* **114**, 1580 (1959).
(11). Murray and Schmitt, *Phys. Rev. Letters* **3**, 360 (1959).

2.3.2. Fission.

2.3.2. Fission. Fission is an important reaction in neutron detection because of the large energy release per fission as compared with the energy release in the average counter due to gamma rays. Theoretically, for example, we should have about 80 MeV per fission fragment released in the counter as compared with at most a few hundred kilovolts released by electrons given off by gamma interaction with the walls of the counter. A fission neutron detector therefore has considerable advantages over other neutron detection where there are high gamma ray fluxes, as, for example, in sectors.

For purposes of this discussion the fissionable detectors can be divided into two kinds, those which are thermally fissile (U^{233}, U^{235} and Pu^{239}) and those which are not thermally fissile but are fissile above a certain threshold neutron energy, usually in the region of several hundred kilovolts. In the first group, the thermally fissile detectors, we have a cross section at thermal energies of between 500 and 750 barns which varies rapidly through its various resonances in the eV region, although the mean cross section drops off steadily. When the neutron energy has reached the order of 100 keV the cross section flattens off and within ± 10 per cent becomes constant up to about 5 MeV. The cross section in this region, taken arbitrarily at 3 MeV for the purposes of Table 2.1, is between 1.3 and 2 barns.

Table 2.1. Relevant Nuclear Properties of the Principal Thermally Fissile Nuclides

Nuclide	$\sigma_{fiss}(th)$ (barns) (2200 m/s)	σ_{fiss} at 3 MeV (barns)	Alpha half-life (years)
U^{233}	530	1.9	1.6×10^5
U^{235}	582	1.3	7.1×10^8
Pu^{239}	750	2.0	2.4×10^4

A third property of these thermally fissile elements which is of some importance in counters is their alpha half-life; since if the half-life is short, that is to say the alpha yield is high, then with a considerable amount of material in the counter one may get build-up of alphas during the duration of the average pulse (see below).

In addition to the thermally fissile nuclides, there is a second group of heavy nuclides which, while fissionable with fast neutrons, are not thermally fissile. From the practical point of view these should be included in the section on threshold detectors, i.e. section 2.4. However, for convenience of classification we will refer to their properties here. Their cross section varies from values such as 0·14 barns for Th^{232} to 1·5 barns for Np^{237}. The rise of cross section near threshold is reasonably sharp. These nuclides are of value in analysing fast neutron spectra because the variation of cross section with energy above threshold is relatively flat and because, taken collectively, their threshold energies cover a range of considerable interest in fast reactor spectra.

At appreciably higher energies, 6 to 10 MeV, the fission cross sections of all these fissionable nuclei are approximately doubled. This is because the compound nucleus at these high energies is in a highly excited state. Therefore, in addition to undergoing fission in the normal way, it can emit the neutron and still be left in a state of energy sufficient to undergo fission. Therefore, two separate modes of fission (n,f) and (n,nf) are available for fission and the cross section approximately doubles. However, this increase of cross section is not of great practical importance.

The properties of these fissionable materials are summarised in Table 2.2. Further details concerning the thermal and fast

Table 2.2.   Relevant Nuclear Properties of Nuclides which are not Thermally Fissile

Nuclide	Threshold (MeV)	Cross section at 3 MeV (barns)	Alpha half-life (years)
Th^{232}	1·3	0·14	$1·4 \times 10^{10}$
Pa^{231}	0·6	1·1	$3·4 \times 10^{4}$
U^{234}	0·4	1·5	$2·5 \times 10^{5}$
U^{236}	0·8	0·85	$2·4 \times 10^{7}$
U^{238}	1·2	0·55	$4·5 \times 10^{9}$
Np^{237}	0·4	1·5	$2·2 \times 10^{6}$

properties of the more important nuclei, viz. the thermally fissile nuclei and Th^{232}, U^{234}, U^{236}, U^{238} and Np^{237} will be found in Appendix IV.

For most of the materials in Tables 2.1 and 2.2, the specific activity for alpha emission is relatively low, so that the problem of build-up does not arise, and up to 2 g of material can be loaded into a counter. If, however, we consider a counter containing 1 mg of Pu, then the number of alphas emitted per microsecond is, on the average, approximately one. Since the alphas are emitted at random, there is an appreciable chance that in a period of minutes 20 alphas will be emitted in 1 microsecond, and the energy expended by 20 alphas in a counter may be approximately the same as that expended by a fission fragment. Hence, if the electronics of the system has time constants of 1 microsecond, there is an appreciable chance that the alpha build-up will register a "fission". (The question is dealt with by Rossi and Staub, Appendix II and by Gillespie p. 118 : Bibliography refs. 0.2 and 2.3.2.) One way of improving the situation is to utilise the difference in differential ionisation between fission fragments and alpha particles (Chapter 1.2). If we detect only the first part of the range, for example by using low pressure or short inter-electrode distances, then, as compared with the average over the whole range, the alpha particle pulses will be depressed, while the fission pulses will be enhanced; even so, however, the maximum amount of plutonium which has been successfully loaded into a conventional ion chamber (where the time constant is limited to about one tenth of a microsecond) to give a reasonable plateau is 10 mg. To improve on this situation, faster detection is required and counters detecting the light emitted when fission fragments pass through xenon have been successfully developed to the point where 100 mg of Pu have been loaded into the counter.

The methods of loading these materials in their counters will be described later (Chapter 3). We should observe that the range of alpha particles in the oxides of the fissile isotopes is ~ 20 mg/cm^2 and the range of fission fragments is ~ 10 mg/cm^2 so that the practical limit on film thickness, for a reasonable plateau, is 1 mg/cm^2 (or, at most, 2 mg/cm^2).

2.3.3. Radiative capture.

As observed in Chapter 1, if a heavy element captures a neutron, the compound nucleus will acquire the binding energy of about 8 MeV. This energy, however, cannot be liberated by charged particle emission, since the Coulomb barrier prevents the emission of charged particles with an energy of only a few MeV. Therefore the bulk of the energy is released in prompt gamma emission. If the compound nucleus is itself a stable nuclide in the ground state (e.g. $Cd^{113} + n \rightarrow Cd^{114}$), all the energy will appear in gamma emission. If the compound nucleus is an unstable nuclide in its ground state (e.g. $Au^{197} + n \rightarrow Au^{198} \rightarrow Hg^{198} + \epsilon^-$) part of the neutron binding energy will appear in the energy release involved in beta emission, K capture etc. The prompt gamma emission, which carries away the bulk of the neutron binding energy in either case, has a spectrum whose character varies from element to element.[12]

Before discussing in detail the properties of elements which are used in neutron detection by radiative capture, a few remarks are relevant on the general subject of neutron interaction with the heavier nuclei at low energies. Apart from fission, only two reactions are possible when a slow neutron is captured by a heavy nucleus: either the neutron is re-emitted with effectively the same energy (elastic scattering) or the neutron is absorbed and the excess energy liberated through gamma emission (radiative capture). The probability of these reactions varies rapidly with neutron energy, and reaches a peak when the energy of the compound system corresponds to an excited state in the compound nucleus. The graph of cross section versus neutron energy shows a peak at these resonances, and much experimental and theoretical analysis has been expended in recent years in their elucidation.

The resonance curve is characterised by the cross section at the peak and the width at half height. In any nuclear reaction, the total width (Γ) is the sum of the partial widths for the decay of the compound nucleus, so that for the case under discussion

$$\Gamma = \Gamma \text{ absorption} + \Gamma \text{ scattering}$$
$$= \text{radiation width} + \text{neutron width}.$$

(12). Mittelman and Liedtke, in *Nucleonics*, **13**/5, 50 (1955), give a brief summary of an extensive subject.

These two widths vary considerably with neutron energy and mass of the initial nucleus. For light elements and fast neutrons, the neutron width is much greater than the radiation width, so that the interaction is primarily one of elastic scattering. In manganese, for example, which is often used as a neutron detector, the first resonance at 300 eV has been shown to be chiefly a scattering resonance. In heavy elements, however, capture resonances predominate in the thermal region. In these elements, the radiation widths are strikingly constant, both with atomic weight and with neutron energy, while the neutron widths vary widely. Finally, the radiative capture cross sections can be shown to vary as $1/v$ at very low energies, while the scattering cross sections tend to a constant. For neutron detectors which are used because of their high capture cross sections, elastic scattering at low energies is of small account.

From the practical point of view, the detection of neutrons by gamma ray emission following capture has been used but not extensively. Gamma rays following capture in cadmium have been detected in the large liquid scintillators developed at Los Alamos and elsewhere (see Chapter 3). Gamma rays have also been detected from neutron absorption in boron (see ref. 3.74 in Bibliography) and from neutron absorption in various heavy elements. More extensive use has been made from studies in which unstable isotopes are produced. Many elements produce unstable isotopes by neutron absorption, but for practical purposes of neutron detection the choice is limited to those elements which are available in a convenient form, which have adequate neutron capture cross sections and which have suitable half-lives. The cross sections and decay schemes of the elements normally used are summarised in Appendix XI and Table 2.3, but it may also be relevant to make comment on individual elements as follows:

Sodium. Sodium has been used as an absolute thermal flux detector by Grimeland (ref. 4.56) using NaI crystals. The capture cross section in the thermal region is effectively $1/v$, since the first resonance is at 3 keV.

Manganese. Manganese activation is frequently used in thermal neutron measurements. Thus, as metal foil, it is used in graphite stack measurements; as $MnSO_4$ solution it is used in baths to determine neutron source strengths, and as $CaMnO_4$ or $NaMnO_4$ it is used in the Szilard-Chalmers reaction (see below).

The first resonance, at 340 eV, is chiefly scattering.

Cobalt. Co^{60} has a half-life of 5·2 years, and is therefore useful as a monitor of reactor flux over long periods.

Cadmium. The importance of thermal neutron absorption in Cd^{113} is well known. There is a high resonance of about 3000 barns (for the natural element) at 0·2 eV, and the cross section decreases rapidly above 0·5 eV. Thus, cadmium effectively absorbs neutrons of energy less than 0·5 eV. Roughly speaking, the thickness required for the attenuation of a thermal flux by a factor of 1000 is about 0·020 in. The total energy of gamma rays released by neutron capture is about 9 MeV. The variation of the capture cross section of cadmium with neutron energy is shown in Appendix V (a).

Indium. Of all radioactive detectors, indium has been most extensively used. This is because of the convenience with which indium can be obtained in the form of pure metal, either by plating or as thin foil, because of the high capture cross section (thermal as well as resonance) and because of the strong resonance at 1·46 eV. The activation of an indium foil screened with cadmium in a slow neutron flux is largely due to the absorption of these neutrons (1·46 eV), and many studies of neutrons of energies slightly above thermal have been made using indium foils. The decay scheme (see Appendix XI) is complex. In^{116} has a 13-sec activity, which must be allowed to decay before the activity is counted. Also the natural element has a less abundant (4·8 per cent) isotope, In^{113}, which produces In^{114}. The latter has two periods, one of 72 sec, which is produced with a small capture cross section (2 barns) and a longer period of 49 days which is produced with a larger capture cross section (56 barns). The latter requires correction if irradiations are prolonged. The variation of cross section with energy is shown in Appendix V (b).

Iodine. Iodine has sometimes been used as a slow neutron detector. It has a convenient half-life (25 min) and the first resonance is at 21 eV.

Gold. Gold is of considerable importance, because its

thermal capture cross section is perhaps the best-established standard in slow neutron flux measurements (Chapter 5). Gold foils can be obtained over a wide range of thicknesses. Their activity can be determined by 4π beta counting, or, because of the gamma ray coincident with the beta ray, by coincidence measurement. The most recent value of the capture cross section is $98\cdot5 \pm 0\cdot7$ barns. The capture cross section as a function of energy is shown in Appendix V (c).

The chief properties of these radioactive indicators are summarised in Table 2.3.

Table 2.3. Isotopes used for Neutron Detection by Radioactive Capture

Capturing isotope	Half-life of product	Radiations emitted (Energies in MeV)	2200 m/s activation cross section for natural element (barns)	First resonance (eV)
Na^{23}	15 h.	$\beta-$, 1·4 γ, 2·76, 1·38	0·50	3000
Mn^{55}	2·58 h.	$\beta-$, 2·8, 1·0, 0·7 γ, 0·82, 1·6, 2·1	13·3	340
Co^{59}	5·2 y.	$\beta-$, 0·3 γ, 1·17, 1·33	36	135
Cd^{113}	—	—	2550	0·18
In^{115}	54 m.	$\beta-$, 0·6, 0·86, 1·0, 2·8 γ, 1·27, 1·5, 2·1, 0·41, 1·1, 0·14	155	1·46
I	25 m.	$\beta-$, 2·0, 1·57 γ, E.C. 5% 0·43	5·5	21
Au	2·7 d.	$\beta-$, 0·96, 1·37 γ, 0·411	98	4·9

2.3.4. The Szilard-Chalmers process.

An early event in the history of neutron detection was the discovery by Szilard and Chalmers[13] that the activity produced in the absorption of neutrons by iodine in ethyl iodide could be concentrated. This was done by extracting the radioiodine by shaking with an aqueous solution containing free iodine as a carrier and subsequently separating off the free iodine. In effect, the combination of neutron absorption and gamma emission are

(13). *Nature*, **134**, 462 (1934).

sufficient to break the chemical bond between the radioactive daughter nucleus and the rest of the molecule. An obvious condition for success is that there should be no exchange between the active material (iodine) and inactive material (ethyl iodide). If we assume that the binding energy of the neutron, 8 MeV, is released by the emission of a single gamma ray and that the mass of the recoiling nucleus is 100, then one can show, from simple consideration of energy and momentum, that the energy of recoil of the nucleus is 340 eV, which is much larger than the energy of the average chemical bond. One might superficially expect, therefore, that the efficiency is invariably 100 per cent, which is by no means always the case: it is necessary also to ensure that there is no recombination between radioactive atoms and parent molecules. However, the efficiency of the Szilard-Chalmers process can be high, and under favourable conditions can approach 100 per cent.

The Szilard-Chalmers process has been frequently used for the detection and estimation of weak neutron sources. The process has been described in several summaries.[14, 15] From the practical point of view, the materials most frequently used are ethyl iodide, as in the original experiment, and manganese in the form of $NaMnO_4$ or $KMnO_4$, from which MnO_2 is precipitated. Of these $NaMnO_4$ is to be preferred, because of the activity produced in the potassium.

2.4. Other neutron-induced reactions: endoergic reactions: threshold detectors

If energy is absorbed, rather than liberated, in a neutron-nucleus interaction, the reaction is energetically impossible with slow neutrons, and the thermal neutron cross section is zero. As the neutron energy is increased, the point will be reached at which the neutron is energetically just possible, but at which the cross section is negligibly small. As the energy is further

(14). McKay, *Prog. Nucl. Phys.* I. (Ed. O. R. Frisch), Pergamon Press, London (1950).
(15). Edge, *Aus. J. Phys.* **9**, 429 (1956).

increased, we reach the point where the cross section is small but measurable. This energy may be called the *effective threshold*. As the neutron energy increases above the effective threshold, the cross section generally increases rapidly, and then flattens off. At higher neutron energies, other reactions become possible, competition sets in, and the cross section for the first reaction declines.

In analogy with chemical processes, we call these reactions *endoergic*, since the kinetic energy of the reaction products is less than the kinetic energy of the initial particles by an amount equal to the reaction energy. This is obviously not true of fast neutron fission (say) of U^{238}, since the energy of the incoming neutron is a few MeV and the energy of the fission fragments is some 160 MeV. Nevertheless, fission in these cases is possible only with fast neutrons because there is a fission barrier, such that, if the compound nucleus has excitation energy less than this barrier, it cannot undergo fission. Therefore there is a threshold with the same characteristics as those described above. Indeed, as compared with other threshold detectors, the cross section variation with neutron energy of fast fission detectors is characterised by sharp thresholds and flat plateaux. Their properties have already been summarised in Table 2.2.

Returning to the general properties of endoergic reactions, we observe that the direct detection of an endoergic reaction is difficult, and one normally measures the activity of the radio-active product. The same considerations of suitability that we observed in the case of radioactive capture then apply : thus, the radioactive product must have a suitable half-life, so that the activity after irradiation can be followed for at least two half-lives. This is important, because other sources of activity may be present in the sample as a result of irradiation. In particular, it is essential that the effect of radiative capture (which, in the presence of a slow neutron background, could be appreciable) is minimised, either by a small radiative capture cross section or a widely differing half-life of the radioactive product.

We consider now specific cases :

(*a*) **(n,n′)**. It has been pointed out by Barschall (see ref. 0.1 in the Bibliography) that the cross section for excitation of isomeric states of certain nuclei (e.g. Au^{197m}, period 7·5 sec, and In^{115m}, half-life 4·5 hours) is relatively high (order of $\frac{1}{2}$ to 1 barn) and that these materials could also be used as threshold detectors.   So far, however, they have not been used, probably because of the high cross section for radiative capture of thermal neutrons in both these materials.

(b) **(n,p), (n,α).**   These reactions are useful in the range of 1 to 4 MeV, where the cross section can be several hundred millibarns.   In this range, the elements concerned are necessarily light, since for heavy elements the high Coulomb barrier precludes particle emission.   The cross section varies rapidly over the range, because of resonances in the compound nucleus. The effective threshold is considerably above the theoretical threshold as calculated from mass values, since, just above threshold, the energy available to the emerging particle is not nearly enough to enable it to surmount the Coulomb barrier.

Table 2.4a.   (np, nα) Reactions

Original nucleus	Radioactive nucleus half-life	Radiation emitted	Effective threshold MeV	Average cross section near peak (barns)
O^{16}	N^{16}, 7·3 sec	β^-, γ	12	0·09
Al^{27}	Mg^{27}, 10 m	β^-, γ	4	0·08
P^{31}	Si^{31}, 2·7 h	β^-	2	0·07
S^{32}	P^{32}, 14 d	β^-	2·5	0·25
Cl^{35}	P^{32}, 14 d	β^-	3	0·1

Table 2.4b.   (n,2n) Reactions

Original nucleus	Radioactive nucleus half-life	Radiation emitted	Effective threshold MeV	Average cross section near peak (barns)
C^{12}	C^{11}, 20 m	β^+	22	0·2
Ni^{58}	Ni^{57}, 36 h	β^+, γ	13	1·1
Cu^{63}	Cu^{62}, 10 m	β^+, γ	12	0·9
Mo^{92}	Mo^{91}, 15·5 m	β^+	14	1·0
I^{127}	I^{126}, 13 d	β^-, γ	11	1·3
Tl^{203}	Tl^{202}, 300 h	E.C., α	12	1·0

Also, the neutron energy at which the cross section becomes appreciable depends considerably on the effect of resonances. Thus, these threshold detectors are, in effect, useful only for qualitative estimates of neutron flux. The variation of the $P^{31}(n,p)Si^{31}$ and $S^{32}(n,p)P^{32}$ cross sections with neutron energy is shown in Appendix VI, and the general properties of these detectors are listed in Table 2.4.

(c) **(n,2n) reactions.** In this reaction, a neutron is, in effect, ejected from the nucleus, so that the threshold will be the binding energy (multiplied by a small factor, allowing for centre-of-mass motion). Above this, the cross section generally rises to a fairly flat peak around 3 to 5 MeV above threshold, and then declines, due to competition. Typical examples, such as that of $Cu(n,2n)$, is given in Appendix VII.

The properties of the main radioactive threshold detectors are given in Table 2.4 a, b. It will be appreciated that the estimates of threshold and average cross section near peak are both qualitative and approximate. For more precise details, the reader is referred to references (2.16) to (2.28) in the Bibliography.

As threshold detectors will not specifically figure in subsequent chapters, we may perhaps conclude with two types of experiments in which they have been used:

(a) For measurements of high intensity bursts of neutrons over short periods, the usual type of electronic detectors can be saturated, whereas threshold detectors can be used to estimate both neutron flux and spectra. Such a technique has been described by Hurst et al.[29] with particular reference to the determination of neutron spectra from bursts of neutrons. To minimise thermal neutron absorption, the threshold detectors were sheathed in boron spheres. The detectors used were:

Thermal neutrons, gold (radiative capture)
Fast neutrons: 1–750 keV, Pu^{239} (fission)
                750–1500 keV, Np^{237} (fission)
                1·5–2·5 MeV, U^{238} (fission)
                Above 2·5 MeV, $S(n,p)$.

(29). *Rev. Sci. Inst.* **27,** 153 (1956).

To the extent that the range of the threshold detectors over-lapped, appropriate subtractions were made.

(*b*) Non-elastic scattering of 14 MeV neutrons from the T-D reaction by various materials can be studied by irradiating a threshold detector, e.g. copper, near the source and then surrounding the source with a sphere of the material under investigation.   If elastic scattering in the material is the only possible reaction, the spectrum of the neutron flux emerging from the sphere will be unchanged, and the copper activation will be unchanged.   If the non-elastic cross section is high (i.e. if there is a high probability that the neutron will be captured, or will be reduced in energy), the copper activation will be considerably reduced.   A typical experiment of this kind has been described by Phillips *et al.*[30]

(30). *Phys. Rev.* **88**, 600 (1952).

3

THE CHIEF
INSTRUMENTS
OF
NEUTRON
DETECTION

In this chapter, we shall discuss the principles and properties of the four main methods of neutron detection. For fuller accounts of individual methods the reader is referred to standard texts (see refs. (1) to (3)).

3.1. The ionisation chamber

Let us consider a parallel plate ion chamber which is filled with a boron compound in gaseous form. A neutron has been captured by a boron nucleus, and both alpha and lithium 7 tracks lie between the plates as shown in Fig. 3.1. To estimate the charge collected on the plates by an applied voltage and the voltage change produced by the collection of this charge, we

(1). Rossi, B. B., and Staub, H. H. *Ionization Chambers and Counters*. N.N.E.S. Dio. V, Vol. 2. McGraw-Hill, New York (1949).
(2). Staub, H. H. *Experimental Nuclear Physics*, Vol. I (a). Detection Methods. Ed. E. Segre. John Wiley & Sons, New York (1953).
(3). Wilkinson, D. H. *Ionization Chambers and Counters*. The University Press, Cambridge (1950).

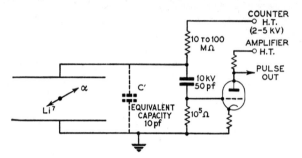

Fig. 3.1.   Schematic of ionisation chamber.

assume for simplicity that there is a single emergent particle with energy 2·4 MeV, and that the energy expended per ion pair is 32 eV.   The number of ion pairs produced is approximately

$$\frac{2\cdot4 \times 10^6}{32} = 75,000$$

and the charge collected on the plates is therefore

$$7\cdot5 \times 10^4 \times 4\cdot8 \times 10^{-10} \text{ e.s.u.} = 3\cdot6 \times 10^{-5} \text{ e.s.u.} \approx 10^{-14}$$
$$\text{coulombs.}$$

If the plates are small, and the interplate capacity C' is 10 pf $= 10^{-11}$ farad, the change in voltage across the plates is 1 mV. It is clear then that detection of individual pulses requires considerable voltage amplification; or conversely, if the current carried by the chamber is to be measured with simple meters, then a high reaction rate is required.

We have assumed here, however, that all electrons and ions are completely and instantaneously collected.   This is, of course, not the case and we consider below the conditions under which this can be approximately realised.

3.1.1. (a) The behaviour of free ions and electrons in gases.   The mean free path of molecules in a gas at N.T.P. is about 10^{-5} cm, and the mean free path of low energy ions and electrons is, roughly speaking, of the same order.   Hence, before the electrons or positive ions formed by a fast moving charged particle from a nuclear reaction can be collected on the plates of the ion chamber, they must undergo very many collisions with the molecules of gas in the chamber. Let us consider, first, the electron. Since it is very light, its mean velocity in the direction of the applied field is high. The velocity, of course, depends on the mean free path which varies inversely as the pressure (p), and on the applied electric field, X. The electron velocity for a number of typical counter gases as a function of X/p, is shown graphically in Appendix VIII. For most practical conditions, it is of the order of 10^7 cm/sec, although it varies with different gases and different conditions over the range 10^6 cm/sec to 10^8 cm/sec. In effect, the average time taken for an electron to travel between the plates of an ion chamber separated by 1 cm is of the order of $\frac{1}{10}$ microsecond.

The positive ions, formed in a gas in the wake of a fast-moving charged particle, being much heavier, move much more slowly, and traverse the chamber in a time of the order of 1 millisecond. Historically, the instruments used in neutron detection aimed originally at collecting both positive and negative charges formed in the gas. This posed many problems: for example, the amplifier time constants had to be long, so that sources of audiofrequency noise, such as microphony in the valves or higher harmonics of the a.c. input, could easily lead to trouble. Hence in modern detection systems, the emphasis is almost exclusively on electron collection, i.e. on fast counting systems.

Returning to the career of electrons through gases, we observe that after a collision the electron can be scattered in any direction. In a frame of reference moving with the drift velocity of the electron, we should observe the electron gaining energy of random motion, through successive elastic collisions. For a monatomic gas like argon, this *agitation energy* can become quite high, e.g. 300 times the thermal energy of the gas atoms. Now, it so happens in argon that for very slow electrons the collision cross section is very low (Ramsauer effect), i.e. a very slow electron would traverse the gas with few collisions. As the agitation energy increases, however, the cross section rises rapidly, and the electron undergoes many more collisions, and the mean drift velocity is reduced. If, however, a small amount of polyatomic gas such as CO_2 is added, then an electron in collision with a CO_2 molecule can undergo an inelastic collision whereby the energy of the electron is absorbed in rotation or vibration energy of the molecule. Consequently, the agitation energy is much reduced, and the drift velocity is increased. The addition of polyatomic gases (such as, for example, CO_2 in A or He^3 filled chambers, or CH_4 in H filled chambers) is fairly common.

3.1.1. (b) Saturation.
In a very pure inert gas, the probability of electron capture by neutral gas atoms is small. Unfortunately, it is difficult to ensure that the gas in a counter is of very high purity, especially as some of the constituent impurities such as oxygen or water vapour must be reduced to concentrations of less than one part in 10^7. Even if the counter is perfectly vacuum tight, one must go to considerable lengths to ensure that impurities which gradually emerge from absorption on the walls of the counter have no effect on the counter performance. If we consider electron capture in oxygen, we observe that the probability of capture varies fairly rapidly as the electron energy is varied (Wilkinson,[3] p. 41). In particular, if the electron energy is low (0·1 eV) the capture probability is high, while if the energy is near 1 volt, the capture probability is low. Hence the normal test, to confirm that electron capture is not taking place, is to vary the voltage. At low voltages, a very small amount of contamination will affect the performance, and the pulse height from the counter will increase with increasing voltage. At higher voltages, the losses due to electron attachment become small and constant, so that the pulse height becomes constant with increasing voltage. When this happens, *saturation* is said to have been reached. One can then be reasonably sure that electron attachment on the impurities has been minimised, and that the residual attachment is constant. It should be made clear, however, that the question of saturation concerns primarily those counters in which a spectrum of pulses is to be accurately determined, and in which it is necessary to ensure that the spectrum is not distorted by the electron attachment. For example, in flux measurement or neutron spectrometry with H_2 or He^3 filled proportional counters (see 3.2, p. 62) it is essential that negative ion formation should be negligible. In many cases, however,

the phenomenon of electron attachment is not so important. We cite two typical cases :

(1) If one is measuring the direct current in a counter and the pressure and counting rate are not high, the phenomenon of electron attachment does not affect the issue. For one is measuring the total current, which includes all negative charges, whether they are electrons or negative ions. If, however, there is a high reaction rate or high pressure, then recombination can take place either between ions produced from different pulses (high count rate) or from ions in a single track (high pressure). This is because, while the probability of recombination between electrons and heavy positive ions is very small, the probability of recombination between positive and negative ions is quite large.

(2) Often one is counting neutrons simply with ionisation chambers lined with boron or fissile material. In these circumstances, the pulses are generally large compared with any extraneous pulses due, for example, to electrons released by gamma rays, or to noise in the amplifier. The spectrum is not important, so that provided the bias is set to eliminate effects of noise and gamma rays, the problem of saturation and negative ion formation is not serious.

Despite what has been said above, it has been claimed by Facchini and Malvicini[4] that as much as 0·5 per cent of oxygen can be added to a mixture of argon and 4 per cent nitrogen without appreciably affecting the electron-collecting properties of the mixture. It is to be presumed that the agitation energy, under experimental conditions, in the nitrogen-argon mixture was such that the resonance for electron capture in oxygen was not reached. However, the use of oxygen as a constituent of counter fillings is not to be recommended, and, in general, the use of clean techniques and pure gases is worth considerable effort.

The fact that the current from a counter varies with applied voltage, below saturation, has been used by McCreary and Bayard,[5] in obtaining a neutron-sensitive boron-lined counter

(4). *Nucleonics*, **13**/4, 36 (April 1955).
(5). *Rev. Sci. Inst.* **25**, 161 (1954).

with electronically adjusted gamma ray compensation. The problem is this. One wishes to measure neutron flux, at low levels, in a pile which, as a result of previous running, may have a considerable residual gamma flux. In principle, one has two equal counters, one with boron lining and the other without boron lining, and measures the difference current, which will then be due to the neutron flux. The principle of the method is shown in Fig. 3.2; one measures the mean current to the signal electrode, which, in the absence of neutrons, would receive equal

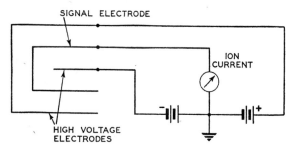

Fig. 3.2. Schematic of compensated ionisation chamber and associated circuit (McCreary & Bayard, ref. 5).

numbers of positive and negative charges on the two sides due to the gamma flux. The method is simple, but in practice the question of mechanically adjusting two counter volumes to equality proves troublesome. McCreary and Bayard overcome this difficulty by varying the voltage on one counter of the type described in 3.1.2 (b) below. Since one is below saturation, the current on this side varies with voltage, and by a fine control of this kind the contribution of the gamma flux can be accurately balanced out, and the range of neutron sensitivity extended. As one would expect, the degree of compensation changes slowly with time.

We conclude these paragraphs with some purely practical considerations.

(i) **High voltages: leakage and breakdown.** Most ionisation chambers operate in the range 200 to 4000 volts, while high pressure chambers may require up to 20,000 volts. As the simple illustration at the beginning of this chapter showed, the insulation in a counter must be very high, and all effects due to leakage or breakdown must be eliminated. The first source of these breakdowns is the signal lead into the chamber, and is very well illustrated by a diagram given by Weill,[6] and shown in Fig. 3.3. Fig. 3.3 (a) states the problem. Fig. 3.3 (b) is the guard ring which is extensively used as a solution to the problem of breakdown or leakage in the signal

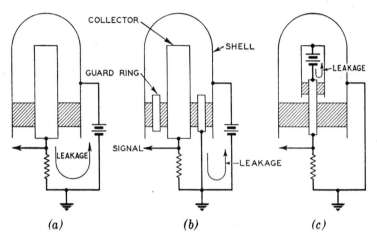

Fig. 3.3.   Leakage schematic (Weill, ref. 6).

lead. Fig. 3.3 (c) shows a neat solution to the leakage problem when the applied voltage is sufficiently low to permit the battery to be built into the chamber.

In addition to the signal lead, insulating supports are normally used elsewhere in the chamber, and the material should be carefully chosen (a useful list is compiled by Wilkinson,[3] p. 106). If, as in (ii) below, a clean technique is adopted, with the whole system capable of being baked, glass-to-metal seals are strongly recommended although quartz insulators used with Invar metal and "Araldite" as a thermo-setting plastic have given good results. Organic materials such as polystyrene can be used; they have the advantage of being machinable, but are a source of gas contaminants, and, if in

(6). *Nucleonics*, **15**/8, 45 (August) 1957.

sufficient bulk, will appreciably moderate fast neutrons. Teflon (tetrapolyfluorethylene) is an excellent inert hydrogen-free machinable insulator. Because of its mode of production, however, it tends to contain appreciable quantities of absorbed gas and must be strongly outgassed. The series capacitor, often used between detecting system and high tension collecting electrode, must be chosen so as to withstand a d.c. voltage two or three times the normal operating voltage. All sharp points and edges inside and outside the chamber must be eliminated. Since most chambers consist of a positive and negative electrode, and since breakdown probability rises rapidly with voltage, it is sometimes useful practice to divide a voltage of 10 kV across the chamber between electrodes of $+5$ kV and -5 kV. Outside the chamber, high tension connecting leads must be reduced to a minimum, and, if possible, the high tension system hermetically sealed and dried with silica gel. Ceresin wax at strategic points outside the chamber can also aid breakdown problems, although the extensive use of wax and polythene in leads can affect, for example, the number of slow neutrons in the vicinity of a fast neutron counter.

(ii) **Anti-contamination techniques.** Prescriptions for counter construction vary with individual tastes. In general clean techniques are good techniques, and the only way to ensure reliable counter performance is by elimination as far as possible of all contaminants. Oxygen and water vapour, as we have seen, capture electrons to form slow moving negative ions which readily recombine with positive ions, and are in any case lost in a fast electronic system. Therefore the counter must not only be thoroughly vacuum tight, but should if possible be capable of being thoroughly outgassed by baking. Water vapour absorbed in the walls of a fast neutron counter, of course, contributes not only to the contamination of the gas in the counter, but is a source of unwanted proton recoils in the counter. This source of difficulty can be considerably reduced by plating the inner walls of the counter with platinum or gold, for which the absorption of water vapour is relatively small: although this means that the counter cannot be outgassed above about 150°C. The solvents used for cleaning the counter and its insulators should also be considered. Chlorine and its compounds are powerful absorbers of electrons, so that a counter which has been cleaned with carbon tetrachloride or trichlorethylene is unlikely to give satisfactory performance. While outgassing by baking is recommended, it is not essential. The counter constructed by Aves and Batchelor for the He^3 spectrometer (Chapter 4) was constructed with quartz insulators cemented into Invar supports with "Araldite", and many authors have reported similar constructions. If necessity demands such construction, the material chosen for the cement should have a negligible vapour pressure, and the counter should be outgassed by long pumping.

If the experiment requires that the counter should be demountable, rubber and O-ring seals should be avoided, unless the experiment is of very short duration. An O-ring seal often gives off enough vapour to give serious deterioration after about a week's use. The counter should be made so that a soft-soldered joint can readily be made or broken. Alternatively, indium in the form of wire or sheet, or indium-plated copper rings filled with air at high pressure (Wills rings) have been successfully used. Other metal gaskets (Cu, Al) in vacuum techniques are becoming more popular but they suffer from the drawback, as regards neutron counters, of requiring heavy flanges which may involve neutron scattering.

Having ensured clean conditions in the counter, it is obviously necessary to ensure clean conditions in the filling gas. Recipes for ensuring purity of the counter gas are briefly summarised as follows:

Hydrogen. Hydrogen may be boiled off liquid hydrogen, or from charcoal in a liquid-air-cooled trap, or (preferably) evolved from pyrophoric uranium which has absorbed hydrogen as UH$_3$ (roughly speaking, 1 cu. in. of pyrophoric uranium will store 6 litres of hydrogen at N.T.P.).

Hydrocarbons (CH$_4$, C$_2$H$_6$, C$_3$H$_8$ etc.). These can be obtained commercially at high purity from prolonged fractional distillation. The last traces of oxygen and water can be removed by storing in glass flasks, on the walls of which sodium has been evaporated.

Noble gases (A, He). These are conveniently maintained in reservoirs, such that a side tube to the reservoir contains heated calcium or magnesium turnings (300°C), over which the gas circulates by thermal convection.

CO_2. CO_2 can be stored in glass flasks with sodium lining, but, for most practical purposes, CO_2 of adequate purity can be obtained by volatilisation from dry ice and repeated fractionation from liquid air traps.

3.1.2. The induction effect. Consider the situation represented in Figs. 3.4 (a) and 3.4. (b). An ion pair has been formed near one plate of an ionisation chamber of capacity C, and, after a period of the order of one microsecond, the electron is collected on the positive electrode. In a period of the order of one millisecond, the positive ion will be collected on the negative electrode, and the full voltage change $-e/C$ appears across the counter. However, as we have explained, "slow" counters involve serious difficulties, and it is with "fast"

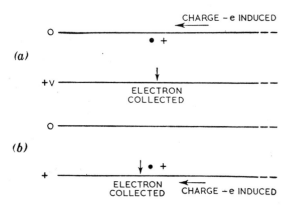

Fig. 3.4. Schematic illustrating effect of induction.

counters, with response times of a few microseconds, that we shall be concerned. Under these conditions, we observe that, in Fig. 3.4 (a), where the ion pair is formed near the negative electrode, the charge induced by the positive ion in the positive electrode is small. A charge of approximately $-e$ is induced in the negative electrode, while a charge $-e$ is collected at the positive electrode, so that nearly the full voltage change $-e/C$ appears across the counter. In Fig. 3.4 (b) however, the positive ion is near the positive electrode. The electron is collected, but a charge of nearly $-e$ is induced in the same electrode. In effect, the collected electron is bound by the proximity of the positive ion, and the net voltage appearing across the counter is small. As we shall see later, it is useful to regard the voltage change as related to the amount of work done on the moving electron.

Thus, according to the position of formation of the ion pair in the chamber, the voltage developed across the counter can vary from zero to a maximum. For example, a parallel plate chamber, filled with BF_3 and irradiated with thermal neutrons, will give a differential pulse spectrum which is continuous from zero to a maximum. The effects of induction, especially as applied to alpha sources, are extensively discussed by Rossi and Staub,[2] and by Wilkinson.[3]

The effects of induction, then, must be eliminated or minimised, as follows:

(a) **Solid sources.** If the source of pulses is a solid (e.g. boron in a thermal neutron beam), the lining can be restricted to the negative plate, and the counter pressure raised so that the track lengths are small compared with the interelectrode distance.

(b) **The Frisch grid.** For a thin solid radiator, the effects of induction can effectively be eliminated by the ingenious method

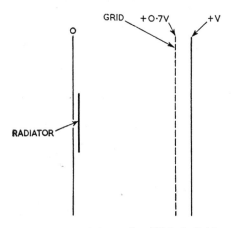

Fig. 3.5. Schematic of Frisch Grid.

suggested by O. R. Frisch.[7]   Consider the situation represented by Fig. 3.5.   Alphas are emitted (e.g. from a boron foil under slow neutron irradiation) at the negative electrode of a parallel plate ion chamber, and the range of the alphas is roughly half the width of the chamber.   In a simple chamber, the pulses produced by tracks at different angles will vary with the position of the track, due to the induction effect.   If now, near the positive electrode, we place a grid of fine wires, held at a voltage near the full positive voltage, the fields in the vicinity of the grid will be such that most electrons from the ionisation will pass through the grid and be collected on the positive

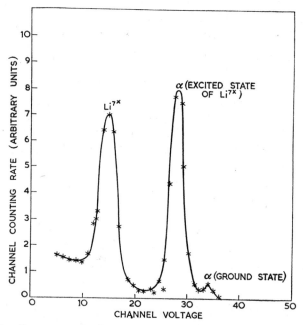

Fig. 3.6.   Spectrum of pulses from gridded ion chamber, using electromagnetically separated B^{10} in a thermal neutron beam (Raffle, ref. 9).

electrode (the transmission of grids under various conditions has been studied by Bunemann, Cranshaw and Harvey[8]).   The charge induced by the stationary positive ions, however, is

(7). British Atomic Energy Report, BR 49 (n.d.).
(8). *Can. J. Res* **A.27**, 191 (1949).

limited to the grid, so that the pulse size is constant, and nearly equal to the maximum pulse size in the absence of a grid.

Such a counter has been developed by Raffle[9] in studies of fission cross sections for thermal neutrons, the boron film being on aluminium sheets on which B^{10} was deposited in an electromagnetic separator. Fig. 3.6 shows the bias curve obtained by Raffle with this counter. Recalling that the reaction involved is

$$B^{10} + n \rightarrow Li^{7*} + \alpha$$
$$\rightarrow Li^7 + \alpha$$

we should expect four particle groups (two alpha groups, a Li^7 and a Li^{7*}) to be observable in the bias curve. Fig. 3.6 shows this clearly, except that the two lithium groups are not resolved.

In general, however, we should observe that the use of Frisch grids arises only in special applications in neutron detection. Another example is in the counter of Nereson and Darden (see Chapter 4.3 (c)).

(c) **The cylindrical ion chamber.** The voltage pulse developed across a chamber, when the electron has crossed the

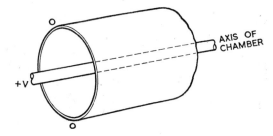

Fig. 3.7.   Schematic of cylindrical ion chamber.

chamber but the residual positive ion is stationary, is related to the work done on the electron by the applied field, as reference to Fig. 3.4 (a) and (b) shows. If now we have a cylindrical ionisation chamber with a narrow positive central electrode, as represented by Fig. 3.7, the electric field (which varies as $1/r$) across most of the counter is low, since most of the voltage drop occurs in the immediate vicinity of the central wire. Therefore, the work done on an electron arising from ionisation in

(9). Private communication, and to be published.

most of the volume of the counter will be approximately constant, and one is much closer to the situation whereby the pulse size is independent of the position of ionised particles in the track. Such a chamber is, for example, described by Larsson and Taylor,[10] who developed the BF_3 counter for precision measurements on neutron sources. Larsson's chamber had an outer diameter of 1·2 cm, with a 1 mm platinum wire for the central anode. The counter was filled with BF_3 at various pressures, and was used to measure the flux of slow neutrons in a water bath. Tracks could occur at any point in the counter, and Larsson calculated the bias curve to be expected under these conditions. His experimental curves are shown in Fig. 3.8, and agreed reasonably well with calculations.

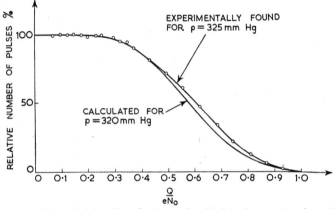

Fig. 3.8. Pulse height distribution of cylindrical ion chamber filled with BF_3 (Larsson, ref. 10).

The effect of boron absorbed on the walls was determined by filling the chamber with argon: when a small correction for this effect had been made, the count rate was shown to be proportional to pressure.

3.1.3. Some practical ionisation chambers.
Ionisation chambers have been used for the study of proton recoil spectra, as described by Rossi and Staub, but their use in this respect

(10). *Ark. f. Fys.* **3**, 9, 131 (1950).

is limited by the fact that there is no internal amplification in an ionisation chamber, and the limit of noise set by the electronics normally corresponds to a noise level of 0·1 MeV. More common in use are ionisation chambers lined with boron and fissile material, which we shall briefly describe. In these, the normal pulse height is large compared with the pulses due to noise or to electrons from gamma rays.

(a) **Boron-lined counters.**   Counters such as that of McCreary and Bayard (Section 3.1.1) are extensively in use. Lowde[11] has described a special slow neutron counter for use with a crystal spectrometer, in which the angular resolution demanded a counter of small physical cross section but high efficiency. This was achieved by a series of thin boron-lined aluminium plates, similar to the fission counters described below. The efficiency depends critically on the number and boron film thickness of the plates. If the boron films are too thick, then many reaction products lose too much energy to be counted, so that the efficiency is low and the counter has a short plateau, if any.   On the other hand, if the boron film is too thin, too many neutrons are lost in scattering in the aluminium.   Lowde's counter, optimised for these effects, had a practical efficiency of 24 per cent as compared with a theoretical efficiency (neglecting scattering in the aluminium) of 50 per cent. The sensitive volume was 0·4 cm³, with a length of 5·7 cm.

The standard boron-lined chamber type, TQT, in use in England has been described by Jaques et al.,[12] and its BF$_3$-filled counterpart, type TPA, has been described by Taylor and Sharpe.[13]   A section diagram of the former chamber is shown in Fig. 3.9.   With the exception of the insulator assembly, it is constructed entirely of aluminium, which has a small neutron capture cross section.   The boron coating is applied to the electrodes as amorphous boron.   When finally assembled, the chamber is filled with pure argon to a pressure of 70 cm Hg, at which pressure the maximum dissipation of the available energy from the $B^{10}(n,\alpha)$ reaction is achieved consistent with the electrode spacing used in the chamber.

(11). *Rev. Sci. Inst.* **21**, 835 (1950).
(12). *Proc. I.E.E.* **100** (I), 110 (1953).
(13). *Proc. I.E.E.* **98** (II), 174 (1951).

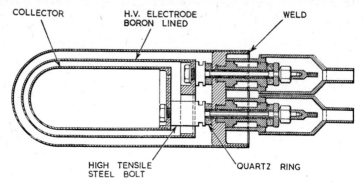

Fig. 3.9. Section diagram of ionisation chamber type TQT. (Jaques *et al.*, ref. 12).

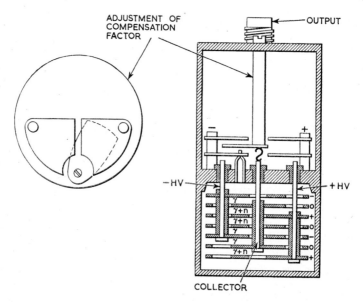

Fig. 3.10. Schematic of parallel plate compensated chamber. (Duchene *et al.*, ref. 14.)

Jaques *et al.* also describe a parallel-plate gamma-ray compensated chamber. In principle, the compensation is similar to that of the counter of McCreary and Bayard, except that a series of parallel plates are employed instead of cylindrical electrodes, and there is no fine adjustment.   A similar counter of French design[14] (Fig. 3.10) shows a simple means of providing fine adjustment in a parallel plate compensated chamber.

(b) **Fission chambers.**   Ionisation chambers lined with fissile material are widely used.   The high average energy of the fission fragments (80 MeV approx.) makes them useful in the presence of high gamma ray flux.   Like boron-lined chambers, they are limited in film thickness to about 1 mg/cm^2 (2 mg/cm^2 at most). This is because, as shown in Fig. 3.11, fission fragments

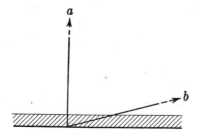

Fig. 3.11.   Particles emerging from solid radiator.

emerging in the direction a will emerge with nearly the full energy, while those emerging as at b will have reduced energy, so that they may fall below the discriminator bias level and be lost to the counting system.   Since the number of particles of type b is much greater than the number of type a, because of relative solid angles, the effect becomes appreciable at film thicknesses (1 mg/cm^2) which are small compared with the total range of fission fragments in the material under consideration (10 mg/cm^2).

A second general point is discussed by Lowde[11] and by Holmes et al.[15]   For maximum efficiency, one has a series of plates, connected alternately positive and negative, with fissile material on both sides of all plates.   This is not necessarily, however, the best arrangement.   Consider Fig. 3.12 (a) and (b).

(14). *J. Nucl. En.* **4**, 1, 26 (1957).
(15). *J. Nucl. En.* **1**, 117 (1954).

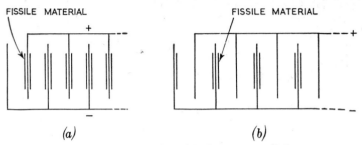

Fig. 3.12.   Schematics of fission counter linings.

(*a*) with fissile material on both plates.
(*b*) with fissile material on negative plates only.

In Fig. 3.12 (*a*) ionisation produced by fission fragments leaving the positive plates, and moving nearly parallel to the plates, will give very small pulses because of the induction effects of Section 1.3. Thus, the gain in efficiency is small, and the deterioration in plateau appreciable. A system such as (*b*) gives more favourable results: induction effects are minimised.

Three main types of ionisation chamber lined with fissile material have been described. The first is the spiral chamber of W. C. Bright, described in Rossi and Staub. The material is coated on both sides of two long strips of aluminium foils. The foils are then wound in a spiral, separated by a nylon thread. In this way a high density of fissile material is achieved, although the method of construction demands considerable technical skill.

A second type of counter is described by Rossi and Staub,[1] p. 219, and has been developed, in much smaller form, by Allen and Ferguson[16] and Ericksen *et al.*[17] Here a series of plates are mounted on a set of three pillars (two in Ericksen's counter). A second set of plates is mounted on three further pillars, and interleaved with the first set, the two sets of pillars being at 60° to each other, with insulating tubes between pillar and alternate plate. With such a counter, several hundred milligrams of fissile material can be loaded into a chamber of volume 15 cc. The chamber is relatively simple to construct and is quite

(16). *J. Nucl. En.* **2**, 38 (1955).
(17). *I.R.E. Trans. on Nucl. Science*, NS-3, **3**, 8 (1956).

robust. The plateau in the chamber of Allen and Ferguson was such that the count rate changed by about 2 per cent for a 10 per cent change in bias voltage in the operating range. The counter was loaded with U^{235}.

A third counter has been described by Aves et al.,[18] and its electrical characteristics by Holmes et al.[15] Fissile material is painted on both sides of accurately drawn nickel tubes of varying diameters, and the tubes mounted on nickel annuli forming a raft. Two such sets of tubes are made so that they fit together (see Fig. 3.13 (c)) with a spacing of any one tube from its neighbour of $\frac{1}{2}$ mm. The collecting time of this counter was shown to be less than 0·1 microsecond. One raft is mounted on an insulator, and is maintained at a potential of 300 V. The counter pressure normal in this type of counter is 10 atmospheres of argon with $\frac{1}{2}$ atmosphere of CO_2.

Developments of this counter have been described by Abson et al.[19] A variety of chambers is described, of which the one with the greatest sensitivity has a total quantity of 3 g of enriched U^{235} in a counter of 200 $\mu\mu F$ (it should be observed that the limiting size of these counters is reached when the total capacity of the counter, including connecting leads is about 400 $\mu\mu F$, since under these circumstances a fission in the counter gives a pulse which is little greater than the noise level in the first valve). Abson et al. compare the fission counter with the BF_3 proportional counter, and observe that for a given size of counter the neutron sensitivity of the BF_3 is considerably greater, by as much as one or two orders of magnitude. The gamma ray sensitivity of the BF_3 chamber, however, is much greater: the maximum permissible gamma ray level of a BF_3 counter is a few hundred r per hour, while the corresponding level for a fission counter of 100 cm^2 surface area is 10^5 r/h. Also, the fission chamber is more suited to high temperature operation (500°C) and, in contrast to the BF_3 chamber (q.v.), there is no evidence of deterioration in characteristics after 10^{12} counts. In sum, the BF_3 chamber is more sensitive, the fission chamber is more robust.

Fig. 3.13 shows schematically each type of fission chamber.

(18). J. Nucl. En. **1**, 110 (1954).
(19). Proc. I.E.E. **105B**, 22, 349 (1958).

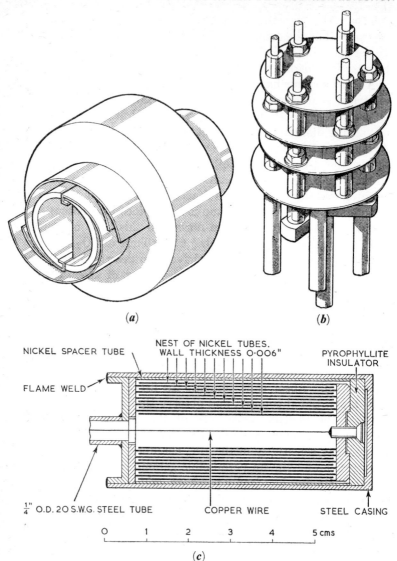

(a)   *(b)*

NICKEL SPACER TUBE   NEST OF NICKEL TUBES.   PYROPHYLLITE
                        WALL THICKNESS 0·006"   INSULATOR

FLAME WELD

$\frac{1}{4}"$ O.D. 20 S.W.G. STEEL TUBE   COPPER WIRE   STEEL CASING

O   1   2   3   4   5 cms

(c)

Fig. 3.13.   Schematics of three types of fission chamber.

(*a*) Spiral type, developed by W. C. Bright and described by Rossi
and Staub (ref. 1).

(*b*) Parallel plate type described by Allen and Ferguson (ref. 16).

(*c*) Cylindrical type described by Aves *et al.* (ref. 18).

(c)   We conclude this section with some technical notes on deposition of boron and fissile material in the linings of these counters.

(i) *Boron.*   An earlier method of deposition of boron was by the cracking of diborane gas on a metal surface heated to 900°C. This method has many difficulties.   The gas must be prepared, starting usually from the $CaF_2.BF_3$ complex, and is rather explosive.   Boron, while inert in the cold, is extremely reactive when hot, and the range of metals which when heated to 900° will accept a thin layer of boron is limited.   Tantalum is the most suitable.

A second method, equally limited in application, is the deposition of boron in an electromagnetic separator.[20]   Boron is unique among elements in that it deposits from a high voltage ion beam without sputtering.   Films can be deposited on any metal, are quite durable, and of high (B^{10}) isotopic content.   A major objection is the expense involved in the separation process.

As we have said, boron when very hot is very reactive, so that boron evaporation presents many difficulties.   Recently, however, several papers have appeared on boron evaporation. Safford[21] uses a boat of carbon, with the centre thinned down to make a hot spot.   The boron initially forms a coating of boron carbide, and thereafter evaporates as boron metal. Hill[22] wraps boron in tantalum wire, and heats by electron bombardment.   As much as 8 g of boron were evaporated in a single run.   Barnes *et al.*[23] discuss various techniques, and conclude that the use of carbon is limited by the appreciable volatilisation of carbon.   They conclude also that electron bombardment of boron, held in tantalum mesh, gives the best results, with least contamination of the resulting boron film.

(ii) *Fissile material.*   There are several reliable methods of deposition of films of fissile material.   The first is that of

(20). Smith, "Enrichment of Stable Isotopes by Electromagnetic Separation", p. 162.   *Prog. Nucl. Phys.* Vol. 6, Ed. O. R. Frisch. Pergamon Press, London (1957).

(21). *Rev. Sci. Inst.* **27**, 972 (1956).

(22). *Rev. Sci. Inst.* **27**, 1086 (abstract) (1956).

(23). A.E.R.E. Report R/M 125 (June 1957).

electrodeposition of a solution of uranium sulphate.[24],[25]
The second is a painting technique.[26] A solution in an organic
solvent is painted on the foil, and then ignited at high temperatures to convert the nitrate to oxide and to drive off the organic
material (this method precludes the use of aluminium and
nickel foils for quantitative work, and platinum is preferred).
After ignition, the film is rubbed with tissue paper to remove
flakes. Some thirty layers are required to achieve a thickness
of 1 mg/cm^2 of material. Though laborious, the method gives
durable results. The third method is of evaporation:[27] it is
simple and speedy, but the metallic film tends to oxidise slowly in
air, and the thick layer of oxide may peel off the target material.

(iii) Finally, we should mention films of hydrogenous material
used in fast neutron counters. Thick films, usually of polythene,
present no problem. Thinner films can be made of polythene,
whose thickness may be uncertain, or by the evaporation of
glycerol tristearate,[28] better known as fat. The composition
of the latter changes little under vacuum evaporation, and has
been used in accurate flux measurements.

3.2. Proportional counters

If a parallel-plate ionisation chamber is filled with BF_3 gas,
and irradiated with slow neutrons, the effect of induction is such
that, with fast collection, all pulses will be recorded from zero
to maximum. In a cylindrical ion chamber with a narrow
positive central conductor, however, the spectrum of pulses will
show a fairly high peak at maximum pulse height since for the
majority of pulses the effect of induction is small. The proportional counter is, in a sense, a development of the cylindrical
ion chamber, except that now the central positive collector is a
fine wire. If the wire diameter is sufficiently small (0·005 in. is
a normal size) and the voltage across the counter is about 2 kV,
the field in the immediate vicinity of the wire is such that some

(24). Hufford and Scott, *Natl. Nucl. En. Series.* Div. IV, Vol. IV B,
Pt II, p. 1167 ; also MDDC 1515.

(25). Fleming, Jr. A.E.C.D. 3395 (1952).

(26). Glover and Borrell, A.E.R.E. Report C/R 1359 (1954).

(27). Milsted, A.E.R.E. Report C/R 1379 (1954).

(28). Strong, *Procedures in Experimental Physics.* Prentice Hall
(1946).

electrons, between collisions, can acquire sufficient energy to ionise the molecules with which they next collide. The ionisation process thus releases a second electron, which, being accelerated near the wire, has a higher probability again of ionisation by further impact. Thus, we have the incipient avalanche of corona breakdown.

At low voltages, then, the proportional counter behaves like an ionisation chamber. If the counter is thoroughly clean, the pulse size from, say, alpha particles liberated from the outer wall is constant with voltage. As the voltage is increased, however, there is a starting voltage at which the multiplication referred to above sets in. Initially, the probability of any one electron causing additional ionisation is small, i.e. most of the electrons are collected by the wire without further ionisation. The rise of multiplication with voltage, just above threshold, is therefore quite slow. The probability of secondary ionisation, however, rises exponentially, so that eventually when the multiplication is 10,000 the increase of multiplication with voltage is very rapid. If the applied voltage is further increased slightly, the counter goes over into the Geiger discharge. This means that a single avalanche liberates not only secondary ions and electrons, but enough photons to trigger off other avalanches on either side along the wire. These avalanches release further photons, and the discharge spreads along the whole length of the wire. There is no proportionality about the Geiger discharge: it can be triggered by a single electron or a thousand.

The amplification in a Geiger discharge is very great, such that a typical counter will deliver about one volt to a counting system, and little further electronic amplification is required. Immediately after the discharge, there is a cloud of residual positive ions in the immediate vicinity of the wire. The field of these ions reduces the effective field at the wire, so that immediately following a discharge a further discharge cannot take place. Until these ions have reached the walls, the counter is not in its normal operating state: the time interval involved is about $\frac{1}{2}$ millisecond, and is called the *recovery time*. When the ions reach the wall, some may release a secondary electron which will again trigger the discharge. Therefore *quenching* is necessary, either by addition of vapours (alcohol) or by reduction of applied voltage for a period greater than the recovery time. An important feature of the Geiger counter is its plateau. As the voltage is increased above threshold, the count rate is effectively constant; eventually, the count rate for high voltages increases, because other effects give spurious pulses. We give only a brief summary of the Geiger counter, since its use in neutron detection is limited to the determination of neutron-induced radioactivity. More detailed accounts will be found in references (3) and (29).

Returning to the situation of low multiplication in a proportional counter (say, 10) we make two further points. First, for a given counter voltage, the multiplication is constant, so that the size of pulse is proportional to the number of ion pairs in the track of the fast ionising particle. Hence the name proportional counter. The second point concerns the statistics of the amplification process. While one incoming electron will on the average liberate nine further electrons, there is still an appreciable chance that an electron will be collected without ionisation, and of course, by implication, a chance that some electrons will liberate many more than 9 electrons. Now, from the statistical point of view, 10 is a small number, and one might superficially expect that the pulse height registered by the counter will show a wide spread due to the wide scatter associated with the probability of ionisation by individual electrons. However, it was shown by Frisch[30] that the straggle in a proportional counter is never more than twice the straggle in the initial number of electrons, and the effect is never serious.

Proportional counters have several important advantages. In the first place, the internal amplification is such that the pulses from low energy particles (down to 10 keV or less) can be registered. By contrast, as we have seen, the ionisation chamber is limited by noise in the amplifier to recoils of energy greater than 0.1 MeV. A second considerable advantage is the fact that the pulse size is independent of the position of the

(29). Korff, *Encyclopaedia of Physics*, Vol. XLV, Nuclear Instrumentation II. Springer-Verlag, Berlin (1958).

(30). *Prog. Nucl. Phys.* Vol. 3. Ed. O. R. Frisch. Pergamon Press, London (1953).

track in the counter. For, with reasonable multiplication, the contribution to the pulse of the electrons from the original track is small compared with the contribution from the electrons released in the immediate vicinity of the wire, so that the induction effects are constant.

For the study of spectra, the resolution of the counter depends critically on constancy of multiplication. In the first place, this requires a high uniformity of wire diameter. Platinum wire is usually quite satisfactory. (It is also essential to ensure that there are no sharp points, such as those due to kinks or dust particles, on the wire). In the second place, one must ensure that the field at the wire is uniform along its whole length. This is particularly affected by the geometry of the end of the wire. The field at the wire is obviously changed abruptly if one proceeds from wire to an end termination of different radius, and this change of field will be distributed along the wire for a distance of the order of the radius of the outer cylinder. The simplest way to ensure uniform multiplication was suggested by Cockcroft and Curran[31] and is as shown in Fig. 3.14. Field tubes at the end of the wire cover the end connection, and are held at the potential, between 0 and V,

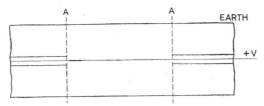

Fig. 3.14. Schematic of proportional counter with field tubes.

corresponding to the equipotential for the radius of the field tube. In this way, there is no discontinuity in field distribution at A, and multiplication is constant along the wire. Another advantage of this system is that it defines accurately the counting volume, if tracks are produced by neutron reactions in the gas, as for example by proton recoils in hydrogen. Thus, the "end" of the counter is the plane denoted by A in Fig. 3.14. A second method of ensuring uniform field in the

(31). *Rev. Sci. Inst.* **22**, 37 (1951).

counter is by terminating the counter at A in a semiconducting sheet. The potential distribution in the sheet is the same as the potential distribution in the main volume of the counter, so that the field at the wire is constant. Such a counter has been developed for hydrogen counters by R. C. Allen.[32] The advantage of such a counter is that it is compact: but it has not been widely used.

Practical considerations. Conditions for proportional counters, as regards saturation and voltage breakdown, are much the same as for ionisation chambers. Because the multiplication varies with voltage, the voltage must be kept constant to 0.1 per cent. The question of negative ion formation is important, because it must be remembered that, in contrast to a parallel-plate chamber, nearly all the voltage drop in a proportional counter occurs in the immediate vicinity of the wire. In the outer regions of the counter the collecting field is low, so that the probability of electron attachment is correspondingly high. This factor determines, in effect, the practical size of wire. If the wire is too large the counter requires a very high voltage to give adequate multiplication. If the wire is too small, the collecting field is too low and the probability of attachment too high. Wire diameters between 0.025 mm and 0·125 mm are normally used.

As regards breakdown, the use of positive and negative voltages has been effectively combined by Skyrme, Tunnicliffe and Ward[33] with the necessity for field tubes (Chapter 4, Fig. 4.5). In their counter, the wire is held positive, the cathode negative, and the field tubes are earthed.

The BF₃ counter. The BF_3 proportional counter is the most widely used of all counters for neutron detection and we shall consider it now in some detail. Some other designs of proportional counter will be discussed in Chapter 4.

The range of α-particles of 1·5 MeV energy in BF_3 at N.T.P. is about $\frac{1}{2}$ cm. With a $\frac{1}{2}$ in. diameter counter and pressures of 40 to 70 cm Hg *end and wall effects*, i.e. effects due to particle tracks which terminate in the walls or end of the counter, and

(32). Los Alamos Report LADC 2442 (unpublished) (1955, decl. 1956); *Phys. Rev.* **105**, 1796 (1957).
(33). *Rev. Sci. Inst.* **23**, 204 (1952).

therefore give pulses less than the full pulse height, will be small but appreciable. Since the energy released in the reaction (2·4 MeV) is high compared with electrons released by gamma rays, there is no need to pay close attention to uniformity of multiplication, and practical counters do not incorporate the field tubes described above, except as protection against voltage breakdown.

Basically, then, the BF₃ counter is a proportional counter in its simplest form. Good BF₃ counters are nevertheless very difficult to make, because BF₃ is a reactive gas and the clean techniques recommended earlier are here not merely preferable but are essential to success. As pointed out by Fowler and Tunnicliffe,[34] a trace of water in a BF₃ counter with glass walls continuously converts BF₃ into SiF₄ by the sequence of the type

$$3H_2O + 2BF_3 \rightarrow B_2O_3 + 6HF$$
$$4HF + SiO_2 \rightarrow SiF_4 + 2H_2O$$

and so on (the presence of SiF₄ in the gas of a counter of poor characteristics was confirmed in Fowler and Tunnicliffe's work by mass spectrometer). The remedy, according to these authors, after the usual precautions of outgassing had been thoroughly carried out, was to "soak" the counters in BF₃ gas for periods up to three months. They consider that the soaking may produce a thin layer on the walls of the counter, which prevents the emergence of further reaction products.

BF₃ counters tend to be temperature sensitive. Increased temperatures were found by Lockwood and Bennett[35] to have a marked deteriorating effect on counter performance, which was attributed to the evolution of electronegative impurities from the walls. Sobermann et al.[36] reported marked deterioration in BF₃ counters due to high counting rates. They operated at rates of up to 10^6 per minute, and after 10^8 counts (at high multiplication) there was a marked deterioration in counter performance. They suggest that the deterioration was due to the action of free fluorine, which is liberated as a result

(34). *Rev. Sci. Inst.* **21**, 734 (1950).
(35). *Rev. Sci. Inst.* **25**, 446 (1954).
(36). *Rev. Sci. Inst.* **24**, 1058 (1953).

of the intense ionisation. The counters showed partial recovery on standing.

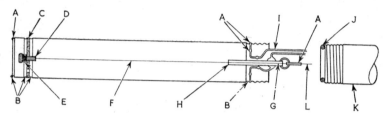

Fig. 3.15. Schematic of BF₃ proportional counter developed by Abson *et al.* (ref. 37).

Counter Body: constructed of high-conductivity oxygen-free copper.

A. Hard soldered at these 4 points using silver-copper eutectic solder, melting point 778°C.

B. Swages rolled into body for location of end caps and for locking quartz disc.

C. Quartz disc.

D. Tube for end termination—spring loaded.

E. Inconel coil spring.

F. Tungsten or inconel wire anode.

G. Spot weld to anode wire.

H. Guard ring electrode.

I. Glass to metal seal.

J. O ring seal.

K. Screwed end cap of appropriate length and fitted with optional end termination provides airtight joint when screwed into counter body.

L. Nickel or ferry wire.

The construction of BF₃ chambers, then, requires considerable care. We shall describe in detail the counter technique developed by the Harwell group (Abson *et al.*[37]). Earlier counters constructed of turned brass for the outer wall gave difficulties, and thin-walled oxygen-free copper is now invariably used, in sizes from ½ in. dia. and 6 in. long, to 2 in. diameter and several feet long (from the point of view of neutron absorption aluminium is to be preferred, but its use involves other technical difficulties). Fig. 3.15 shows a schematic of a 1 in. diameter counter. All metal parts are brazed by R.F. heating, using silver-copper eutectic without flux, in an atmosphere of 70 per cent nitrogen and 30 per cent hydrogen. The BF₃ for the counters is prepared by heating the BF₃.CaF₂ complex to 250°, and passing through traps cooled to dry ice temperatures to remove water vapour, and NaF to remove HF.

(37). A.E.R.E. Report EL/R. 2280 (1957); *Proc. I.E.E.* **105B**, 22, 357 (1958).

Eventually the gas is frozen into a liquid nitrogen trap, and transferred to a storage flask. The counters are vacuum baked at 400°C for three hours, then "soaked" in BF₃ gas for several hours. The counters are next pumped hard, and the BF₃ filling gas is frozen into a trap connected by a mercury cut-off valve to the filling manifold. The frozen BF₃ is then allowed to warm up until the counters are filled to a pressure slightly less than atmospheric, when the trap is again cooled to reduce the pressure by a factor of two or three. This process is carried out at least three times quickly in order to enable all the gas to come into contact with the cold trap but without completely freezing it again. Remaining impurities with higher freezing points may thus be removed. The gas pressure is finally allowed to rise to the required filling pressure, the mercury cut-off closed, and the counter sealed off at the glass stem.

As regards counter life, Abson and his co-workers find that

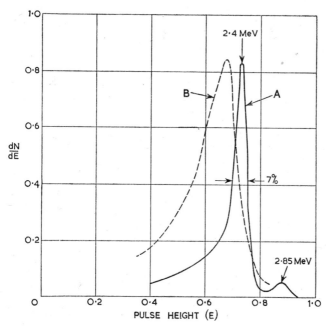

Fig. 3.16.   Differential Bias Curves of two BF₃ proportional counters.
A. 2 in. diameter counter.   **B.** 2 in. diameter counter.
BF₃ pressure, 40 cm.Hg. (Abson *et al.*, ref. 37).

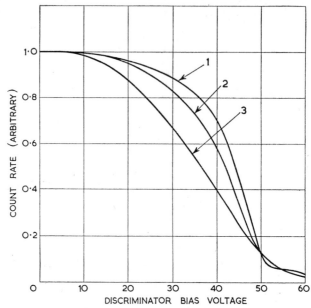

Fig. 3.17. Integral Bias Curves for 1 in. diameter BF_3 counters with 0.002 in. diameter anode wires.

  1. BF_3 pressure 70 cm.Hg. anode voltage 2,400V (M = 40).
  2. BF_3 pressure 40 cm.Hg. anode voltage 1,800V (M = 40).
  3. BF_3 pressure 20 cm.Hg. anode voltage 1,200V (M = 40).

(Abson *et al.*, ref. 37).

with gas multiplication factors of 8, 40 and 400 the life is of the order of 10^{11}, 10^{10} and 10^9 counts respectively. The counters recover after heating for several hours at 180°C, when the rate of deterioration is apparently less. The reduction in rate of deterioration is not fully understood. As regards temperature sensitivity, the counters show no change over a period of several months at 100°C, while at 150°C a change is observable after a few weeks. This is to be contrasted with the observations of Lockwood and Bennett,[35] who noted a change in integrated yield of 2 per cent per degree C, and of Schultz and Connor[38] who report considerable change in counter response for temperature changes between 92°F, 160°F and 196°F.

As regards pulse height spectra, Fig. 3.16 shows a typical

(38). *Nucleonics*, **12**/2, 8 (1954).

differential bias curve. The reproducibility of the counters is such that when several are connected in parallel, the ground state group at 2·8 MeV is still resolved. Fig. 3.17 shows the effect of pressure: it is seen that the end and wall effects at pressures of 20 cm in a 1 in. diameter counter are appreciable.

Time delay in BF₃ counters. Since BF_3 counters are frequently used in time-of-flight experiments, the delay in a BF_3 proportional counter can be of importance. This delay arises from the fact that some tracks will be formed near the centre wire to which the counter will respond almost immediately, while other tracks, near the outer wall, will release electrons

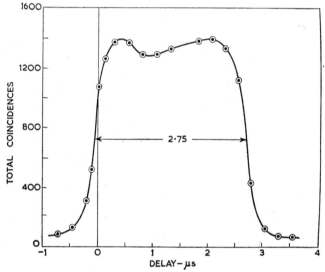

Fig. 3.18. Variation with delay of coincidence between counter pulse and gamma ray signal in an adjacent scintillation counter (Nicholson, ref. 39).

which take a time of the order of microseconds to reach the wire. This delay has been studied by Nicholson[39] who detected the 480 keV gamma rays from the $B^{10}(n,\alpha)Li^{7*}$ in a large NaI crystal placed near the counter, and determined the distribution of counts in the BF_3 counter as a function of delay

(39). A.E.R.E. Report N/R. 1639 (1955); *Proc. Phys. Soc.* **A-69**, 413 (1956).

between counter and crystal. Now, it can be assumed that the drift velocity W is proportional to the electric field (Appendix VIII), and therefore inversely proportional to the radius. Near the wire, the delay is small but the number of counts from the small volume is low. Near the outer wall, the number of counts is large, but the drift velocity is low, so that the delay is large and the pulses are more spread out in time. Calculation shows that the number of pulses, as a function of delay, is constant, i.e. it is in the form of a rectangle, whose width was experimentally determined to be of the order of two to three microseconds. Nicholson's studies of a number of counters of differing pressures, voltages and dimensions gave results in reasonable agreement with the theoretical formula. The curve relating coincidence rate to delay is shown in Fig. 3.18.

3.3. The scintillation counter

An important point, mentioned only in passing in the previous sections, is the question of counter efficiency. Ionisation chambers and proportional counters register only the charge collected from the ionisation products in the track of fast particles in a gas. These particles must therefore arise either from thin films or from the gas, i.e. in both cases from a relatively small quantity of material. With thermal neutrons, the high cross sections of boron or of the thermally fissile elements make high efficiency reasonably possible: as we saw, Lowde's[11] boron-lined counter had an efficiency for thermal neutrons of 25 per cent, and BF_3 proportional counters can have correspondingly high efficiency. For neutrons of energy more than, say, 1 keV, however, the efficiency of these counters drops off rapidly, and the efficiency of an ion chamber or proportional counter for neutrons of 1 MeV energy is usually of the order of 0·1 per cent.

A solid counter, therefore, with its much greater mass of material, offers the possibility of much higher efficiency. Such a detector is the scintillation counter, of which many varieties have been developed. In addition to its efficiency, the scintillation counter has the second considerable advantage of speed. We have seen that the speed of an ion chamber is limited to 0·1 microsecond or thereabouts, while the proportional counter is appreciably slower. An organic scintillator, however, has a speed of response of the order of one millimicrosecond (ignoring the delays in the photomultiplier). Against these major advantages, however, must be offset the fact that while neutron-sensitive ion chambers and proportional counters discriminate against gamma rays, scintillation counters are usually more sensitive to gamma rays than they are to neutrons. The development of the neutron-sensitive scintillator, therefore, has involved much effort in finding ways of reducing the effectiveness of the scintillator for gamma rays.

3.3.1. The principles of scintillator detection.

The use of scintillators is an old-established and highly respectable practice in nuclear physics. It was with ZnS screens that Rutherford conducted his early experiments on alpha particles, and it was ZnS which enabled him "almost to see the little beggars". The method of counting individual alphas by visual observation was, however, very tedious, and was superseded in the pre-war years by other types of detector and by electrical methods of counting. At about this time, however, the photomultiplier was developed, and during the war Curran and Baker showed that the scintillations from alpha particles could be registered by pulses from the photomultiplier. Since then the technique has developed rapidly, particularly as applied to gamma ray detection. However, the applications to neutron detection are important and numerous, as the succeeding pages will show.

The literature on the subject is very extensive, and the reader is referred to references (40) to (43) for details. We shall consider briefly the principles of scintillator detection, and then discuss in more detail their application to neutron detection.

(a) **The photomultiplier.** The photomultiplier consists of a photosensitive cathode and a series of secondary emitters maintained at appropriate voltages. Light falling on the

(40). Birks, *Scintillation Counters*. Pergamon Press, London (1953).
(41). Curran, *Luminescence and the Scintillation Counter*. Butterworth, London (1953).
(42). Brooks, "Organic Scintillators". *Prog. Nucl. Phys.* Vol. 5, p. 252. Ed. O. R. Frisch. Pergamon Press, London (1956).
(43). Mott and Sutton, "Scintillation and Cerenkov Counters". *Encyclopaedia of Physics*, Vol. XLV, p. 86. Springer-Verlag, Berlin (1958).

photocathode releases electrons which are accelerated to the first electrode (or dynode, as it is usually called). The number of secondary electrons emitted from this dynode is greater than the number of incident electrons, and with a suitable arrangement of electric fields these electrons are drawn to a second dynode, where further secondary electrons are emitted, and so on. The voltage on successive electrodes is obtained by tapping off a resistor chain. Typical values for an 11-stage multiplier are a gain of 10^7 for an applied overall voltage of 2 kV. The multiplication per stage, and therefore the overall gain, varies rapidly with the applied voltage, which should therefore in general be kept constant to 0·1 per cent.

As with the ionisation chamber, it is instructive to consider the efficiencies of the various stages of a photomultiplier system. We consider a thin layer of boron-impregnated ZnS(Ag), for which the conversion efficiency of kinetic energy of alpha particles into fluorescent radiation is about 20 per cent. Thus, for 2·4 MeV of initial alpha energy, we shall have approximately 0·48 MeV converted into fluorescent radiation with a mean photon energy of 3 eV, so that about 160,000 photons are liberated. We allow a factor of 50 per cent for overall transmission through the ZnS layer, and 50 per cent for the fraction of the emitted photons which reach the useful part of the photocathode, i.e. we have 40,000 photons at the photocathode. If the photosensitivity is that of a good cathode, it will be of the order of 40 μA per lumen, i.e. about 10 electrons per 100 quanta of light of energy 3 eV (4000 Å), so that 4000 electrons are emitted. Finally, we have the collection efficiency at the first dynode, which may be taken as 50 per cent. Thus 2000 electrons are injected into the photomultiplier, which, with a gain of 10^7 gives 2×10^{10} electron charges, or about 3×10^{-9} coulombs, at the output of the multiplier. If this charge is stored in a capacity of 20 μμF, the voltage change across the condenser will be 150 volts. It is obvious that, for the normal application, little or no amplification beyond the photomultiplier is required.

This example raises a further distinction between ionisation chambers and scintillation detectors. The number of electronic charges collected as a result of the capture of a neutron by a boron nucleus in BF_3 gas is, as we have seen, about 75,000. The number of electrons injected in a photomultiplier is nearly two orders of magnitude less. Hence the straggle in pulses in a scintillation detector, due to statistics alone, is much greater than in the average ion chamber or proportional counter. The resolution, for example in the study of neutron spectra, by proton recoil in organic crystals, is therefore less. However, scintillation counters have not often been used directly for studies of neutron spectra.

Returning to the photocathode, we observe that the spectral sensitivity varies widely with the material employed, and it is essential for optimum performance to ensure that the emission of the phosphor approximately matches the spectral sensitivity of the photomultiplier. In liquid scintillators, in particular, the emission is normally in the region of the ultraviolet, and *wavelength shifters* are added which change the emission bands so as to match more closely the spectral sensitivity of the photomultiplier.[44],[45]

A factor of some importance in neutron detection by proton recoil in organic crystals is that of noise pulses in the photomultiplier, which limit the operation of the scintillation counter to neutrons of energy greater than 300 keV. Some factors in these noise pulses (cold emission, ionisation of the residual gas) are a function of the multiplier construction, but others are, to a certain extent, under the control of the experimenter. These include:

(i) Direct leakage through and over insulators. As before, a protective coating of wax on high-tension leads can often help.

(ii) At high gains, the output stages of a photomultiplier can show negative resistance characteristics, giving apparent "breakdowns".[46] If the potentials of these stages are drawn from a chain of stabilised gas discharge tubes, rather than from the resistor chain, the number of "breakdowns" may be considerably reduced.

(iii) Thermal emission at the cathode. Photosurfaces sensitive to red light are particularly sensitive to thermal emission,

(44). Hayes et al.' Nucleonics, 14/1, p. 42 (January 1956).
(45). Avivi and Weinreb, Rev. Sci. Inst. 28, 427 (1957).
(46). Stump and Talley, Rev. Sci. Inst. 25, 1132 (1954).

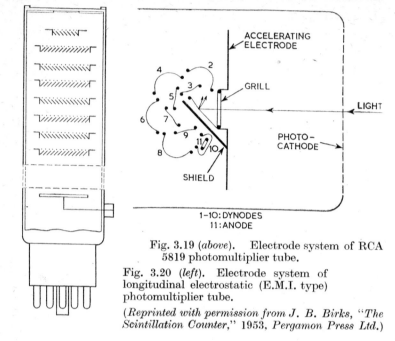

Fig. 3.19 (*above*). Electrode system of RCA 5819 photomultiplier tube.

Fig. 3.20 (*left*). Electrode system of longitudinal electrostatic (E.M.I. type) photomultiplier tube.

(*Reprinted with permission from J. B. Birks, "The Scintillation Counter," 1953, Pergamon Press Ltd.*)

and cooling the tube, even to 0°C, can yield a marked reduction in noise pulses.

Finally, we show, in Figs. 3.19 and 3.20, two characteristic types of photomultiplier. The first (Fig. 3.19) employs electrostatic focusing, which makes for short transit times and good time resolution (10^{-9} sec). The second (Fig. 3.20) is less sensitive to magnetic fields, and has a very low dark current, but has a poorer time resolution (10^{-8} sec).

(b) The luminescence process. Scintillation detectors can be divided broadly into two types: solid inorganic scintillators, and solid and liquid organic scintillators.

(1) *Solid inorganic phosphors.* Free atoms possess electronic energy levels to which an electron in the ground state can be excited, and from which, in a time usually of the order of 10^{-8} sec, the electron can return to the ground state with the emission of characteristic radiation. In an assemblage of atoms such as an inorganic crystal lattice, these levels are broadened by mutual interaction into continuous *allowed*

energy bands, separated by *forbidden* regions of energy. A schematic diagram of the energy band system of an insulator is shown in Fig. 3.21. In the normal state, the lower energy bands are filled and the upper bands are empty. The separation between the bands is only a few electron volts. If an electron is raised to the conduction band, for example, by the absorption of radiation or by the passage of a fast particle, the electron can move through the crystal, and may experience a variety of fates. It may enter a luminescence centre, from which the excess energy is liberated with the emission of a

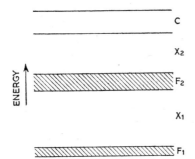

Fig. 3.21.   Energy bands in an insulator.
C   empty conduction band.
F_1F_2 filled bands.
X_1X_2 forbidden bands.

(*Reprinted with permission from J. B. Birks*, "*The Scintillation Counter*", 1953, *Pergamon Press Ltd.*)

photon; it may reach a quenching centre, from which the energy is lost in thermal agitation without the emission of radiation : or it may reach an electron trap, from which it may return to the conduction band by gaining thermal energy, or fall to the ground state by radiationless transitions. The long period decay of phosphors is well known from the behaviour of the luminous parts of clock dials. Experimental data on electron traps have been obtained from studies of thermoluminescence, in which luminous substances are irradiated in the cold and their subsequent re-emission of light studied as the sample is warmed up. An alternative mode of propagation postulates the transport of energy by *excitons*. In this picture, the excited atoms of the material transmit the excitation to one another in a chain-like fashion, and this chain frequently terminates in an activator atom which possesses a high efficiency for electron excitation.

While luminescence centres can exist in pure crystals due to lattice defects, the quality of most phosphors depends on, or is greatly improved by, the inclusion of impurity atoms in the crystal lattice. Such foreign substances are known as *activators*, and they play an essential part in most inorganic substances used in neutron detection.

(2) *Organic scintillators.* The luminescence of organic materials differs considerably from that of inorganic materials, in that the luminescence is a fundamental property of the molecule, and is shown not only in the crystalline state but in the liquid and vapour phases. The implication is that in the solid state the molecules are loosely stacked, and the electronic levels are little affected by their environment. The chief factor in determining the energy levels of the molecule is the distance between the atoms, and the energy system of the molecule can be represented in principle by a potential energy diagram in which the abscissa is the interatomic distance (Fig. 3.22). Normally the system is in its ground state at A, with low energy vibrational states shown by the short horizontal lines. Absorption of energy, for example by radiation, raises the system to a higher excited state. This process will be represented by a vertical line through A, since, as with the slow-moving positive ions of section 3.1.2, the atoms are relatively immobile. If the absorbed energy is high, and the system reaches the point C, the atoms will move apart along the line cCc', and the molecule will dissociate. If the energy of the radiation is less, however, and the system reaches the state D, then molecules will be in the excited state represented by bBb'. The excess vibrational energy is rapidly dissipated as heat, until the molecule is in the relatively excited state B. If the molecule is sufficiently stable, it may return to the ground state by the emission of radiant energy corresponding to BE (note that the energy represented by BE is less than the energy represented by AD: this explains the action of wavelength shifters noted above). The molecular mean life is the order of 10^{-8} seconds, so that it is important that the energy cannot be dissipated in other ways. For example,

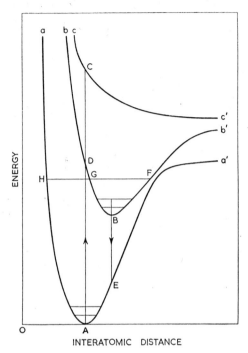

Fig. 3.22. Molecular potential energy configuration of an organic molecule. (*Reprinted with permission from J. B. Birks, "The Scintillation Counter", 1953, Pergamon Press Ltd.*)

if there is a point *F* in the curve *bBb'* from which radiation of low energy can readily be released, most of the energy will be dissipated by thermal agitation. Thus, for efficient fluorescence, the potential curves of the normal and excited electronic states should be well separated, so that the probability of transitions from *B* to the ground state, other than radiative transitions, should be small.

Many kinds of organic scintillator have been studied. Those which have been most successfully developed include anthracene, stilbene and plastic scintillators among solids, and terphenyl in various solvents among liquids. These will be discussed below.

The organic scintillator has two major advantages for neutron detection, particularly for fast neutrons. The speed of the organic scintillator is some two orders of magnitude greater than that of the inorganic scintillator (10^{-8} to 10^{-9} sec as compared with 10^{-6} to 10^{-7}). Secondly, the organic scintillator, by definition, has hydrogen built into its chemical constitution. On the other hand, for neutron detection, the organic scintillator has one major disadvantage, namely, that its light response to fast heavy particles (recoiling protons) is much less than for electrons of equal energy. We have mentioned above, without discussion, the action of *quenching centres*; these are impurity atoms which absorb the electron energy by radiationless transitions. However, the dissipation of energy, by other than radiative transitions, can occur by the action of the damaged molecules which are left in the wake of a fast ionising particle. This is most simply shown (Birks and Black[47]) by exposing a scintillator such as anthracene to a powerful alpha source. After exposure to some 10^{10} alpha particles, the scintillation efficiency begins to drop off rapidly, owing to the accumulation of damaged molecules. This also occurs not only after long bombardment but in the track of a fast particle. Fig. 3.23 shows, for example, the scintillation pulse height S observed by electrons, protons, deuterons and alpha particles of energy E. Clearly, the heavier the particle, the less the pulse height. To explain this, Birks[48] has considered the luminescence dL produced by a particle which loses energy dE in an element of track dx. The initial excitation is proportional to dE/dx. However, there are damaged molecules in the track also proportional in number to dE/dx, and the probability of energy transfer to a damaged molecule is BdE/dx. The resultant luminescence may then be written

$$\frac{dL}{dx} = \frac{A\ dE/dx}{1 + BdE/dx}$$

This may be resolved into two extreme cases. If the rate of energy loss is very small (fast particles, such as electrons) the loss of luminescence due to damaged molecules is negligible, and $\frac{dL}{dx} = A\ dE/dx$. The total luminescence is then proportional to

(47). *Proc. Phys. Soc.* **A-64**, 511 (1951).
(48). *Proc. Phys. Soc.* **A-64**, 874 (1951).

the energy, as is shown by the linear relation for electrons in Fig. 3.23. If, however, the loss of luminescence due to damaged molecules is high (B large) we have $\dfrac{\mathrm{d}L}{\mathrm{d}x} = A/B = \text{constant}$, so

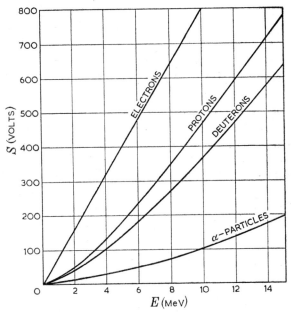

Fig. 3.23.   Relative scintillation response S of anthracene to different particles of energy E.

(Reprinted with permission from J. B. Birks, "The Scintillation Counter", (1953), Pergamon Press Ltd.)

that the luminescence is proportional to the range, i.e. to $E^{\frac{3}{2}}$ (Chapter 1). The shape of this curve is shown for alpha particles in Fig. 3.23. Birks showed that this simple theory gave a good account of the variation of luminescent response of anthracene to different types of ionising particles. More recent developments, while accepting the validity of the equation postulated by Birks, tend to seek other explanations to account for it (see for example references (49) and (50)).

The significance of these phenomena for neutron detection is

(49). Bell and Hayes, *Liquid Scintillation Counting*, p. 268. Pergamon Press (1958).

(50). Wright, *Proc. Phys. Soc.* **B-69**, 358 (1956).

obvious.   Neutrons are detected in organic scintillators by the action of the recoiling protons, and, as Fig. 3.23 shows, the pulse height of a proton of 2 MeV energy entering an anthracene crystal will be only about $\frac{2}{5}$ the pulse height from an electron of the same energy liberated in the crystal by a gamma ray. Therefore the pulse heights due to fast neutrons are appreciably smaller than those due to gamma rays of the same energy, and much effort has been expended in seeking methods of increasing the discrimination in favour of fast neutrons.   These will be briefly described below.

In some neutron detecting systems, the event recorded is the gamma ray released following the capture of an incident neutron by an absorber.   In these experiments, a high efficiency gamma ray detector is required, and a NaI or CsI crystal is to be preferred.   This is because the absorption of gamma rays in an organic scintillator is primarily by Compton effect (Chapter 1) whereas in a sodium iodide crystal, in which the iodine has a relatively high atomic weight, the absorption of the gamma rays is primarily by the photoelectric effect, which for a high Z material has a higher cross section than the Compton effect.

3.3.2. Organic scintillators as neutron detectors. (a)

Slow neutron detectors. For slow neutrons, attempts to incorporate compounds containing boron into scintillating liquids have been made.   Borazole has been tried as a solvent,[51] and the Argonne fast chopper group[52],[53],[54] have developed the method of dissolving esters such as methyl borate in solutions of terphenyl (the scintillator) in phenylcyclohexane (the main solvent).   When used with neutrons of intermediate energy (say 1 keV) a scintillator 4 in. in length can have an efficiency as high as 30 per cent, since the organic liquid slows down (moderates) some of the neutrons before capture.   The chief difficulty, even more than with other neutron detectors using organic scintillators, is the problem of gamma ray background.   A 2 MeV alpha particle produces a pulse only $\frac{1}{40}$

(51). Hoorn and Dohne, *Rev. Sci. Inst.* **25**, 922 (1954).

(52). Muelhause and Thomas, *Nucleonics*, **11**/1, 44 (Jan. 1953).

(53). Bollinger and Thomas, *Rev. Sci. Inst.* **28**, 489 (1957).

(54). Bollinger, Geneva Conference on the Peaceful Uses of Atomic Energy, Vol. IV, Paper P/580, p. 47 (1955).

as great as an electron of the same energy. Apart from gamma background, this means that only 10 to 15 electrons are released at the photocathode of the multiplier for each neutron captured, and noise pulses from the photomultiplier must be minimised. This can be done in two ways. The photomultiplier is kept at the temperature of dry ice (section 3.3.1) to reduce thermal noise and the scintillator is viewed by two photomultipliers in coincidence. A light pulse from the scintillator is then recorded, while noise pulses from the individual photomultiplier, being random, are not registered. An important factor in the work of the Argonne group is the type of reflector used to line the cell of the scintillating liquid. Light from the scintillator may be reflected several times before reaching the photomultiplier, and the reflectivity of the lining is thus important. For aluminium metal (a lining frequently used) the reflectivity was only 83 per cent, but for several oxide powders (TiO_2, Al_2O_3, MgO) reflectivities of 95 to 97 per cent were observed. For a large cell of scintillating liquid, this factor is of considerable importance.

An interesting variant on the problem of overcoming the problem of gamma ray sensitivity has been developed by Brooks,[49] following the work of Wright.[50] A study of the pulse shape as a function of time, from an organic scintillating liquid containing a dissolved boron compound, shows that the decay curve depends on whether the pulse comes from a gamma ray or from neutron capture in boron. This means that electrical discrimination against gamma rays becomes possible. The method is under development, and shows considerable promise, particularly in discriminating pulses due to recoil protons (fast neutrons) from pulses due to gamma rays.

(b) **Fast neutron detectors.** For fast neutron detectors, organic scintillation counters have been widely developed, because of their speed and efficiency. We consider three types. The first is the simple crystal, normally of stilbene or anthracene, used in neutron studies, particularly of neutron spectra. We have seen that n,p scattering is isotropic, so that, if pulse height were linear with energy, the differential spectrum should be a flat plateau, i.e. all pulse heights are equally probable from zero to the full neutron energy. However, as we have seen (Fig. 3.23) the pulse heights from proton recoils in an organic crystal are not linear with energy, and the differential spectrum from n,p scattering will show a piling up of pulses at the low energy end. Two other effects, however, must be taken into account. If the crystal is too small, boundary effects from protons which leave the scintillator without dissipating all their energy in the crystal must be taken into account (the range of a 3 MeV proton in a scintillator is about $\frac{1}{10}$ mm). At the other extreme, however, the crystal must not be so large that multiple scattering can become appreciable. For example, if the neutron loses most of its energy in a recoil with a proton, then with its reduced energy it will have considerably enhanced probability of further collision with a proton (Appendix I (a)), so that the full neutron energy is dissipated in the crystal and the spectrum is distorted in favour of higher energy pulses. The apparently flat differential spectra observed by some experimenters may have been distorted in this respect, although the spectra reported differ appreciably. Some of the papers concerned are listed in references (55) to (57). Poole[55] has analysed the pulse height from an anthracene crystal in the light of Birks' theory, and has obtained good agreement with the experimental curve.

For neutrons of rather higher energy (3 to 10 MeV) an interesting approach to the problem of reducing gamma ray sensitivity has been made by Bonner and his co-workers.[58] This employs the fact that the range of recoil protons is much smaller than that of a gamma-induced electron of the same energy, so that in a small scintillator the relative sensitivity to gamma rays is greatly reduced. The detector therefore consists of a large number of small spheres of plastic phosphor, embedded in a liquid containing no hydrogen (Kel-F). The function of the liquid is simply to provide optical matching between phosphor and photomultiplier. In such a counter, of course, high energy gamma rays may prove troublesome, since the electrons

(55). *Proc. Phys. Soc.* **A-65**, 453 (1952); *Phil. Mag.* Series 7, **43**, 1060 (1952).
(56). Berlman and Marinelli, *Rev. Sci. Inst.* **27**, 858 (1956).
(57). Allen, R. A. *et al.*, *Proc. Phys. Soc.* **A-65**, 295 (1952).
(58). *Phys. Rev.* **100**, 174 (1955).

released in pair production would give a greater pulse than an electron liberated by a single gamma ray.   Bonner's counters have been extensively used in studies of non-elastic cross sections by sphere techniques.   The construction of the detector is shown in Fig. 3.24; the response of the detector in Fig. 3.25.

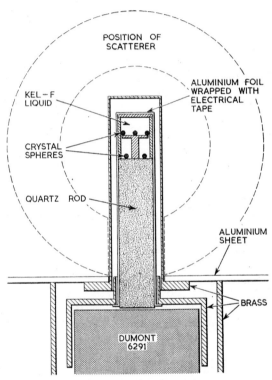

POSITION OF
SCATTERER

KEL – F
LIQUID

ALUMINIUM FOIL
WRAPPED WITH
ELECTRICAL
TAPE

CRYSTAL
SPHERES

QUARTZ ROD

ALUMINIUM
SHEET

BRASS

DUMONT
6291

Fig. 3.24.   Ball scintillator counter developed by Bonner *et al.* (ref. 58). The counter was used to determine non-elastic cross sections by sphere transmission methods, to which the "scatterer" refers.

(c) **Large liquid scintillators.**   The large liquid scintillator is of considerable importance in neutron detection.   This counter was first developed by Reines, Cowan and their co-workers[59] in their search for the neutrino, but it has also been widely used in various neutron studies because of its high efficiency.

(59). *Rev. Sci. Inst.* **25**, 1061 (1954).

Normal dimensions are of the order of 1 to 3 ft, (see Plates I and II) so that the chance of capture of an incident neutron of incident energy, say 2 to 5 MeV, is of the order of 99 per cent. After the neutron has been slowed to thermal energies, it is captured by cadmium in solution (a typical concentration is 5 per cent by weight), and the many photomultipliers surrounding the counter detect the gamma rays following neutron capture in cadmium. In view of what has been said above, one might think that such a counter would be impossible to use because of

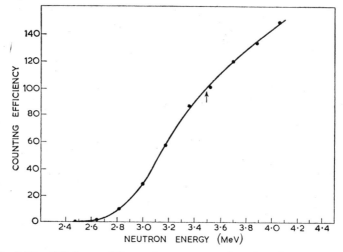

Fig. 3.25.   Efficiency of Bonner's counter as a function of neutron energy (Bonner *et al.*, ref. 58).

its very high gamma detection efficiency. The gamma background, however, is virtually eliminated by the use of appropriate coincidence techniques. If, for instance, one is studying the number of neutrons emitted in fission, then the trace of an oscilloscope is started by the pulse from the fission chamber (placed at the centre of the scintillator), and subsequent gamma rays from neutron capture which take place in the next few microseconds are registered on the time base of the oscilloscope. The chance of a pulse from background gamma rays in these few microseconds is small, and can be estimated. Or an incoming neutron of several MeV energy will give a light pulse from proton recoil, followed a few microseconds later by the gamma rays released when the neutron, having been moderated to thermal energies, is captured.

Reines *et al.* consider in some detail the time involved before neutron capture, i.e. the time required for the incoming neutron is slowed down to thermal energies. The best neutron capturing material is cadmium, since the total gamma ray energy released on neutron capture is high (8 MeV), and, as compared with boron, the effective capture cross section is high only at thermal energies. In effect, the neutron must be slowed down to thermal energies before it can be captured, so that the time between the timing signal and the pulse following neutron capture is sensibly constant. These times were computed by Monte Carlo methods, and agreed well with experimental observations. The lapse of time before capture is not, however, a sharply defined quantity, and the time required to ensure 100 per cent capture is of the order of several tens of microseconds (depending, of course, on the cadmium concentration).

From the practical point of view, terphenyl solutions in benzene or toluene are most frequently used. Contaminants such as water, oxygen and any sulphur-containing compounds must be eliminated, since they act as quenching agents. The sealing of these large counters (sizes of 12 in. × 20 in. × 20 in. represent the order of size) is an appreciable problem, since the liquids leak through organic agents such as normal rubber, and are contaminated by them, so that special rubbers such as silicone are required. Also, in these large counters, the light collection efficiency of the photomultiplier is a major factor. The reflector on the walls is important, and titanium dioxide is frequently used. It is important also to employ wave length shifters,[44],[45] i.e. organic solutes which are represented by initials such as POPOP or BBO. These agents shift the spectral response of the scintillator from the short wavelength (blue-violet) region of the spectrum to the longer wavelengths. The conversion to longer wavelengths has three advantages; (1) the longer wavelengths have a longer mean free path in the solute i.e. less absorption, (2) they have better reflection properties at the walls of the detector, (3) they give more efficient matching to the photomultiplier efficiency curves.

Another application of the large liquid scintillator is in the detection of neutrons in the region of 100 MeV. The scintillators described (Thresher et al.,[60] and Christie et al.[61]) have both been used in experiments with large electron synchrotrons, so that clearly discrimination against gamma rays, while still a problem, is not as great a difficulty as it is at 1 MeV. There are several reasons for this. In the first place, for high energy pulses the scintillator output is much more nearly proportional to energy for all particles, and the difference in pulse height between a 100 MeV electron and a 100 MeV proton is much less than at 1 MeV. In the second place, the range of a 100 MeV proton in benzene is 8·8 cm, while the range of a 100 MeV electron is 50 cm, so that if the counter dimensions are less than say 30 cm no electron can deliver its full energy to the scintillator. As a neutron monitor, therefore, the large liquid scintillation counter is satisfactory : the efficiency of the large counter of Christie et al. (30 in. dia. × 5 in. long) was estimated at 8 per cent.

3.3.3. Inorganic scintillators. (a) ZnS.

Having outlined the properties of organic scintillators, we shall give an account of the types of inorganic scintillator most frequently used in neutron detection. The first of these is ZnS, usually activated with silver, which has been used in a variety of forms. It is one of the most efficient of all phosphors, and as much as 20 per cent of the energy of a fast particle can be converted into light energy. Its chief limitation is its opacity : ZnS cannot be grown in transparent crystal, so that the only suitable form is that of a powder in which the effective thickness is limited to about 50 mg/cm². A second objection to ZnS has been its relatively slow response time. Thus, not only does it have a very long decay period (ZnS must be kept in the dark for many hours before it can be used as a scintillator) but it has a shorter decay period of 10^{-5} sec. In addition, however, Koontz et al.[62] have shown that there is a third decay period of 0·04 microseconds, so that detectors incorporating ZnS can, with

(60). Rev. Sci. Inst. **26**, 1186 (1955).
(61). Rev. Sci. Inst. **27**, 127 (1956).
(62). Rev. Sci. Inst. **26**, 352 (1955).

suitable amplifier differentiation, be used at reasonably high counting rates.

A detector which has many advantages in the thermal and low energy neutron range is the ZnS–B_2O_3 glass mixture, in which alpha particles from the $B^{10}(n,\alpha)Li$ reaction cause scintillation in the ZnS. Such a detector has been described by Gunst, Connor and Bayard.[63] Fused B_2O_3 is a transparent

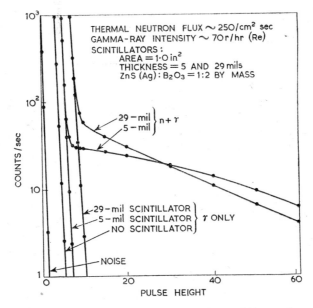

Fig. 3.26. Response of the ZnS–B_2O_3 scintillator of Gunst, Connor and Bayard[63] to neutrons and gamma rays for two representative thicknesses of scintillator.

glass, and scintillators which are thin to the range of gamma-ray-induced electrons but thick to the range of $B^{10}(n,\alpha)Li^7$ reaction products can readily be prepared. Powdered B_2O_3, with 30 to 50 per cent by weight of ZnS(Ag) powder (10 microns average particle diameter) are mixed and laid on 0·005 in. aluminium foil. The mass is selected to give the desired thickness and heated to about 540°C. A second foil is then

(63). *Rev. Sci. Inst.* **26**, 894 (1955).

placed over the melt and the sandwich is compressed by a suitable press to the desired thickness at 480°C. The cooling before compression gives bubble-free scintillators and facilitates the removal of the second foil. The bottom foil remains firmly attached to the scintillator, and serves as a reflector. Since B_2O_3 becomes cloudy on water absorption, the scintillator is protected by wetting with silicone or mineral oil. Thickness between 0·005 in. and 0·085 in., and diameters up to 5 in. have been achieved. Fig. 3.26 shows the integral bias curves for neutrons in the presence of a high gamma ray flux. It is clear

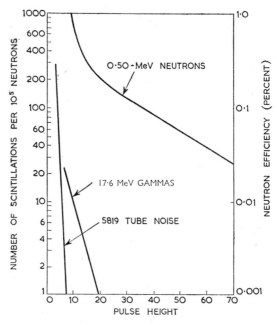

Fig. 3.27.   Efficiency of Hornyak detector for gamma rays and 0·50 MeV neutrons, as a function of bias voltage (ref. 65).

that the thicker scintillator gives a considerably greater sensitivity to gamma ray background. Similar detectors have been described by Bailey and Prescott.[64]

(64). *Aus. Jour. Phys.* **11**, 135 (1958).

In the fast neutron region, the place of the B_2O_3 glass is taken by a transparent organic material like lucite or "Perspex", and the place of the alphas from $B^{10}(n,\alpha)Li^7$ is taken by recoil protons from the lucite. Such a detector was first reported by Hornyak.[65] ZnS powder and lucite powder of sensibly the same grain diameter (8 to 25 microns) were mixed intimately and moulded at 2000 p.s.i. and 120°C. The ZnS:lucite mixture by weight was found to be optimum at 1·5:10, and with this

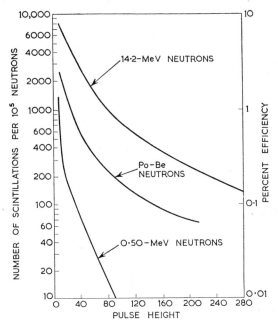

Fig. 3.28. Efficiency of Hornyak detector for 0·50, Po-Be and 14·2 MeV neutrons, as a function of bias voltage (ref. 65).

mixture buttons of $\frac{1}{4}$ in. thickness were found to have adequate transparency. With such a composition, the detector has a low response to gamma radiation, and the efficiency as a function of integral pulse height for neutrons of various energy and for 17·6 MeV gamma rays is shown in Figs. 3.27 and 3.28. The

(65). *Rev. Sci. Inst.* **23**, 264 (1952).

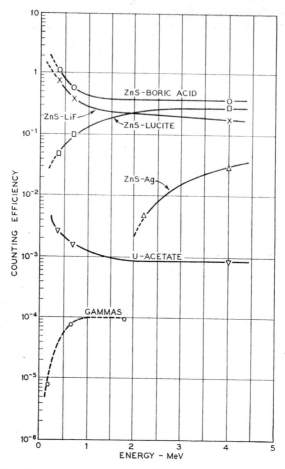

Fig. 3.29. Neutron detecting efficiencies of various mixtures as determined by Koontz, Keepin and Ashley (ref. 62).

relatively high efficiency, as well as compactness of this counter, illustrate the comparative advantages of the fast neutron scintillation counter as compared with the ionisation chamber. A modification to the Hornyak detector has been suggested by Seagondollar et al.[66] using as organic material a liquid called

(66). *Rev. Sci. Inst.* **25**, 689 (1954).

bioplastic which, when activated by an organic catalyst, sets to a transparent solid with properties similar to lucite. The ZnS powder is mixed in when the liquid is partially polymerised, when its high viscosity inhibits the further settling of the grains.

Keepin[67] suggests that part of the response of a detector of the Hornyak type to fast neutrons comes from (n,p) or (n,α) reactions in the sulphur of the ZnS. These reactions have thresholds around 2 MeV, and probably contribute appreciably to the response of the higher energy neutrons.

Koontz, Keepin and Ashley[62] have studied the properties of mixtures of ZnS(Ag) with various neutron-sensitive detectors. The efficiency of these mixtures for fast neutrons, as a function of neutron energy, is shown in Fig. 3.29.

(b) **Lithium iodide.** The $Li^6(n,\alpha)T$ reaction has some attractive properties for the purposes of neutron detection (Chapter 2). Since, however, there are no suitable gaseous compounds of lithium, it is in solid detectors such as scintillators and photographic plates that lithium finds a use. The possibility of using LiI in a phosphor was first suggested by Hofstadter *et al.*[68] Schenck[69],[70],[71] studied a large variety of lithium compounds, and his results have been confirmed by the studies of Nicholson and Snelling[72] on lithium iodide phosphors. These studies indicate the importance of choosing the right activator for the scintillator. Thallium is quite satisfactory for NaI. When LiI crystals are activated with thallium, however, they give very broad peaks, because the activation in different regions varies in efficiency. LiI(Sn) can be grown readily, and the spectra show fair resolution: but the crystals are chemically unstable, and the emitted light does not match the average photomultiplier spectrum. Europium-activated crystals do not show these defects, except that the decay time constant is rather long ($1\cdot4\ \mu$ sec).

A crystal of LiI one cm thick, grown from natural lithium

(67). *Rev. Sci. Inst.* **25**, 30 (1954).
(68). *Phys. Rev.* **82**, 749 (1951).
(69). *Nucleonics*, **10**/8, 54 (August 1952).
(70). *Phys. Rev.* **85**, 923 (1952).
(71). *Nature*, **171**, 518 (1953).
(72). A.E.R.E. Report EL/R. 1350; *Brit. J. Appl. Phys.* **6**, pp. 104–6 (1955).

iodide, has an efficiency for thermal neutrons of 65 per cent. As regards pulse height, inorganic crystals in general do not have the low luminous efficiency for heavily ionising particles that is characteristic of organic scintillators. Results vary slightly, but can be summarised by saying that for energies of a few MeV the pulse height from an alpha particle in an inorganic scintillator will be some 10 to 30 per cent less than the pulse height from an electron of the same energy. Thus, for LiI(Sn), Nicholson and Snelling find the effective energy of the alpha particles, when calibrated with the 0·661 MeV gamma rays from Cs^{137}, is 4·1 MeV (the true value is 4·8 MeV). The resolution of the average crystal (full width at half height) is about 12 per cent. The decay time constant varies with the activator, being 1·4 μ sec for LiI(Eu) and 0·25 for LiI(Sm) (cf. NaI(Tl) which has a decay time constant of 0·34 μ sec).

As regards gamma sensitivity, a flux of 20 mr per hr of gamma rays less than 3 MeV can be tolerated without serious interference from pile-up.

(c) **Observations of gamma rays in neutron detection.** Frequently gamma rays are detected resulting from neutron inelastic scattering or capture. In some of these experiments, such as studies of inelastic scattering, the gamma rays and their excitation functions are of intrinsic interest, and the study, strictly speaking, does not involve neutron detection. In other experiments, however, the neutrons are detected by the gamma rays emitted on capture by an absorber. In time-of-flight spectrometers in the range 100 to 1000 eV, for example, the efficiency of BF_3 chambers falls off appreciably, unless they are very long, when the timing uncertainty is increased. The detection of gamma rays emitted by a neutron absorber is a favourable alternative. Thus, if we consider a cylinder of thin-walled aluminium 3 cm deep filled with amorphous B^{10}, placed axially in a neutron beam of energy 1 keV, the boron is nearly "black" to the beam of incident neutrons. In 94 per cent of the reactions, a 480 keV gamma ray is liberated, which is detected in a NaI(Tl) crystal. Such a system was suggested by Duckworth *et al.*[73] and developed by Rae and Bowey.[74]

(73). *Nature*, **165**, 69 (1950).
(74). *Proc. Phys. Soc.* **A-66**, 1073 (1953).

Above 1 keV, the losses become appreciable: at 50 keV, for example, the neutron absorption of the cylinder used by Rae and Bowey was only 50 per cent. Also the low energy of the gamma ray necessitates heavy gamma ray shielding and single-channel pulse analysis of the 480 keV peak, to minimise background. The overall efficiency at 1 keV, in the experiments of Rae and Bowey, was 2·6 per cent. An advantage of the system is that this efficiency remains constant up to the point where neutron losses become appreciable, i.e. up to 1 keV.

A similar system has been described by Albert and Gaerttner,[75] with a betatron time-of-flight apparatus. As absorber they used samarium, which emits several gamma rays on neutron absorption with a total energy release of 8 MeV. Background was reduced by coincidence counting with two liquid scintillators in coincidence. Coincidence counting, however, involves reduced efficiency. As regards size of absorber, the efficiency is limited by gamma ray absorption in the heavy element.

(d). Lastly, we shall mention some other inorganic scintillators which have been used in neutron detection. Harding[76] developed a scintillator analogous to the Hornyak detector, except that the scintillator was KI and the organic substance alpha-bromonaphthalene, which has the same refractive index as KI. The proportions were chosen so that the scintillator had the thickness of the mean proton range, while the organic material had thickness equal to the mean electron range for gamma-ray induced electrons. Brown[77] substituted for the alpha-bromonaphthalene a polystyrene polymer with which a solid button could be made. As compared with the ZnS detector, the neutron efficiencies are comparable, but the gamma ray sensitivity of the KI button is higher.

3.3.4. Miscellaneous scintillation techniques. There remain to be mentioned a few further techniques using photo-multipliers. Erickson and Kaufman[78] have developed photo-

(75). *Rev. Sci. Inst.* **26**, 572 (1955).
(76). *Nature*, **161**, 437 (1951).
(77). *Rev. Sci. Inst.* **26**, 970 (1955).
(78). *Rev. Sci. Inst.* **27**, 107 (1956).

multiplier tubes which do not employ scintillators. The inner face of the front glass of the photomultiplier, before tube assembly, is coated with a paste of B^{10} or $U_3{}^{235}O_8$ in oil, baked, and assembled in the photomultiplier. The particles or fragments from neutron interaction with B^{10} or U^{235} interact directly with the photocathodes and release electrons, which are multiplied in the usual way.

Scintillators have also been used to detect the light emitted when fission fragments pass through a gas (Nobles[79]). A quaterphenyl wavelength shifter serves to match the light output of the gas to the response of the photomultiplier. Xenon is appreciably better than krypton or argon, and the resolving time is 1 $m\mu$ sec or less. This very short resolving time is of advantage in some applications. In efficiency, however, the system resembles the thin film ionisation chamber, and its application is more in fission studies than in neutron detection.

3.4. Neutron detection by nuclear emulsions

3.4.1. Photographic plates.
As a neutron detector, the photographic plate has several advantages. In the first place, it integrates the complete record of all processes occurring in the plate during the period of observation. For low fluxes, e.g. checking health tolerances for slow or fast neutrons, or, for the very low fluxes of neutrons in cosmic rays the integrating properties of the plate, without the need for maintaining associated electrical or other equipment, may be of value. Furthermore, the track lengths in foils for particles of energy say 2 MeV are quite short (40 microns), so that the physical size of the emulsions (normal thickness 200 microns) can be quite small. This in turn means that the plates can be placed close to the source, without involving a large solid angle subtended at the detector. The emulsions developed for nuclear physics are relatively insensitive to gamma rays, and indeed special plates and processes are needed to show electron

(79). *Rev. Sci. Inst.* **27**, 280 (1956).

PLATE I

Interior of the partially assembled detector tank of a large liquid scintillator. End plates for mounting the tubes are seen, with the rear one in place.

(From Reines and Cowan, *Physics Today* **10**, 8, 12 (1957))

PLATE II

View of a tube bank of 55 multipliers on one end of a large liquid scintillator. Tubes were staggered to obtain tighter packing.

(From Reines and Cowan, *Physics Today* **10**, 8, 12 (1957))

PLATE III

Neutron radiograph of a waxed string in a block of lead 2 in. thick; an example of the reversal of absorption coefficients of X-rays and neutrons.

(J. Thewlis, *Brit. J. App. Phys.* **7**, 345 (1956))

PLATE IV

Neutron radiograph of plant tissues.
(J. Thewlis, *Brit. J. App. Phys.* **7**, 345 (1956))

tracks. Finally, because of its small size and mass, the photographic plate gives a minimum of scattering and consequent distortion of the incident flux. As against these advantages, there is one major disadvantage : the scanning of plates is very tedious. Even if tracks are recorded from a radiator (e.g. a film of hydrogenous material) external to the plate the recording of say 1000 tracks is a lengthy procedure. This is the simplest case : if the tracks are initiated within the emulsion and are due to a reaction such as $Li^6(n,\alpha)T$, for which energy and momentum balance are required to give the neutron energy, the process becomes prohibitively expensive in time.

Various attempts were made before the war to use ordinary photographic plates for nuclear studies. The photographic plate is affected by the passage of a fast nuclear particle in much the same way as by light, but in ordinary plates the emulsion has too large a grain size to be of much use in recording tracks from nuclear reactions. The advances made by Powell[80] in collaboration with Ilford Ltd., were chiefly along the direction of reducing grain size, and of increasing the proportion by weight of AgBr. Various emulsions are available which will record the path of various types of particle, but in all of them the AgBr content is about 80 per cent by weight. For neutron studies, this means that the hydrogen content is relatively low and the attenuation of a neutron beam in the plane of the plate is appreciable. Another factor arising from the high bromide content is the large shrinkage which occurs on fixing, when the residual silver bromide is dissolved out. This is about 60 per cent compared with 10 per cent for a half-tone emulsion.[81]

The use of photographic plates in nuclear physics has been reviewed by Rotblat[81] and by Beiser.[82] Rotblat's curves for ranges of alpha particles and protons, and for straggling in emulsions (on which the resolution in energy of the photographic plate depends) are given in Appendix IX. The application of

(80). *Nuclear Physics in Photographs*, Oxford University Press (1947).

(81). *Progress in Nuclear Physics.* Ed. O. R. Frisch, Vol. I, p. 37, Butterworth-Springer (1950).

(82). *Rev. Mod. Phys.* **24**, 273 (1952).

the photographic plate to neutron physics has been reviewed by Rosen.[83],[84],[85] We consider these applications below.

(a) **Slow neutrons.** One of the first applications of emulsions in the measurement of dosage from thermal neutrons in a pile was reported by Cuer *et al.*,[86] who used the natural nitrogen content in the emulsion to give tracks of protons of energy 0·625 MeV (Chapter 2.1). The method, however, suffers from many disadvantages, including the uncertainties of cross section and of nitrogen concentration.

The sensitivity of the plate to slow neutrons can be greatly increased by impregnating the emulsion with boron or lithium. Kaplan and Yagoda[87] have described the technique of loading a plate with lithium or boron for use in detecting cosmic ray neutrons. By soaking the plates in suitable emulsions, concentrations of 34 mg of boron and 12 mg of lithium per ml of emulsion could be achieved. With the use of evaporation loading, this concentration could be increased to 72·5 mg of boron and 17·5 mg of lithium per ml of emulsion. It is clear that with these concentrations, integrated slow neutron fluxes of a few neutrons per sq. cm can be detected. For example, the daily tolerance rate of slow neutrons will give 100 tracks in a 100 microns square of plate. Various other authors[86],[88] have reported the use of Li- and B-loaded emulsion. It has been pointed out by Baker[89] that for neutron flux density measurement, there is appreciable thickening of the film towards the edge. For accurate measurement ($\pm$ 3 per cent) it is necessary to work with discs cut from the centre of the plate.

(b) **Fast neutrons.** Many experiments have been conducted with photographic plates as fast neutron detectors. Let us consider first measurements of neutron spectra using proton recoils from the hydrogen in the plate. Here there are two limiting factors. In the first place, the neutron density

(83). *Nucleonics*, **11**/7, 32 (1953).

(84). *Nucleonics*, **11**/8, 38 (1953).

(85). International Conference on the Peaceful Uses of Atomic Energy, Vol. IV, Paper P/582, p. 97 (1955).

(86). *Comptes Rendus*, **228**, 6. 557 (1949).

(87). *Rev. Sci. Inst.* **23**, 155 (1952).

(88). Titterton, *Brit. J. Rad.* **23**, 465 (1950).

(89). *J. Sci. Inst.* **31**, 187 (1954).

required to give an adequate counting rate, in a unidirectional neutron flux, is of the order of $10^8/cm^2$. The resolution of neutron energy is about 50 to 100 keV, and the lowest neutron energy that can be easily detected is about 500 keV (tracks can be detected for proton recoils of 300 keV energy, but the results must be corrected for reduced sensitivity). Hence, where the method is used to detect primary neutrons from a reaction such as a (d,n) reaction, the technique is reasonably adequate, since all these conditions are met. In such investigations, the plate is placed at a slight angle to the incident neutron beam. In this way, the attenuation of the neutron beam is kept low (5 MeV neutrons are attenuated by a factor of 0·6 in 3 cm of emulsion). The proton recoils in the forward direction, which are limited to an angle of about 15° to the incident neutron direction, are retained within the plate (correction of course must be made for the recoils which, starting near the surface of the plate, emerge from it). In this way, satisfactory spectra can be recorded. Experiments of this kind are many, and are typified by references (90) to (93).

A second type of experiment, with similar geometry, is that in which the neutrons resulting from the inelastic scattering of 14 MeV neutrons by various materials are studied. In these experiments, a T-D neutron source (for which 10^{10} neutrons per sec, of 14·1 MeV energy isotropically emitted from a target, is a typical example), is surrounded by a sphere of the material under study. The neutrons emerging from the sphere include the neutrons of 14 MeV emerging without interactions, and neutrons of lower energy resulting from inelastic collisions. The spectra of these lower energy neutrons is of considerable interest, and has also been the subject of several papers, of which some are listed in references (94) to (97). From the spectrum of the low energy group of neutrons, an equivalent

(90). Gibson and Thomas, *Proc. Roy. Soc.* **A-210**, 543 (1952).
(91). Johnson, *Phys. Rev.* **86**, 302 (1952).
(92). Evans *et al.*, *Proc. Phys. Soc.* **A-66**, 108 (1953).
(93). Gibson, *Phil. Mag.* **44**, 297 (1953).
(94). Stelson and Goodman, *Phys. Rev.* **82**, 69 (1951).
(95). Whitmore and Dennis, *Phys. Rev.* **84**, 296 (1951).
(96). Whitmore, *Phys. Rev.* **92**, 654 (1953).
(97). Graves and Rosen, *Phys. Rev.* **89**, 343 (1953).

nuclear "temperature" of the compound state, formed by the incident neutron and the scattering nucleus, can be deduced. The shape of the spectrum, however (in the region of 0·5 to 2 MeV), depends critically on the accuracy of response of the emulsion in this region. Rather different values of "temperature" have been reported by time-of-flight methods, and it is possible that the earlier data were affected by the reduced sensitivity of the emulsion at low energies.

A third type of experiment is the study of spectra of neutrons inelastically scattered from various materials. The energy of the monoenergetic incident neutrons is between 2 and 5 MeV. In these experiments, the detector is shielded from the target but detects neutrons scattered from the material under study. However, the yield of scattered neutrons is usually less by a factor of about 1000 than the primary source, and experiments are difficult to carry out. Typical examples are given in references (98) to (100), and one example is shown in Chapter 4.3, Figs. 4.14 and 4.15.

Finally, the determination of the spectrum of an isotropic flux by proton recoil in photographic emulsion has been attempted by Nereson and Reines.[101] However, one has here isotropic scattering of an isotropic flux, and the double differentiation involves many difficulties. Another method of determining the spectrum of fast neutron flux has been developed by Keepin and Roberts,[102] using Li loaded plates. The problems here, too, are considerable: the $Li^6(n,\alpha)T$ excitation function, with its high thermal value and resonance peak at 260 keV must be taken into account, the problem of distinguishing alpha and triton tracks is not easy, and each individual event requires separate analysis. The problem of determining accurately the spectrum of an isotropic flux of fast neutrons is considerable.

(c) **External radiators.** In all the above applications, the source of tracks has been in the emulsion itself. There is an interesting group of experiments, however, in which the reac-

(98). Jennings et al., Phys. Rev. **98**, 582 (1955).
(99). Stelson and Preston, Phys. Rev. **86**, 132 (1952).
(100). Snowdon et al., Rev. Sci. Inst. **24**, 876 (1953).
(101). LA 1192 (1950) (decl. 1957).
(102). Rev. Sci. Inst. **21**, 163 (1950).

tions occur in a radiator external to the emulsion, and the reaction products (protons or deuterons) are recorded in the emulsion. Considerations of energy and intensity limit these studies to sources of 14 MeV neutrons. The radiator and plate are housed in a vacuum chamber, to eliminate air scattering, and only those tracks are counted which start in the surface of the emulsion and lead away from the radiator. In the experiments of Rosen *et al.*,[103] the source is shielded from the

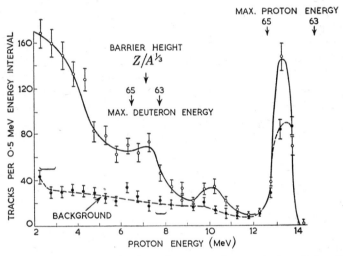

Fig. 3.30. Energy distribution of protons from reaction Cu(n,p)Ni.
(D. L. Allan, ref. 104).

plate by collimators of iron and paraffin. However, the condition that the tracks should start in the emulsion surface and lead away from the radiator reduces very considerably the relative background of tracks arising from neutron-proton recoils in the emulsion, and in the experiments of D. L. Allan[104] no shielding is necessary. Background is determined by removing the radiator. A typical spectrum from the reaction Cu(n,p)Ni is shown in Fig. 3.30.

(103). *Phys. Rev.* **91**, 90 (1953).
(104). *Proc. Phys. Soc.* **A-68**, 925 (1955); *Proc. Phys. Soc.* **A-70**, 195, (1957).

3.4.2. Neutron radiography. As is well known, neutrons can be used in many studies for which hitherto X-rays have been the only source of penetrating radiation. Neutron beams can be reflected from crystal planes, and monochromatic beams of neutrons are thus obtained in the same way that monochromatic beams of X-rays are produced. The use of neutron beams for studies of the solid state are of the greatest importance. For most of these studies, the neutron detectors used are the same as those referred to elsewhere in these pages. A different application, however, is the use of neutrons in radiography,[105] which we shall briefly outline here.

The value of X-rays as a tool for the radiographer lies not only in their penetrating power but in the fact that the absorption in different elements varies rapidly approximately as Z^4. For this reason, the bones of a skeleton, composed of C, Ca and O, are clearly contrasted with the flesh which is composed of H, C and O, as is familiar from any medical X-ray photograph. With neutrons, similar contrasts in absorption occur, but are necessarily related to the absorptive power of the nuclei concerned. Thus hydrogen (50 barns in the solid state for thermal neutrons) scatters much more strongly than lead (10 barns). Plate III shows a picture of a waxed string in a lead block, where the absorption is the opposite of what would have been observed if X-rays had been used. Plate IV shows a photograph of plant tissue taken by neutron radiography.

Since photographic plates are not sensitive to slow neutrons, the chief problem in neutron radiography is that of a suitable converter for changing neutron density into film blackening. Three methods can be used:

(*a*) The neutrons impinge on a thin film of boron or lithium, the alpha particles from which give light flashes on a screen of ZnS, which in turn blacken an underlying photographic plate. The difficulty here is that most thermal neutron beams are normally also accompanied by sufficient gamma rays to fog the plate.

(*b*) The neutrons impinge on a material such as cadmium, the gamma rays from which blacken the adjacent plate. As

(105). Thewlis, *Brit. J. App. Phys.* **7**, 345 (1956).

in (a), the plate tends to be fogged by gamma ray scattering and background.

(c) A more satisfactory method is to absorb the neutrons in a radioactive converter such as a plate or foil of Ag, In or Au. After irradiation, the foil is removed from the beam and placed in contact with the photographic film, and the subsequent beta and gamma rays from the foil blacken the emulsion.

3.5. Miscellaneous other methods

There are various other detectors which do not fit into the previous sections of this chapter, and which we shall summarise here:

(a) **Cloud chambers.** The cloud chamber shares with the photographic plate the major disadvantage that the analysis is excessively tedious, but it does not possess the advantages of the emulsion of capacity for integration, small size, small scattering and simplicity. There is, however, one problem to which the cloud chamber is peculiarly well suited, and that is the study of low energy recoil tracks in a spectrum. Thus, the spectrum of the neutrons emitted in fission, which extends from roughly 10 keV to 10 MeV can be readily measured by various methods from its peak (800 keV) to the maximum energy. Below 500 keV, however, the photographic method fails, and any electrical method encounters serious difficulties in determining the shape of the low energy neutron spectrum in the presence of a high flux of fast neutrons. Bonner et al.[106] used a chamber 30 cm diameter and 20 cm deep, with a minimum of scattering material in the walls and filled with a pressure of $\frac{1}{3}$ atmosphere of hydrogen and water vapour. The stopping power of hydrogen is about one quarter that of air, so that recoil protons of 50 keV energy had a length of 7 mm and could be measured reliably. The neutron spectrum could so be determined.

Another example is the problem of the determination of the spectrum in a fast reactor. There is no moderator in a fast reactor, and degradation of neutron energy proceeds by inelastic scattering until the capture cross section exceeds the

(106). *Phys. Rev.* **87**, 1032 (1952).

inelastic scattering cross section, so that the peak in the spectrum occurs somewhere between 50 and 300 keV. Since the fission cross section of U^{235} is varying with moderate rapidity in this region, the determination of the spectrum is of importance but involves many difficulties. The Argonne fast reactor group[107] have used a cloud chamber in an external beam to determine the spectrum. Here the main problem is to ensure that the neutrons which proceed from the part of the reactor which the cloud chamber "sees" represent a true sample of the flux of neutrons in the reactor. If this condition can be satisfied, the cloud chamber represents the best method of spectrum analysis.

Cloud chambers can be used for other studies in which the range of recoil particles is low. Thus, Connor[108] has studied the reaction products from the interaction of 14 MeV neutrons with oxygen. For elastic scattering, the range of oxygen recoil is small, but by using oxygen and water vapour at $\frac{1}{5}$ atmosphere pressure, Connor obtained readable tracks.

An application of the diffusion cloud chamber has been the determination of the spectrum of D-D neutrons from ZETA by Rose et al.[109] The problem is a difficult one. The total yield per pulse over the whole torus is of the order of 10^6, so that the yield along any one tangent is appreciably less. The cloud chamber was situated some 3 metres from the mean centre of the neutron source. However, the efficiency of the chamber, filled with 7 atmospheres of hydrogen, was high, and energy determinations could be made on a large proportion of observed tracks (E recoil $\geqslant 1 \cdot 5$ MeV) with an accuracy of 4 per cent i.e. 100 keV. It so happens, also, that the neutron energy from the D-D reaction, in the forward direction, varies rapidly with incident deuteron energy at low energies. By operating the machine, therefore, so that the direction of current was first towards and then away from the cloud chamber, a difference of peak neutron energy amounting to 200 keV for the two cases was observed. This would correspond to a situation in which stationary deuterons were struck by deuterons of energy 17 keV.

(107). A.N.L. TID-7506 (Part 1, July 1956).
(108). *Phys. Rev.* **89**, 712 (1953).
(109). *Nature*, **181**, 1630 (1958).

A recent development of great importance in high energy physics is the bubble chamber, which is, in effect, the liquid counterpart of the cloud chamber. In the bubble chamber, the pressure on the liquid is suddenly reduced, so that the liquid becomes superheated, and bubbles grow on nucleation centres provided by the ions and electrons. Many technical difficulties are involved, and the bubble chamber is one of the most expensive instruments of nuclear physics. However, as its use develops, it may find application for neutrons in the MeV energy range.

(b) Neutron thermopiles. In a reactor, a simple monitor for high fluxes is the neutron thermopile. One junction of a thermocouple is painted with a paste to give a coating of amorphous boron powder, so that in a high flux the junction is heated by alphas from the $B^{10}(n,\alpha)$ reaction. Such a system

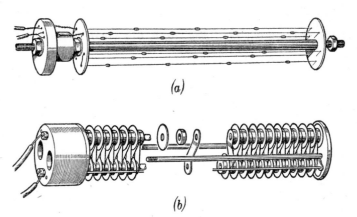

(a)

(b)

Fig. 3.31. Neutron thermopiles described by Jaques (ref. 110).

(*a*) Bead type. (*b*) Disc type.

has been described by Jaques *et al.*[110] and is shown in Fig. 3.31. Two types were developed. The first was a bead type, which has also been described by several authors. The bead, which was deposited by diborane decomposition at 600°C, was 1·5 mm diameter, which is a useful compromise between sensitivity and

(110). A.E.R.E. Report EL/M.45 (1950, decl. 1956), and 46 (1950, decl. 1957).

8—N.D.

time constant. For this size, the output was about 300 μV per bead in a flux of 10^{12} n/cm^2 sec. The time constant was about 12 sec. An alternative type, made with discs of 2 per cent boron steel, is shown in Fig. 3.31 (b). This type is more robust, and involves no constructional difficulties, but has a time constant of 40 seconds.

Various other types of thermopiles have been described, and are listed in references (111) to (114). In one of these, in which the active material has a thickness of 0·006 in., a time constant of 0·037 sec is reported.[113]

(c) Miscellaneous other methods have been occasionally described in neutron detection. These will not be discussed in detail, but are listed in references (115) to (121) in the Reference Index and Bibliography.

(111). Leonard, U.S. Report AECD 3325 (1951, decl. 1952).

(112). Weaver *et al.*, *Elec. Eng.* **76**, 8, 665 (1957); *Trans. A.I.E.E. Comm. & Elec.* **76**, 573 (1957).

(113). Grim *et al.*, *Elec. Eng.* **76**, 8, 678 (1957); *Trans. A.I.E.E. Comm. & Elec.* **76**, 368 (1957).

(114). Lapsley, A.N.L. 4869 (1952).

4

APPLICATIONS
OF
NEUTRON
DETECTORS

In the previous chapter, we described the principle and practice of several forms of neutron detecting devices. In this chapter we shall consider the application of some of these devices to various types of measurement. We cover in the first section some general points: subsequent sections deal with specific applications.

4.1. Measurement of relative intensity: shielding and collimation

We begin by considering measurements in which only ratios are involved, i.e. measurements of relative intensity. The most important of these is the measurement of total cross section. Thus, suppose that a monoenergetic source of neutrons produces at a detector a flux of neutrons $I_0/\text{cm}^2/\text{sec}$. An absorber or scatterer, of cross section σ, containing N atoms per cm^2 in the direction of the neutron beam, is interposed so as to screen the detector from the source, and the flux is reduced to $I/\text{cm}^2/\text{sec}$. Then we have $I = I_0 \exp(-N\sigma)$, from which σ may be determined. The absolute values of I and I_0 are irrelevant: only the ratio I/I_0, i.e. the ratio of counts recorded by the counter, is involved. Usually one varies N by taking several thicknesses of absorber, and confirms that $\log(I/I_0)$ is proportional to N.   Correction must be made for neutrons scattered into the detector from the air and walls of the room; this is usually determined by interposing a thick absorber (a "shadow cone") between source and detector.   Correction must be also made for inscattering, i.e. for neutrons which, although scattered in the absorber, are deflected through so small an angle that they still reach the detector.   To minimise this correction, the size of the absorbers should be made as small as possible consistent with full screening of the detector.   The disposition of source, absorber and detector is usually chosen as a compromise between these corrections : the absorber is half-way between source and detector, and the distance between source and detector is a compromise between maximum count rate and minimum room background on the one hand, and minimum inscattering on the other.

Various other experiments involve the measurement of relative neutron intensity, although in many the variations of detector sensitivity are of major importance.   For example:

(*a*) Sphere transmission experiments involve the ratio of neutron intensity with and without the scatterer in place. One such experiment has been described in Chapter 2.4(b); others have been described by Graves and Davis,[1] by Bonner *et al.*[3,58] and by Batchelor.[2]

(*b*) Angular distribution of fast neutron scattering requires the measurements of relative intensity at various angles around the scatterer.   Examples are the experiments of Barschall & Walt.[3]   Willard *et al.*[4] and R. C. Allen,[5] whose experimental arrangement with a shielded proportional counter is shown in Fig. 4.1.

(*c*) Slow neutron measurements in graphite stacks usually involve the measurement of relative neutron intensity as a function of position in the stack.[6]

(1). *Phys. Rev.* **97**, 1205 (1955).
(2). *Proc. Phys. Soc.* **A-69**, 214 (1956).
(3). *Phys. Rev.* **93**, 1062 (1954).
(4). *Phys. Rev.* **98**, 669 (1955).
(5). Paper P/573, Geneva Conference on the Peaceful Uses of Atomic Energy, Vol. IV, p. 62 (1955); *Phys. Rev.* **95**, 637(A) (1954).
(6). Hughes, *Pile Neutron Research*, p. 123, Addison-Wesley Publishing Co., Cambridge, Mass., U.S.A. (1953).

Another meter of relative intensity, the neutron monitor, is widely used. In experiments with radioactive neutron sources, the source can be assumed to be constant with time, or its variation with time can be accurately assessed. Most neutron physics, however, is conducted with reactors or machines, and in these the source strength cannot be assumed constant, and must be monitored. The requirements of the monitor are that

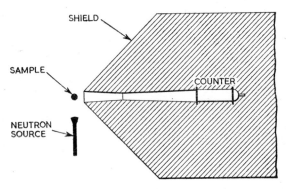

Fig. 4.1.   The shielded proportional counter of R. C. Allen (ref. 5) for obtaining angular distribution of elastic scattering of neutrons of energy 1 MeV.

it should be of high efficiency and should be insensitive to gamma rays and electronic drift. The advantage of the fission chamber as a monitor is obvious. The BF_3 chamber, in a variety of forms, is also extensively used as a monitor for both slow and fast neutrons. For fast neutrons, it can be used in a shaped block of paraffin to give a response which is nearly flat between 20 keV and 5 MeV. This arrangement, christened the *long counter* by Hanson and McKibben, who first developed it, is described in detail in 4.2(e) below. The Hornyak button (Chapter 3.3) has also been used for monitoring fast neutrons. Although it is more sensitive to bias changes than the BF_3 chamber, its compactness and efficiency for fast neutrons (1 to 4 per cent) are often of advantage. A third fast neutron detector has been developed by Langsdorf and his co-workers.[7] The counter

(7). *Phys. Rev.* **85**, 595 (1952).

assembly, shown in Fig. 4.2, consists of a large number of BF_3 chambers surrounding a scatterer situated centrally in the collimator hole in a large paraffin shield. With sufficient BF_3 chambers, detecting efficiencies of 20 per cent for fast neutrons can be achieved.

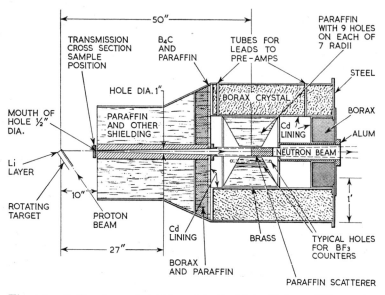

Fig. 4.2. Collimator and shield used in the high efficiency BF_3 counter assembly developed by Langsdorf and co-workers. (Ref. 7.)

Figs. 4.1 to 4.3 have been included primarily as illustrations of shielding required for fast neutron experiments. The design of the collimators and shields referred to will depend on the type of experiment. For a purely thermal beam and background, cadmium shielding of about 1 mm thickness is sufficient. For neutrons of fission spectrum energies (mean energy 1·6 MeV), shields of water, paraffin or oil, with some iron, are frequently used. Normally, the source is external to the shield, and the detector at the centre. To estimate the efficacy of the shield, we shall have recourse to a reciprocity theorem due to Bethe.[8] In this theorem, which applied to the

(8). Los Alamos Report La 1428 (1952).

related problem of sphere transmission. Bethe showed that the source and detector could be interchanged without affecting the number of counts recorded in the detector.* This proposition is introduced, because it is easier to visualise and estimate the attenuation of a source at the centre of a shield, with a detector outside, than it is with the source outside and detector inside. A full discussion of the properties of water and concrete shields has been given in *Radiation Shielding*[(9)]. Roughly speaking, a sphere of 1 metre radius surrounding a fission source will attenuate the intensity of emerging neutrons by 10^4 in the case of water and rather more than 10^3 in the case of concrete. The attenuation of slow neutrons can be increased in hydrogenous substances by the addition of boron, e.g. by stirring about 10 per cent by weight of B_2O_3 into paraffin wax as it hardens, or by using borax in solution. For a fast neutron source, however, the attenuation of the fast neutrons is only slightly affected by the presence of the boron. The effect of the boron additive is to reduce the diffusion of neutrons which have slowed to thermal energies : since the diffusion length of thermal neutrons in pure paraffin is about 1 in., this effect can be appreciable. Both boron and hydrogen emit gamma rays on neutron capture, so that for a gamma-sensitive detector, e.g. an organic scintillator, lithium is used. Lithium is almost unique in that it does not emit gamma rays on neutron capture, and, as the carbonate, it can be dissolved in water or stirred into paraffin wax during setting. Another additive which can be added to paraffin, to reduce gamma intensity, is calomel (HgCl).

Two other points should be made concerning fast neutron shields. The first is that in most experimental arrangements, the flux of air- and wall-scattered neutrons is about 10 per cent of the direct beam, so that shielding around the detector can be less, but not less by a large factor, than the shielding between detector and source. The second point is that, with

(9). Price, Horton and Spinney, *Radiation Shielding*, Pergamon Press, London (1957).

* Specifically, the reciprocity theorem states: "The number of neutrons coming from an isotropic source at the centre of a spherical shell of matter and detected by an isotropic detector outside the sphere is equal to the number detected if the positions of source and detector are interchanged."

fast neutrons, the attenuation is a critical function of neutron
energy. Thus, with 1 MeV neutrons the characteristic attenuation length in water is about 5 cm, so that a thickness of 10 in.
is sufficient to provide an attenuation of about 10^4. Between 1
and 10 MeV, however, the cross section for hydrogen falls from
4·2 barns to 0·95 barns, while that of carbon falls from 2·6 barns
to 1·2 barns. The attenuation of water for fission neutrons,
quoted above, is considerably less than that of 1 MeV neutrons:
this is largely due to the high energy tail of the fission spectrum.

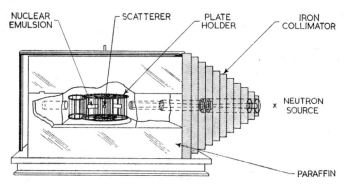

Fig. 4.3.   Collimator assembly employed by Rosen (ref. 10) for angular
distribution measurements.

For 14 MeV neutrons, a much more effective attenuator is iron,
for which the total cross section is 2·6 barns and the non-elastic
cross section is 1·4 barns. As an example, the collimator used
by Rosen,[10] using photographic plates as detector, is shown in
Fig. 4.3. In general, the most efficient shields for neutrons of
10 MeV energy are heavy elements such as iron, in which
scattering and energy degradation begin, followed by hydrogenous materials in which moderation and capture can proceed.

The variation with energy in the MeV range of the total cross
sections of carbon and oxygen, which with the total cross section of hydrogen are often of use in estimating attenuation and
shielding, are shown in Appendix I (b) and (c).

(10). Paper P/582, Geneva Conference on the Peaceful Uses of Atomic
Energy, Vol. IV, p. 97 (1955).

4.2. Measurement of fast neutron flux

We have described in Chapter 1.3 the main sources of fast neutrons. The measurements of neutron flux to be described in this section refer to flux measurements on monoenergetic neutron sources from machines. This means that the source strengths are of the order of $10^8/4\pi$ neutrons per cm^2 per steradian in the forward direction, and the total energy spread is of the order of 1 to 5 per cent of the mean neutron energy. Relative measurements are most readily carried out by a flat-response detector such as the long counter (see below), although at any one energy, almost any of the methods of detecting fast neutrons, e.g. scintillation counters with organic crystals, or proportional counters, can be used.

The absolute measurement of fast neutron flux depends primarily on the scattering of neutrons by protons, which has been discussed in Chapter 2.1. When neutrons strike protons, the only reaction that can occur is that of elastic scattering, and below 10 MeV incident neutron energy, the scattering is isotropic. The cross section has been determined with an accuracy of 1 to 2 per cent. If, therefore, one can determine the number of proton recoils, for example in a volume of gas containing a known number of hydrogen atoms, the neutron flux can be accurately determined. The number of hydrogen atoms can be determined easily enough, but the total number of recoiling protons is not so easily determined. There are various reasons for this. In the first place, for neutrons of say 2 to 3 MeV energy, the recoiling proton has a range of some 10 cm in air at N.T.P., and one either has moderate pressures in the counter, with considerable "end and wall" effects, or high pressures, with short recoil tracks but considerable sensitivity to gamma rays. This raises the second point: at energies below 2 MeV, all tracks have to be counted, including the short, low-energy tracks which represent a glancing collision, and it is difficult to estimate these tracks accurately in the presence of protons from background neutrons and of electrons from gamma-ray interactions. A third factor, of importance to some counters, is the background in the counter itself, caused, for example, by proton recoils from hydrogen absorbed in the walls of the counter, or, for 14 MeV neutrons, from neutron-induced reactions in the counter gas (4.2 (d) below).

A fourth factor, of importance in accurate experiments, is the purity of the primary neutron spectrum. Thus the target material on to which the proton or deuteron beam impinges should be as light as possible, to minimise neutron scattering. Air- and wall-scattered backgrounds must be accurately determined by the use of shadow cones. In the use of D-T neutrons, the intensity of D-D neutrons due to deuterium build-up in the target must be assessed. At higher energies, both protons and deuterons will yield neutrons from the metallic parts of the target, such as nickel in nickel foil windows for gas targets. These can be assessed by filling the target with helium. Finally, higher energy deuterons (6 MeV), in bombarding deuterium, can yield low energy deuterons owing to the break-up of the deuteron.

The methods of measurement of fast neutron flux prior to 1952 have been described by Rossi and Staub[3.1] and by Barschall *et al.*[11] We describe below six developments of these methods which have been made in recent years and which have to a certain extent been intercompared.

(a) **The associated particle method.** A widely used source of monoenergetic neutrons is the reaction

$$T + D \rightarrow He + n + 17 \cdot 6 \text{ MeV.}$$

The importance of the reaction comes from the fact that at a relatively very low-incident neutron energy (120 keV) the reaction cross section is as high as 5 barns. Since deuteron currents up to 500 microamperes (i.e. $3 \cdot 10^{15}$ deuterons/sec) are easily obtainable at these energies, total source strengths of 10^{10} per second are often obtained. From simple considerations of energy and momentum, the neutron, at low incident deuteron energies, carries four-fifths of the reaction energy (viz. $14 \cdot 1$ MeV) and the alpha particle has one fifth of the reaction energy ($3 \cdot 5$ MeV). An alpha particle of $3 \cdot 5$ MeV is readily detected, for example, by a scintillation counter, and for each neutron

(11). *Rev. Mod. Phys.* **24**, 1 (1952).

emitted at angle θ there is an alpha particle emitted at an angle α. The relation between θ and α is given by (cf. Chapter 2.1):

$$m_{\text{neutron}} \cdot v_{\text{neutron}} \sin \theta = m_{\text{alpha}} v_{\text{alpha}} \sin \alpha,$$

or

$$\sin \alpha = (m_n E_n / m_\alpha E_\alpha)^{\frac{1}{2}} \sin \theta.$$

Now, the number of alphas emitted at angle α can be readily determined by counting the alphas passing through a small aperture, of accurately known dimensions, into a counter: from this, the number of neutrons can be accurately determined, to within 1 to 2 per cent.

This method is the simplest and most accurate of fast neutron flux determination. It is applicable, however, to this one reaction, and is therefore very limited in scope. Attempts have been made to apply it to the reaction:

$$D + D \rightarrow He^3 + n + 3 \cdot 2 \text{ MeV},$$

where the He^3 and the neutron share one-quarter and three-quarters of the total energy respectively. The reaction cross section ($0 \cdot 1$ barns at $1 \cdot 5$ MeV) is much lower than for the T-D reaction, so that higher bombarding energies are required. Thus, if the He^3 product particle has an energy of 1 MeV, it must be distinguished by magnetic separation from the elastically scattered deuterons, of similar energy; and although the method has been attempted, too many practical difficulties have prevented its being applicable to accurate flux measurement.[12]

(b) The hydrogen-filled proportional counter. In Chapter 3.2 we discussed the BF_3 proportional counter: here we discuss the proportional counter as applied to flux measurement. The range of a recoiling proton of energy 100 keV is about 2 mm in air: if it has energy 2 MeV, the range is 8 cm, while at 10 MeV the range is about 100 cm. Therefore, at 10 MeV, a gas-filled counter would require inordinately high pressures, and the film counter method (see below) is more suitable. For the range 30 to 3000 keV, however, the gas-filled proportional counter is well suited.

Proportional counters have frequently been used to measure

(12). Franzen *et al.*, *Helv. Phys. Act.* **28**, 328 (1955).

relative intensity, but, as reference to Rossi and Staub will
show, problems associated with "end and wall" effects present
difficulties, and the proportional counter will correctly measure
flux only when the end and wall effects are accurately estimated
and the differential recoil spectra determined by experiment
agree with the calculation.   Fig. 4.4 shows how the "end and
wall" effects arise: recoiling protons 1, 2 and 3 will all give
pulses which are smaller than those which would be expected if
the recoil lay entirely in the sensitive volume.   Now, n,p
scattering at these energies is isotropic in the centre of mass

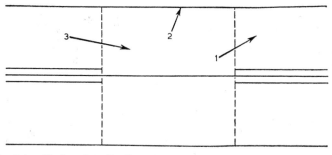

Fig. 4.4.   End and wall effects in a gas-filled proportional counter.

system, so that ideally the differential spectrum is a flat plateau,
with all recoil energies between 0 and E_n equally probable
(Chapter 2).   Because of end and wall effects, however, the
spectrum is changed so as to have an excess of pulses at the
low-energy end.

A satisfactory solution, in theory and experiment, was first
worked out by Skyrme, Tunnicliffe and Ward,[3.33] whose
counter is shown in Fig. 4.5.   It employs.many of the devices
recommended in Chapter 3.2.1.   The sensitive volume is
defined by guard tubes, the anode and cathode are maintained
positive and negative with respect to earth, the construction
permits baking, all constructional material is as thin as possible,
and so on.   Over the whole energy range, the type of gas (H_2
or CH_4) and its pressure are chosen to give a suitable compromise
between excess in range due to proton recoils on the one hand,
and excessive sensitivity to gamma-induced electrons on the
other.

In their development of this counter, for purposes of flux measurements in fission cross section determinations, W. D. Allen and Ferguson[13] encountered various difficulties in making the method self-consistent.   One of the difficulties was associated with the effective range and ionising power of the recoil protons: in hydrogen the observed recoil spectra were slightly flatter than theoretical, while in methane the curves were slightly steeper than theoretical, due to a slight variation in ionising power with energy in this gas.   Eventually the self-consistency between flux measurements with different counters

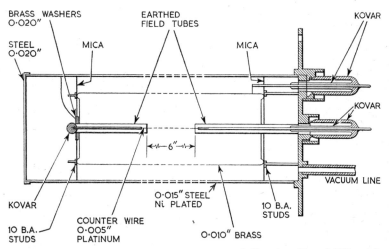

Fig. 4.5.   Gas-filled proportional counter of Skyrme, Tunnicliffe and Ward (ref. 3.33).

filled with H_2 or CH_4, at different pressures, was 2 per cent, and the overall accuracy 3 per cent.   Agreement with flux measurements with the long counter ((e) below) was good.   As an illustration of the agreement between theory and experiment, Fig. 4.6 shows calculated and experimental points for 2·2 MeV neutrons incident on a counter filled with 2 atmospheres of methane.   In this illustration, the proton range was nearly equal to the diameter of the sensitive volume of the counter. Another illustration, in which the proton range was negligible, has been shown in Chapter 2, Fig. 2.2 (a).

(13). *Proc. Phys. Soc.* **A-70**, 639 (1957).

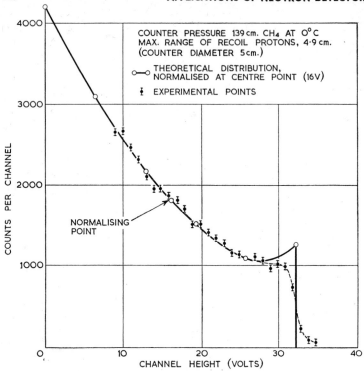

Fig. 4.6. Differential recoil spectrum of 2·2 MeV neutrons incident on counter filled with CH₄ at 139 cm. mercury pressure. The theoretical curve is normalised at the centre point (W. D. Allen and A. T. G. Ferguson, A.E.R.E. Report NP/R 1720).

(c) The thin film radiator. For the range of energies 0·5 to 2 MeV, the thin film radiator has been used. This is described by Rossi and Staub[3.1] and developed by Diven in the determination of the fission cross section of U^{235}.[14] In this method, recoils are observed from a thin film of glycerol tristearate, which is in a plane normal to the direction of the incident neutrons, and are counted in an ionisation chamber or proportional counter. In contrast to the gas filled counter, the number of recoils of low energy is less than that of

(14). *Phys. Rev.* **105**, 1350 (1957).

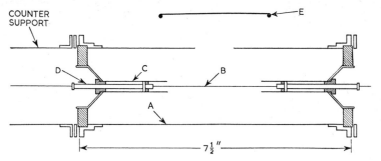

Fig. 4.7.   Double counter of Diven (ref. 14) for detection of recoil protons (proportional counter) and fissions (ionisation chamber).

Proportional counter components:—
   A—outer grounded cylinder
   B—wire at positive high voltage
   C—field tubes
   D—guard ring, at wire potential but insulated from it.

Ionisation chamber:—
   E—collecting electrode.

Not shown: foils with fissile material on upper side and hydrogenous material on lower.

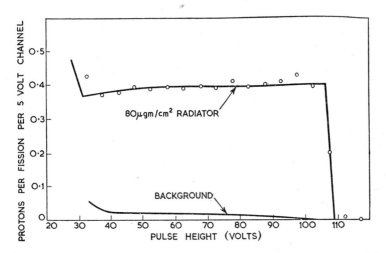

Fig. 4.8.   Differential spectrum of recoils from an 80 microgram/cm² glycerol tristearate radiator when irradiated with 1 MeV neutrons.

   Circles—observed points (background subtracted).
   Solid curve—theoretical spectrum, assuming neutron energy spread of 0·03 MeV.   (Diven, ref. 14.)

the number of recoils of maximum energy (Chapter 3.1) since some of the protons emerging at an angle to the incident beam spend most of their career in the film and emerge with reduced energy. (These effects are discussed in detail in Rossi and Staub.) In Diven's counter, the film was on a platinum foil bent to form a part of the wall of a proportional counter (Fig. 4.7) and the foil carrying the fissile material was placed on the outer wall of the counter. The differential spectrum obtained with the proportional counter is shown in Fig. 4.8.

For the determination of fast fission cross sections, the method has some considerable advantages. In particular, scattered and background neutrons are common to hydrogenous and fissile material films, so that errors due to distance measurement and scattered neutrons are minimised. On the other hand, the technique requires very thin films (a few hundred microgrammes per sq. cm) so that effects of water vapour absorbed on the walls of the counter can be appreciable. This is determined by replacing the foil carrying the film with a blank foil, and in Diven's experiments involved a correction of less than 5 per cent at 1·2 MeV. The fission cross sections determined by the film method and proportional counter method of flux measurement agreed to within ± 3 per cent in the range 0·4 to 1·6 MeV.

(d) The film radiator: proportional counter telescopes.

At higher neutron energies, the film counter developed in (c) is limited by the rapidly increasing range of the recoiling protons, so that above say 3 MeV excessive counter pressures are required. For neutron energies above 3 MeV, the best flux measurements employ a counter which is the equivalent of the "low geometry" counter in alpha particle measurements. Only forward recoils, which pass through an aperture of known dimensions, are counted by a scintillation counter, so that the differential spectrum, instead of being a plateau, is a peak. Since there are many sources of pulses of low energy, the space between radiator and scintillation counter is occupied by a pair of proportional counters. Coincidence between the three systems then effectively rejects all particles except those which start from the radiator and end in the scintillator.

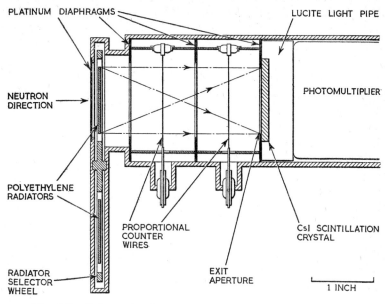

Fig. 4.9.   Schematic of counter used by Bame *et al.* (ref. 19).

This system has been described by many workers.[15–19] We shall limit our discussion to the counter of Bame *et al.*,[19] a schematic diagram of which is shown in Fig. 4.9. In the front of the counter, i.e. towards the neutron source, is a radiator wheel which permits discs of varying polythene thickness, and a carbon radiator, to be introduced successively into the system. The n,p cross section varies roughly as $E_n^{-\frac{1}{2}}$, so that with a given radiator the efficiency will vary as $E_n^{-\frac{1}{2}}$. However, the relative proton energy loss in the radiator varies approximately as $E^{-\frac{3}{2}}$, so that if, for each limited energy range, the radiator thickness is varied so that the percentage energy loss in the radiator remains constant, the efficiency of the system will increase approximately linearly with E_n. The efficiency is also

(15). Kinsey *et al.*, *Proc. Camb. Phil. Soc.* **44**, 96 (1948).
(16). Gossick, *Rev. Sci. Inst.* **26**, 754 (1955).
(17). Cochran and Henry, *Rev. Sci. Inst.* **26**, 757 (1955).
(18). Johnson and Traill, *Rev. Sci. Inst.* **27**, 468 (1956).
(19). *Rev. Sci. Inst.* **28**, 997 (1957).

a critical function of the geometry of the radiator and scintillation diameter, i.e. of their respective radii and distance apart.
We note that a proton recoiling at angle θ to the incident
neutron direction has energy $E_n \cos^2 \theta \approx E_n(1 - \theta^2/2)$, so that
moderately large angles (10° to 20°) can be accepted without
great loss of resolution. However, the geometry will depend
here on the object of the exercise. For a neutron spectrometer,
efficiency is reduced to give an optimum resolution, while for a
flux meter the geometry is chosen so as to give maximum
efficiency. For such a geometry, the effective solid angles require
numerical integration, for which tables are given in ref. 19.

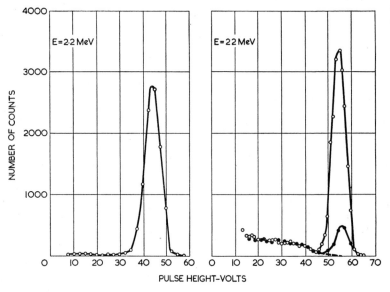

Fig. 4.10. Typical pulse-height distributions obtained from monoenergetic neutrons by Bame et al.
    No backgrounds have been subtracted from the data. For the 2·2
MeV spectrum a 1·3 mg/cm² polyethylene radiator was used, while in
the 22 MeV spectrum radiators of 5 and 37 mg/cm² were used. The
rather large tail below 45 volts in the 22 MeV is caused predominantly by
neutron interactions in the counter walls and gas.

The counter wires in the counter of Bame et al. traverse the
proton tracks, although in the design of Johnson and Traill[18]
the counter wires lie at the side of the counter. The gas pres-

sure is chosen so that the energy loss of protons in the gas is 50 to 200 keV. At high neutron energy (10 to 20 MeV) care must be taken to correct for extraneous neutron reactions. Those such as $C^{12}(n,\alpha)Be^9$, occurring in the carbon of the polythene, are corrected for by examining the spectrum from a carbon radiator. Those occurring in the gas are minimised by the use of krypton as the counter gas, and by varying the pressure and extrapolating to zero. Typical pulse height spectra obtained by Bame *et al.* are shown in Fig. 4.10. The accuracy of the flux measurement is of the order of 2 to 3 per cent. It should be mentioned that one of the errors above 10 MeV concerns uncertainty about the angular distribution of n,p scattering at these energies. Comparison with flux measurement by associated particle method at 14 MeV showed agreement within 4 per cent.

(e) The long counter. All the measurements described above depend basically on the knowledge of the n,p cross section and the detection of proton recoils. A completely different method depends on the response of a BF$_3$ counter in a shaped

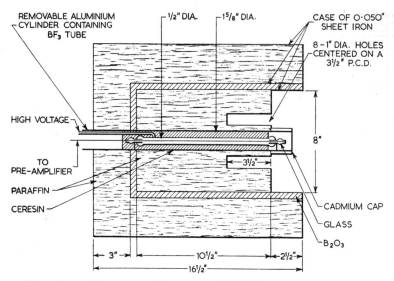

Fig. 4.11. Schematic of Hanson and McKibben's "long counter" (ref. 20).

block of paraffin. This was described by Hanson and McKibben,[20] who showed that by judicious sculpture of the paraffin (Fig. 4.11) the response of the counter was within ± 5 per cent, independent of energy between 25 keV and 5 MeV. Such a system has many advantages: it is simple, robust and has a high efficiency. Recently, however, it has been shown that the response of the long counter is not as flat as had been thought, and Fig. 4.12 shows a composite curve of the response of the long counter as a function of energy, measured at Harwell by proportional counter for energies of 100 to 2000 keV and at Los Alamos[21] by counter telescope above 2 MeV. The rapid

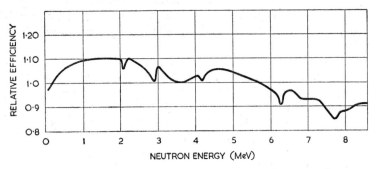

Fig. 4.12. Relative long counter efficiency as a function of neutron energy: a composite curve from Harwell results (0·02–2 MeV) and Los Alamos results (greater than 1 MeV) matched in the flat region 1–2 MeV.

(Reprinted with permission from Allen and Henkel, "Progress in Nuclear Energy," Series I, Vol. II. Ed.: Sanders and Harvey (1958). Pergamon Press Ltd.).

variations in response above 2 MeV correspond to resonances in the total cross section of carbon. It has also been observed by W. D. Allen[22] that, although the long counter approximates remarkably well to a point detector, the point of reference (i.e. the effective centre of the counter) varies with neutron energy; this variation must be taken into account in flux measurement.

Long counters are frequently calibrated with Ra-α-Be sources, i.e. with neutrons with a mean energy of 4 to 5 MeV and a peak of 13 MeV. As Fig. 4.12 shows, this procedure will lead

(20). *Phys. Rev.* **72**, 673 (1947).
(21). Perry, J. E. Private communication (1958).
(22). A.E.R.E. Report NP/R 1667. Also ref. (13).

to errors if the response is assumed flat. A correction of 9 per cent should be applied, for neutrons of energy 1 MeV, if the counter is calibrated with an Ra-α-Be source of mean energy 5 MeV (i.e. the counter sensitivity at 1 MeV is 1·09 times the sensitivity to Ra-Be neutrons). Alternatively, and better, the counter should be calibrated with a source (e.g. Ra-γ-Be) whose energy is nearer 1 MeV. It has been shown[13] that proportional counter measurements and long counter measurements give good agreement at 200 keV neutron energy, the energy of the neutron source (RdTh-D_2O) used in the long counter calibration.

(f) **The homogeneous ionisation chamber.** This chamber was originally developed by Bretscher and French.[23] It has been used by Larsson[24] to cross-check the neutron flux from a T(d,n) reaction, and agreement within 3 per cent with the flux determined by the associated particle method was obtained. In the homogeneous ionisation chamber, the neutron flux is determined by measuring the direct current due to proton recoils in a hydrogenous gas. A fraction of this current, as we have seen, arises from proton recoils which begin or end their tracks in the wall of the chamber, without releasing their full energy in ionising processes in the gas. This defect can be compensated simply by lining the walls with a solid chemical composition similar to the gas. Thus, a chamber filled with ethylene (C_2H_4) would have its walls lined with polythene (C_nH_{2n}). As far as the neutrons are concerned, there is no discontinuity in material at the boundary, so that as many protons are ejected from the walls as end their tracks on the walls. The flux can then be calculated from the assumption that all recoils will end in the gas, and that the number of hydrogen atoms concerned is the number of hydrogen atoms in the gas. Correction must of course be made for carbon recoils. At low energies, where (σ_C/σ_H) is relatively small, the correction is small. At high energies (14 MeV) the correction for carbon reactions poses a problem for accurate flux measurement, since the contribution of $C^{12}(n,n')3\alpha$, the angular distribution of elastically scattered neutrons and the volts

(23). British declassified report BR-386 (1944).
(24). *Ark. f. Fys.* **9**, 293 (1954).

expended per ion pair of recoiling carbon ions, all have to be taken into account. Another problem with the homogeneous chamber in accurate work is that the current will include a proportion due to gamma ray flux. This can in principle be allowed for by comparing currents in two counters, one containing C_2H_4 and (C_nH_{2n}), and the other containing C_2D_4 and (C_nD_{2n}). The homogeneous ionisation chamber is now chiefly used, in modified form, as a fast neutron health monitor (see 4.6 below).

4.3. Neutron spectrometry

Neutron spectrometry is an important branch of neutron physics. In the lower energy regions (0·001 to 1000 eV) the problems concern chiefly time-of-flight techniques and crystal spectrometers, which we describe in 4.4. In the energy range 0·1 to 10 MeV, many different methods of spectrum analysis have been developed. These we shall briefly describe: most are of historical interest, since the millimicrosecond time-of-flight technique is emerging as the most generally applicable instrument in fast neutron spectrometry.

(a) **Direct methods using proton recoils.** Most of the methods of neutron detection described in Chapter 3 have been used for neutron spectrometry. For example, a hydrogen proportional counter with a filling of 375 p.s.i. of H_2 has been used by R. C. Allen[5] to study the low-lying energy levels of heavy elements such as uranium. A feature of the geometry of this experiment is that it employs the technique of surrounding the detector with a sphere of material under investigation, which implies that the counter has to be non-directional and small.

In the same way, Beghian et al.[25] and Segel et al.[26] have used organic scintillators to study inelastic neutron scattering from various substances under bombardment from D-D neutrons. In the experiments of the former, pulses from a stilbene crystal record the differential spectrum with and without a scatterer interposed between the source and the crystal.

(25). *Phys. Rev.* **94**, 144 (1954).
(26). *Rev. Sci. Inst.* **25**, 140 (1954).

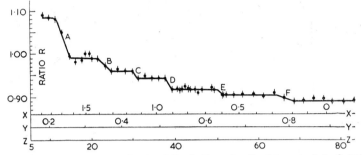

Fig. 4.13. Ratio plot obtained for indium by Beghian *et al.* (ref. 38).

As the normal method of subtraction of spectra involved difficulties in monitoring, ratios of counts of corresponding channels in the two spectra were obtained. In this way, spectra showing steps due to inelastic neutron groups and gamma rays were obtained: gamma rays were identified from NaI crystal spectra. Fig. 4.13 shows, for example, the spectrum obtained for indium.

Finally, photographic plate techniques have been used by several authors to study inelastic neutron spectra. As an example, the arrangement used by Stelson and Preston,[27] and the results obtained for iron are shown in Figs. 4.14 and 4.15.

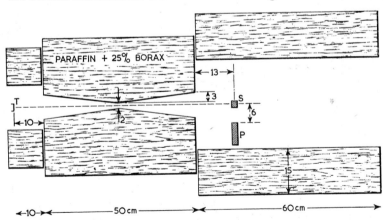

Fig. 4.14. Experimental arrangement for inelastic scattering of fast neutrons, as used by Stelson and Preston (ref. 27).

(27). *Phys. Rev.* **86**, 132 (1952).

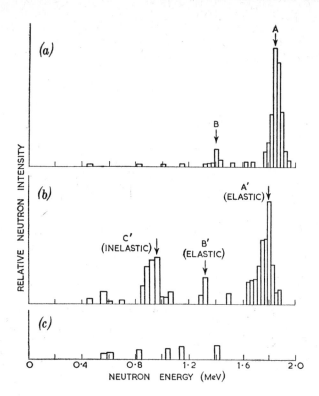

Fig. 4.15. Histogram of neutron energy versus neutron intensity from recoil proton track lengths in emulsion. (Stelson and Preston (ref. 27).) (a) direct beam, Li(p,n) neutrons ; (b) scattered neutrons ; (c) background.

These methods all suffer from the difficulty of resolving an inelastic group in the presence of a strong elastic group, in a spectrometer in which the spectrum is a plateau, not a peak. An interesting alternative spectrometer has been developed by Perlow,[28] who used proportional counters to detect protons scattered in the forward direction only. The experimental arrangement is shown in Fig. 4.16. Protons recoiling from the counter A, filled with a hydrogenous gas, pass through the collimating grid between the counters A and B, and a pulse is

(28). *Rev. Sci. Inst.* **27**, 460 (1956).

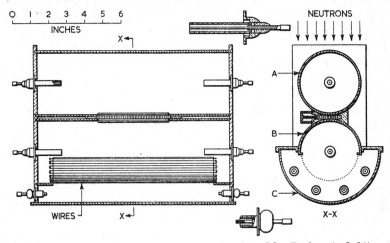

Fig. 4.16.   Triple proportional counter developed by Perlow (ref. 28).

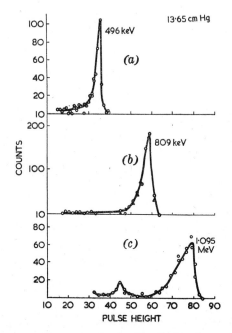

Fig. 4.17.   Differential spectra obtained by Perlow for neutrons of energy 496, 809 and 1095 keV.   Gas filling, hydrogen at 13·65 cm mercury pressure.

recorded when A and B are in coincidence without triggering C. The spectrum records the sum of pulses in A and B, and a typical spectrum is shown in Fig. 4.17. The advantage of such a counter is that there are no wall corrections, and that the spectrum for monoergic neutrons is a peak. The disadvantage is that the low hydrogen pressures involved, and selection of only forward recoiling protons, mean that the overall efficiency (0·001 per cent) is quite low. Another gas-filled counter, using anticoincidence methods to eliminate wall effects, has been described by Giles.[29]

(b) The He³ spectrometer. The region of 100 to 1000 keV has until recently presented difficulties for neutron spectrometry, and a useful detector in this region is the He^3 spectrometer. We recall that the reaction $He^3 + n \rightarrow T + p + 765$ keV has a slow neutron cross section of 5400 barns, and a fast neutron cross section of 0·8 to 1 barn in the region of interest. There are no resonances and no competing reactions, and the peak due

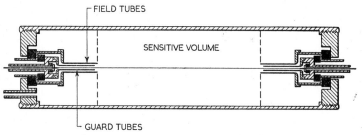

Fig. 4.18. He^3 proportional counter developed by Batchelor *et al.* (ref. 30).

to thermal neutrons at 765 keV makes a convenient calibration check, both for pulse height and resolution.

The development of the He^3 proportional counter has been carried out by Batchelor,[30] whose counter is shown in Fig. 4.18. The filling gas is He^3 with 2 atmospheres of krypton and 2 cm of CO_2. Thermal neutrons are eliminated by a thin covering of cadmium, though a strong peak at 765 keV due to epithermal

(29). *Rev. Sci. Inst.* **24**, 986 (1953).
(30). *Rev. Sci. Inst.* **26**, 1037 (1955).

neutrons is always present. Depending on the He³ concentration, the efficiency is about 0·01 per cent and the resolution such that the full width at half height of the peaks is 8 per cent (i.e. at 1 MeV the width is 80 keV). The pulse height spectrum obtained by surrounding the counter with spheres of uranium

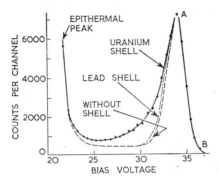

Fig. 4.19. Pulse height distributions obtained by Batchelor with neutrons of 500 keV energy, for the bare He³ counter and for the counter placed in shells of lead and uranium. The ordinates of the three curves have been adjusted to match in the region AB.

and lead and bombarding the system with neutrons of energy 500 keV is shown in Fig. 4.19. Inelastic scattering is negligible in lead at 500 keV, so that, from the difference between uranium and lead shells, the spectrum of neutrons inelastically scattered from uranium at 500 keV can be determined.

(c) Other telescope techniques. A variety of telescope techniques have been developed for fast neutron spectrometry. The oldest, and perhaps the most widely used, has already been described in Section 4.2.4. In their studies of average neutron cross sections in the range 3 to 12 MeV, Nereson and Darden[31] employed a telescope in which the main detector was an ionisation chamber with a Frisch grid (Fig. 4.20). An anti-coincidence chamber beyond the main chamber eliminates protons of excessive energy.

In the counter of Holt and Litherland[32] the recoiling proton is stopped in a third chamber, and the time zero is established

(31). *Phys. Rev.* **89**, 775 (1953).
(32). *Rev. Sci. Inst.* **25**, 298 (1954).

when the first two chambers are in coincidence. From the time taken for the electrons released in the third chamber to reach a grid on the far side of the chamber from the recoiling proton, the depth of penetration of the proton into the chamber, and hence its energy, could be determined.

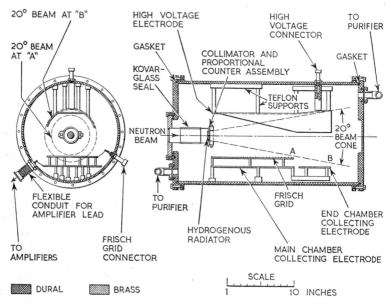

Fig. 4.20.   Front and side view of telescope employed by Nereson and Darden (ref. 31).

A similar counter, with a different emphasis, has been developed by Ribe and his co-workers.[33]   In this counter interest centres in the energy loss in the first two proportional counters (Fig. 4.21). The heavier the particle produced in a reaction, the lower its velocity and the greater the energy loss. The pulse height in the chamber thus discriminates between protons and deuterons. With this counter, Ribe has studied (n,d) reactions in elements such as boron and fluorine, and obtained angular distribution patterns which are the inverse of the normal stripping (d,n) process.

Several other similar counters have been described (see refs.

(33). *Phys. Rev.* **94**, 934 (1954).

12 to 16).   The difficulty with them all is the low efficiency
arising from the film-telescope technique.   A different situation
arises if one adopts a scintillation counter technique, such as
first proposed by Mozley and Shoemaker.[34]   In essence, this
spectrometer consists of a pair of adjacent anthracene crystals,
aligned along the direction of the incident neutrons, and in
coincidence, so that proton recoils starting in the first crystal
are stopped in the second.   In effect, the radiator is the first

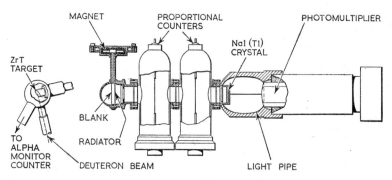

Fig. 4.21.   Apparatus developed by Ribe and Seagrave for measuring
B^{10} (n,d) Be^9 cross sections, showing $T(d,n)He^4$ neutron source and
coincidence-telescope spectrometer.

detector.   The pulses are summed, and the spectrum recorded
on a pulse analyser.   Because of the variety of ways in which
a gamma ray can cause coincidence between two such crystals,
a low-pressure proportional counter is placed between the
crystals.   A triple coincidence is then registered only when a
heavily ionising particle has traversed the proportional counter.
The efficiency, in the range 2 to 18 MeV, was 2.10^{-4}, and the full
width at half height $4\frac{1}{2}$ per cent.

This counter suffers from the difficulty that the scintillation
efficiency of anthracene crystals is in this energy range quite
non-linear in proton energy.   An alternative spectrometer,
which reduces this difficulty, has been developed by Calvert *et
al.*[35]   The second detector in this spectrometer is a sodium
iodide crystal.   The pulses from the two crystals are applied to

(34). *Rev. Sci. Inst.* **23**, 569 (1952).
(35). *Proc. Phys. Soc.* **A-68**, 1005 (1955).

the X and Y plates of an oscilloscope and recorded photographically. For monoenergetic neutrons, then, one should obtain a narrow trace on the oscilloscope, whatever the variation of light response in anthracene with energy (if the response were linear, the trace would be the quadrant of a circle). The resolution obtained was 5·7 per cent. Fig. 4.22 is representative of the geometry, and Fig. 4.23 shows a typical spectrum obtained with this counter.

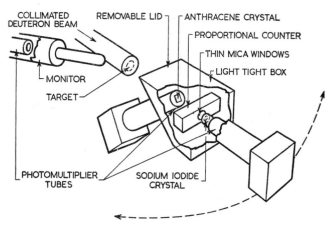

Fig. 4.22. Diagrammatic sketch of spectrometer, monitor and target arrangements developed by Calvert *et al.* (ref. 35): (spectrometer in 0° position).

In the above counters, the spectrum is determined in effect by pulse height analysis of the recoiling proton. In the experiments of Chagnon, Owen, Madansky[36] and of Draper,[37] the recoiling particle detected in the second detector was the neutron. However, with twelve organic crystals in coincidence for the second detector, the efficiency was only 10^{-4} and, as compared with proton telescopes, the system suffers from many disadvantages. A variation on the theme was investigated by Beghian *et al.*[38] and more recently by Patro.[39] Use was made of the fact that a neutron recoiling at nearly 90° to its initial

(36). *Rev. Sci. Inst.* **26**, 1165 (1955).
(37). *Rev. Sci. Inst.* **25**, 558 (1954).
(38). *Phys. Rev.* **86**, 1044 (1952).
(39). *Ind. J. Phys.* **30**, 99 (1956).

direction will have low energy, and that an efficient second detector can be a sodium iodide crystal, detecting the capture gamma rays from a sheet of silver in which it is wrapped, or a lithium iodide crystal. The low velocity of the recoiling neutron was taken into account with a suitable delay. While this modification slightly improves the efficiency and resolution of the original system, it does not eradicate the main disadvantages.

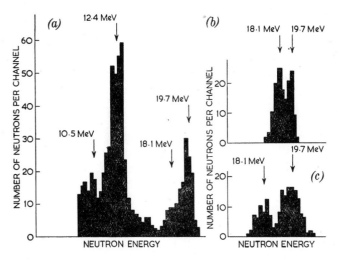

Fig. 4.23. Typical spectra obtained by Calvert *et al.* (ref. 35):
(*a*) Neutron energy spectrum obtained at 0° from $F^{19}(d,n)Ne^{20}$.
(*b*) 15° spectrum showing neutrons corresponding to ground and first excited states.
(*c*) The same as (*b*), but with 260 mg/cm² aluminium placed between the crystals.

A fast neutron threshold spectrometer of a very different kind has been developed by Kinsey[40] and described by Ferguson and Paul.[41] It is in effect an extension of the principle of the counter of Langsdorf *et al.* (Fig. 4.2). The scatterer is a cylinder of lithium, and the beam, after passing through the scatterer, enters and is trapped by a second high efficiency detecting assembly of paraffin moderators and BF_3 counters. In effect, the spectrometer consists of two Langsdorf

(40). *Can. Jour. Phys.* To be published.
(41). *Nucl. Phys.* **12**, 426 (1959).

counters in series, with lithium as the scatterer in the first. Now, the total cross section of lithium varies slowly and smoothly, except for a sharp resonance at 260 keV. The ratio of counts in the two counters will therefore be slowly varying, unless there is a component in the incident neutron spectrum of energy 260 keV. This will give increased counts in the first counter, and reduced counts in the second, and the ratio of the two counts will vary accordingly. The instrument has been used, for example, to study the energy levels of A^{37}, Sc^{48} and Cr^{51} by proton bombardment of Cl^{37}, Ca^{48} and V^{51}. As the proton energy is varied, the ratio of counts shows dips wherever there is a component of the incident beam of energy 260 keV.

4.4. Time-of-flight spectrometry

A discussion of millimicrosecond time-of-flight belongs logically to the preceding section, but since time-of-flight spectrometry is common to all ranges of neutron energy, we shall consider the various applications collectively in this section. We are concerned primarily with the neutron detectors employed, but mention must be made of certain details of apparatus and technique.

Common to all time-of-flight equipment is the fact that the neutrons are produced in a burst, or short interval of time, i.e. short compared with the longest time taken for any neutron in the neutron range considered to traverse the spectrometer flight path. For very slow neutrons, this time interval will be many tens of microseconds, for fast neutrons a few millimicroseconds. At the end of the flight path, a detector records the neutrons arriving at varying intervals of time after the burst. Thus, a direct conversion of the number of neutrons arriving at time t to the number of neutrons arriving with energy E gives the spectrum of neutrons emitted during the burst. The change in this spectrum produced by an absorber in the beam path will give the attenuation in the absorber as a function of neutron velocity, and hence the cross section as a function of energy; the number of neutrons with energy E scattered from a scatterer gives the scattered spectrum, and so on. The main features of the apparatus and results for a wide range of neutron energies has been described in many of the papers of Volume IV of the Geneva Conference (1955) Proceedings, and will be briefly summarised here.

(a) The thermal neutron range. A thermal neutron travels with a velocity of some 2000 m/sec, or 1 metre in 500 μsec. A beam of thermal neutrons (for example, from a reactor) impinges on a cylindrical rotor, normally with its axis at right angles to the beam. The beam is cut off except during the short interval (say 10 μsec) when a cadmium-lined slit or set of slits in the rotor is in line with the beam direction. At a distance of 1 to 2 metres, a detector counts the neutrons arriving in a series of time intervals, each (say) 10 μsec wide. Such a system constitutes a simple thermal neutron time-of-flight spectrometer, or *slow chopper* (the adjective "slow" refers to the relative neutron velocity). It is often used in the region below 0·1 eV. A particularly interesting application of these very slow neutrons has developed in studies of crystals. The neutron velocity is so low that in collision with the atoms of a crystal they gain energy, and the study of the spectrum of scattered neutrons gives information about the direction and velocity of thermal vibrations in the crystal.

Above 0·025 eV, slow choppers are sometimes used, but they suffer in intensity by comparison with the crystal spectrometer. In the latter instrument, neutrons are reflected from a crystal in the same way that X-rays are reflected, so that higher energies are reflected at lower angles. Since the beam from the crystal is continuous, rather than interrupted as in the case of a chopper, the mean neutron intensity is considerably higher. As compared with the slow chopper, this advantage is partially offset by the fact that scanning over the energy range is not automatic, as it is in the slow chopper.

Neutron detection in this energy range presents few problems. The time uncertainty associated with BF_3 proportional counters (2 μsec) is relatively small, and efficiencies of 50 per cent for BF_3 proportional counters are normal. Ionisation chambers lined with boron, and crystals of LiI(Eu) have been used.

(b) The range I eV to I0 keV. Two main types of spectrometer for this energy range are currently in use. The first, the

10—N.D.

fast chopper, is an extension of the principle of the slow chopper. By comparison, however, the difficulties of detection are considerably increased. A neutron of 1 keV energy travels at a speed of 4.10^5 metres per second, i.e. 20 metres in 50 μsec. The increased distance required between chopper and detector means either a much larger detector, to give the same solid angle as in the slow chopper system, or a smaller detector with lower count rate. To maintain resolution at higher energies, the burst from the rotor must be cut down to the order of 1 μsec or less. The spectrum from a pile, in the intermediate energy range, falls off in intensity as $1/E$ with increasing neutron energy. Finally, most detectors depend on nuclear reactions whose cross sections fall off as $1/v$.

Some, but not all, of these difficulties are also encountered in the second type of time-of-flight spectrometer, in which the neutron burst is produced by a machine. Historically, the method was first developed with a cyclotron as a neutron source, but recently the neutrons are more often produced from (γ,n) reactions following a high current pulse of electrons falling on a heavy element target. The pulse of electrons has been produced by a 100 MeV betatron (K.A.P.L. spectrometer), which has the advantage of a very short burst, or by an electron linear accelerator (Harwell spectrometer) where the advantage lies in very high currents. A project nearing completion aims at an electron current rate during the burst of $\frac{3}{4}$ amp and a peak neutron production rate of 10^{17} to 10^{18} neutrons per second during the burst. One of the problems in these machines is the screening of the detectors from the flash of gamma rays, which is intense.

There are many alternatives to the problem of a high efficiency detector, none of them ideal, and all described in principle in Chapter 3. A single gas-filled BF_3 proportional counter suffers from low efficiency and increased timing uncertainty, since there is appreciable length of the counter in the direction of travel of the neutrons. Also the timing uncertainty of 2 μsec in counter response is, in this application, by no means negligible. An alternative, a large battery of small diameter counters at right angles to the beam, offers appreciable improvement, but the efficiency, for a given timing uncertainty, is still only moderate. LiI crystals have high sensitivity, but the efficiency varies with neutron absorption in iodine, and the gamma sensitivity is high. Liquid scintillators loaded with methyl borate also have high gamma sensitivity, together with timing uncertainty due to the time involved in the moderation of the neutrons by the organic liquid. With sufficient concentration of B^{10}, however, this can be reduced to about 0·5 μsec. The detection of the 475 keV gamma ray from capture of neutrons in a large block of boron 10 has only moderate efficiency and a high gamma ray sensitivity. ZnS fused in B_2O_3 probably gives the best combination of the various factors of speed, short length in the path of the neutron beam, high efficiency and insensitivity to gamma rays. The ideal detector for kilovolt neutrons in time-of-flight spectrometry, however, has yet to be developed.

(c) The range I to I00 MeV: millimicrosecond time-of-flight.

As observed in Chapter 1, a neutron of energy 2 MeV has a velocity $2 \cdot 10^9$ cm/sec, i.e. it travels 1 metre in 50 mμsec. The two chief problems in fast neutron spectrometry are efficiency and gamma sensitivity. In a time-of-flight system, the gamma rays travel 1 metre in 3 mμsec, i.e. they are almost "prompt". They are therefore resolved from the neutron pulses, and no further discrimination is necessary. Also, as regards studies of angular distribution in inelastic neutron scattering in, say, Fe^{56}, the angular distribution of the gamma rays from inelastic scattering is of interest and is simultaneously determined. As regards efficiency, the only limit to the thickness of scintillator one can use is the time taken to traverse the crystal, so that crystal thicknesses of 3 to 5 cm and efficiencies of 30 to 50 per cent, depending on the neutron energy, are common (in view of the times involved, fast organic scintillators are the only possible detectors). Neutron and gamma backgrounds, of course, remain a problem. The neutron burst is absorbed by the walls of the experimental room, and both neutrons and gammas emerging from the walls contribute to the delayed background. Also, the machine is operating for the full interval between bursts, and machine background from a variety of sources can become important. In the ideal arrangement, the neutron target is high above the ground, in a room which has light walls and is completely screened from machine and beam when the latter is off the target.

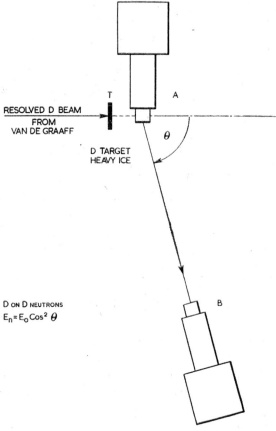

Fig. 4.24. Geometry of the experiment of Nielson and James (ref. 42).

Various types of millimicrosecond time-of-flight have been described. In some of these, the system bears resemblance to the spectrometers described in 4.3, except that neutron energy is determined by time-of-flight methods. For example, Nielson and James[42] employed a spectrometer essentially

(42). *Rev. Sci. Inst.* **26**, 1018 (1955).

similar to that of Draper and of Chagnon *et al.*, except that the neutron was timed in its flight from A to B (Fig. 4.24). The time resolution of the circuit was checked by annihilation radiation from Na^{22}, and the half-width of the delay curve was 1·5 mμsec. The neutron spectrum was determined by a time-to-pulse-height converter, which translates times of flight into pulses which could be registered by a pulse analyser. By a minor rearrangement in geometry, the starting pulse in counter A (Fig. 4.24) could be a gamma ray from, for example, a (d,n,γ) reaction, rather than a recoiling proton. A similar spectro-meter has been described by O'Neill,[43] in which the neutron source was the T(d,n) reaction and the starting signal was the alpha particles from the reaction.

Several time-of-flight spectrometers have been developed in connection with machines. Two such spectrometers[44],[45] operate in conjunction with small cyclotrons. These depend on the fact that in a conventional cyclotron the operating frequency (about 15 Mc/s) is of the right order for millimicrosecond pulse technique, and on the fact that in the course of its rather lengthy path through the cyclotron the protons become bunched in a narrow phase angle. If, therefore, a beam is extracted from the cyclotron, it emerges in short bursts of 2·0 mμsec, in the case of the Brookhaven cyclotron. Since a mean current of 1 mA has been extracted from the cyclotron, the peak current in these bursts is very high, as compared with the current obtainable from an electrostatic generator. This high intensity can be used in various ways, such as the use of rather longer flight paths and in the use of essentially single-channel methods of time analysis. There is, however, inflexibility in the proton energy and frequency, and the high repetition rate may involve overlap between neutron groups of differing energies, i.e. the fast group from one cycle and the slow group from the cycle before.

Time-of-flight spectrometers have, however, chiefly been used with electrostatic generators. The system we shall describe is that of Cranberg[46] who has developed the technique

(43). *Phys. Rev.* **95**, 1235 (1954).
(44). Malmfors *et al.*, *Nucl. Inst.* **1**, 186 (1957).
(45). Bloom *et al.*, *Phys. Rev.* **103**, 720 (1956).
(46). *Phys. Rev.*, **103**, 343 (1956).

to cover a wide range of neutron studies. The power of this technique is illustrated by the fact that much of Cranberg's work has to date been concerned with the study of spectra from inelastic neutron scattering. The difficulties of these studies are considerable, since if the primary neutron source strength is $10^9/4\pi$ neutrons/sec/steradian, the number of neutrons scattered from a scatterer is of the order of $10^6/4\pi$ n/sec/steradian and the detector efficiency needs to be high.

In Cranberg's experiments, the proton beam passes between a pair of deflector plates to which a r.f. voltage of 10 kV at 4·5

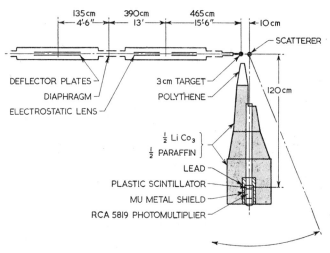

Fig. 4.25. Schematic diagram of the physical layout of the apparatus for measurement of neutron scattering by multimicrosecond time-of-flight (Cranberg, L., and Levin, J. S. (ref. 46)).

Mc/s is applied (Fig. 4.25). This deflects the beam across a slit. The target is not situated at the slit, because of the background of neutrons coming from the parts of the system bombarded by the beam when the latter is off the slit. Instead, it travels a further 3·85 metres through a quadrupole lens which refocuses it on to the target, usually of tritium gas. The bursts of neutrons from the target impinge upon the scatterer, from which the scattered neutrons are detected by an organic scintillator heavily shielded by lead and lithium-loaded paraffin. The time resolution of the system is determined by a number of

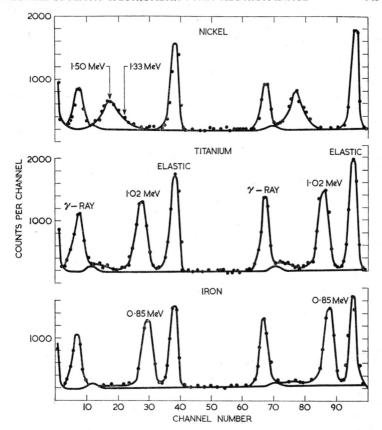

Fig. 4.26. Time spectra obtained by Cranberg and Levin at 90° for neutron scattering at 2·45 MeV from nickel, iron and titanium. The solid line under each curve is the background in the absence of a scatterer. The gamma rays elastically scattered neutrons, and the principal groups of inelastically scattered neutrons are identified. A flight path of 1·5 metres was used.

factors: in addition to the instrumental resolution, there are the time spread of protons in the gas target, the time spread of neutrons scattered from the scatterer and the time spread of detection in the detector. The overall resolution is about 5 mμsec, for this particular experiment. The timing signal is taken from the r.f. cycle, and the time-to-pulse-height-converter[47]

(47). Weber et al., Rev. Sci. Inst. **27**, 166 (1956).

is arranged to operate only when a pulse is received between the r.f. pips. One of the problems in this work lies in establishing the exact time of arrival of the neutron burst. This will be a function of the bias of the electronics and of the rise time (and, by implication, of the pulse height) of the pulse from the neutron detector.

As illustrations of the results obtained with this technique, we reproduce the spectrum determined for nickel, titanium and iron (Fig. 4.26) which shows the gamma ray peak, the elastic and inelastic scattering from these elements at 2·45 MeV and the background. Also, (in Fig. 4.27) the result from inelastic scattering in uranium is shown, with the elastic group omitted, plotted in such a way as to illustrate the concept of nuclear temperature. The neutron group from fission (on the right) is clearly shown : while the main body of low energy neutrons from inelastic scattering lies on the left.

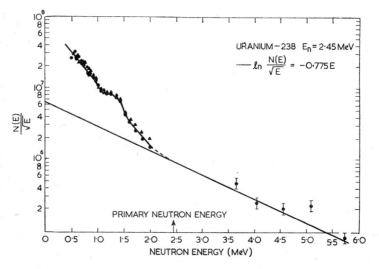

Fig. 4.27.   Analysis of spectral data obtained on U^{238} by Cranberg et al. (ref. 46).

In a second application, Cranberg et al.[48] have studied total cross sections with high resolution. These studies have been

(48). Rev. Sci. Inst. **28**, 89 (1957).

extended to low energies by the use of cooling baths and double
photomultipliers (see Chapter 3.3).   The efficiency of a crystal
$1\frac{1}{4}$ in. deep was constant at 47 per cent between 80 keV and 1
MeV, and fell to one-half this value at 30 keV.

At higher energies (100 to 150 MeV) a similar time-of-flight
technique has been described by Stafford and his co-workers at
Harwell[49] for use with the Harwell cyclotron.   At these
energies, no monoenergetic source is available, so that time-of-
flight spectrometry opens up considerable possibilities for
accurate neutron studies.   The considerably greater neutron
velocity ($1 \cdot 5.10^{10}$ cm/sec) necessitates considerably greater
flight paths (25 m), but the intensity, with this long flight path,
is improved by the fact that the neutrons are strongly peaked
in the forward direction of the proton beam.   In a f.m. cyclotron, the protons near the outer radius are distributed in a
"sausage", which is deflected in a direction parallel to the
magnetic field by a high voltage electrostatic pulse on to the
neutron-producing target.   The high voltage pulse starts
the timing sweep, which can be conveniently monitored by
the gamma ray yield from the target.

4.5. Slow neutron flux measurements

4.5.1. Introduction.   When we speak of *fast neutron flux
measurements*, we mean in most experiments measurement of
flux of approximately monoenergetic neutrons of intensity of
the order of 10^4 n/cm^2 sec.   Fluxes several orders of magnitude
less would be difficult to measure, while fluxes several orders of
magnitude greater would be difficult to produce.   The term
slow neutron flux covers a much wider range.   Thus, fluxes of
slow neutrons from cosmic rays are normally considerably less
than 1 n/cm^2 sec in intensity, while in high flux reactors
measurements of intensity of the order of 10^{14} n/cm^2 sec are
involved.   Also, in the experiments discussed below, the spectrum of neutrons is far from monoenergetic.   Thus, the beam
from the thermal column of a reactor (Chapter 1.3) will contain
neutrons of the range of energies characteristic of a Maxwellian

(49). *Rev. Sci. Inst.* **28**, 749 (1957).

distribution corresponding to a temperature of 300°K.   A beam from a reactor which has not passed through the thermal column will contain, in addition to the thermal beam, a group of neutrons with a spectrum such that the intensity falls off as $1/E_n$. In addition to flux measurements in beams, however, we are often concerned with flux measurements in moderators.   Thus, if a source, say Ra-α-Be neutrons, is placed at the centre of a large graphite stock, then at a distance of about 1 metre from the source (Chapter 5.2.1) the neutrons will be mainly thermal, i.e. they will have a Maxwellian distribution of energies. Nearer the source, the spectrum will contain neutrons of higher energies, including fast neutrons and neutrons in the 1 eV (resonance) range.

The various reactions involved in slow neutron measurement have been described in Chapter 2.   In all these reactions, the cross section falls off rapidly above energies of, say, 1 keV, so that in general the effect of fast neutrons on the detector can be ignored.   The neutrons with which we are concerned therefore fall into two groups, the thermal group and the resonance group. Distinction between the two is made by determining the activities induced in the bare foil and the foil screened by about 1 mm thickness of cadmium.   The ratio so observed, the *cadmium ratio* is an important factor in obtaining an approximate estimate of the energy spectrum of neutrons under investigation.   It should be remembered, however, that the absorption in cadmium is not negligible in the resonance energy range.   Thus, a screening foil of 1 mm thickness may require a correction factor of 9 per cent of neutrons of energy 1·44 eV and 2 per cent of neutrons of energy 4·9 eV.[50]

The choice of detector will be determined by the conditions of the experiment.   For the lowest fluxes, large BF_3 counters or photographic plates loaded with BF_3, with their property of long-term integration, are used.   In the type of experiment to which we shall mainly refer in this section, the slow neutron flux is of the order of 10^3 n/cm^2 sec, and the choice lies between detectors whose absorption cross section varies as $1/v$, or approximately so (boron, manganese, sodium), or detectors

(50). Martin, *Nucleonics*, **13**/3, 52 (March 1955).

with marked resonances in the resonance region (In, whose principal capture resonance is at 1·44 eV, and Au, 4·9 eV). Both the latter have high thermal capture cross sections, and also the effect of capture in higher energy resonances cannot always be ignored.   Thus, Roberts *et al.*[51] in studying the slowing-down of 25 keV neutrons in graphite found that near the source, where the mean neutron energy was high, appreciable correction had to be made for the absorption of neutrons of energy higher than 1·44 eV in their indium foils.   For the highest fluxes, boron is still often used, but the problem of burn-up of the boron becomes an appreciable factor.   Elements with a lower cross section (Co, Cu) have been used, and even bismuth, with an absorption cross section of only 5 mb, has been suggested as a flux meter for high-flux reactors.

Finally, we should observe that a $1/v$ detector enables one to measure not neutron flux but neutron density.   For if the density of neutrons with velocity v is $\rho(v)$, the flux of neutrons with velocity v is $v\rho(v)$, and the rate of capture by an absorber of cross section σ is $\sigma v \rho(v)$, so that the total rate of absorption is $\int \sigma v \rho(v) dv$.   For a $1/v$ absorber, $\sigma \propto 1/v$, so that

$$\sigma v = \sigma_0 v_0,$$

where σ_0, v_0 usually refer to the velocity of 2200 m/sec, which is the most probable velocity of the Maxwellian distribution at 20°C.   The total rate of absorption is therefore $\sigma_0 v_0 \int \rho dv$, i.e. it is proportional to the integrated neutron density.

4.5.2. Relative measurements.   (a) Radioactive decay.
Since many relative measurements are made by activation methods, we begin by considering the effects of decay during and after irradiation.   Suppose the radioactive isotope produced decays with period τ.   If the rate of neutron absorption is R_0, and N is the number of radioactive nuclei existing in the sample at time t, we have

$$\frac{dN}{dt} = R_0 - N/\tau \qquad (4.1)$$

If the irradiation began at $t = 0$, and concluded at $t = t_0$, then

(51). *Phys. Rev.* **80**, 6 (1950).

the activity (number of disintegrations per second) at t is by integration

$$R(t_0) = R_0(1 - e^{-t_0/\tau}) \tag{4.2}$$

so that at a time t after the end of the irradiation the activity will be

$$R(t, t_0) = R_0(1 - e^{-t_0/\tau})e^{-t/\tau} \tag{4.3}$$

which can be rewritten

$$R_0 = \frac{R(t, t_0)e^{t/\tau}}{(1 - e^{-t_0/\tau})} \tag{4.4}$$

The quantity R_0 is independent of neutron exposure. It is referred to as the *saturation activity*, since it is the activity resulting from irradiation for an infinite time t_0. If the activity is detected in a counter of efficiency ϵ, and a total number of counts C is recorded between times t_1 and t_2 after the end of the irradiation, then integration of (4.3) gives

$$R_0 = \frac{C}{\epsilon\tau(1 - e^{-t_0/\tau})(e^{-t_1/\tau} - e^{-t_2/\tau})} \tag{4.5}$$

(b) Counting methods. Relative measurements of thermal neutron density can be made in graphite, water, or other moderators by BF_3 chambers, which have the advantage of high efficiency. In these measurements, the only correction required is that for flux perturbation and depression (section 4.5.4 below). Measurements with radioactive indicators, however, are frequently preferred. They are normally of small physical size, they are not encumbered with electrical connections and can contribute information on the relative intensity of the neutrons of different energy groups.

Normally the determination of radioactive intensity is made with the use of Geiger counters of the end-window type, i.e. the beta activity is determined. The advantages of counting beta rays with Geigers are:

1. The counter is triggered by every beta particle which has sufficient energy to penetrate the window, so that the counting efficiency is high.
2. The Geiger has normally a plateau of a few hundred volts,

with a slope of about 0·02 per cent per volt, so that it is insensitive to small changes of E.H.T. voltage.

3. It has an output of about $\frac{1}{2}$ volt, which is sensibly constant, so that little is required in the way of amplification and the count rate is insensitive to small changes of bias.

These advantages are substantial. Disadvantages include:

(i) The fact that the Geiger counter has a long dead time (a few hundred microseconds) which makes counting difficult for rates much greater than about 100 per sec, for which correction has to be made. Since the dead time is not a fixed quantity, an external *quenching* circuit is usually used such that, after one pulse has triggered the counter, the E.H.T. across the counter is lowered below the Geiger threshold for a fixed known period, say 500 μsec. An electron passing through the counter during this period will not trigger the Geiger discharge. If, for example, the count rate is 100 per sec, and the fixed dead time is 500 μsec, the dead time correction is 5 per cent.

(ii) If the radioactive material produces electrons of low energy, the number of electrons with sufficient energy to escape from a thick foil is low.

A scintillation counter detecting gamma radiation will have the reverse of the advantages and disadvantages described above: thus, it may respond to high count rates from thick foils, but will be less efficient and will be much more sensitive to drift in the electronic apparatus.

For accurate measurement, it is essential to ensure that the foils are all counted under identical conditions. The Geiger counters should be monitored periodically with some standard radioactive material, e.g. uranium. To ensure that the variation of distance of each foil from the counter, during counting, does not affect the measurement, it is customary to count the foils in a system which employs two counters back-to-back in a lead castle (Fig. 4.28). In such a system, if a foil is buckled so that it is, say, nearer to one counter, then it will be further from the other counter, and the effects of variation of distance from the counter are to a first order cancelled out.

We shall, in section 4.5.3 below, be discussing various

absolute methods of determining thermal flux, but it may be worth enumerating some of the difficulties attendant on any attempt to measure absolute activity by beta counting. Apart from the problems of relating the measured activity to thermal flux, there are considerable difficulties in determining the absolute beta activity. In a system such as is shown in Fig. 4.28, for example, there are corrections to be applied for electrons scattered in the window of the counter, in the gas on

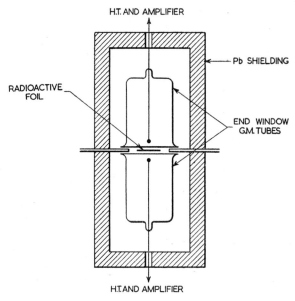

Fig. 4.28.   Schematic of shielded back-to-back beta counting apparatus.

either side of the windows, and from the sides of the aperture. In a true 4π counting geometry, the foil is placed at the centre of a counter, so that every electron emerging from either side of the foil is counted. Any beta ray spectrum, however, has a peak at very low energies (a few kilovolts), and foils of thickness commonly used for slow neutron detection, i.e. about 10 mg/cm^2, are very thick for electrons of this energy. Correction for self-absorption in the foil is therefore comparatively large and uncertain.

(c) **Some practical details.** We shall conclude this section by describing briefly a practical case. The foils used were of 0·015 in. aluminium, plated on each side with 0·002 in. of In, and protected by 0·001 in. of aluminium foil. The irradiation time was 50 to 100 min, i.e. between one and two half-lives of In^{116} (54 min). Much shorter periods increase the error in time corrections, and decrease the net activity: much longer periods may build up appreciable intensity due to In^{114} (50 days). After irradiation, a time of 15 min was allowed for the decay of In^{116} (ground state) and of aluminium (period 2·3 min) and the foils counted in an arrangement similar to that shown in Fig. 4.28, correction being made for dead time. As several foils were used in the experiment, their relative efficiencies were determined by placing them equispaced on a rotating table beneath a source of thermal neutrons, and counting the resulting activity.

When several foils are used to determine the thermal flux at various points in a moderator, it is important that the foils should not interact, within the accuracy of experiment. Thus, in an isotropic flux in graphite, two foils face to face must be separated by a distance at least equal to one scattering mean free path (about 1 in.). If the flux is anisotropic, the "shadow" cast by a foil can be considerable. Similarly, the effect of the foil on the neutron distribution in the surrounding medium needs to be taken into account. We shall be discussing this in Section 4.5.4.

4.5.3. Absolute determination of thermal flux. Absolute determination of radioactive intensity. We have seen above that the absolute determination of the intensity of beta radiation presents many problems. The method of absolute determination which avoids these difficulties is that of coincidence counting.[52] Consider a source which emits N_0 beta and gamma rays per second in coincidence. A beta counter, efficiency ϵ_β, records N_β counts per second, while a gamma detector, efficiency ϵ_γ, records N_γ counts per second, while the coincidence rate is $N_{\beta,\gamma}$ per second. We assume that the gamma emission is isotropic with respect to the beta radiation (as is the

(52). Dunworth, *Rev. Sci. Inst.* **11**, 167 (1940).

case with most sources) and that the two counters are at 180° with respect to the source. Then we have

$$N_\beta = N_0\epsilon_\beta, \qquad N_\gamma = N_0\epsilon_\gamma, \qquad N_{\beta,\gamma} = N_0\epsilon_\beta\epsilon_\gamma$$

from which

$$N_0 = \frac{N_0{}^2\epsilon_\beta\epsilon_\gamma}{N_0\epsilon_\beta\epsilon_\gamma} = \frac{N_\beta N_\gamma}{N_{\beta,\gamma}}$$

independent of the overall efficiency of either counter. Random coincidences are determined by delaying the pulses from one detector relative to the other.

The decay scheme of gold (Chapter 2) almost fulfils the requirements of the ideal simple decay scheme, and gold activation has often been used as a means of measuring thermal neutron flux. There is the additional advantage that the thermal neutron absorption cross section for gold has been established to 1 per cent. Above 0·02 eV the cross section does not vary exactly as $1/v$, and there is a strong resonance at 4·9 eV. The contribution to the activity from this resonance can be determined by Cd difference. The use of gold foils to measure thermal flux has been described by Raffle,[53] who irradiated gold foils in a uniform beam of thermal neutrons. The following corrections need to be determined or estimated:

1. It is necessary to ensure that the activity varies linearly with surface area.
2. In the above elementary derivation, we have assumed ϵ_β and ϵ_γ are constant for all parts of the foil. For a foil of finite thickness, this is not the case, and a correction $p = (1 + \overline{\Delta\epsilon\Delta f})$ must be applied, where $\overline{\Delta\epsilon\Delta f}$ is the mean product of the deviations of the sensitivities of the β and γ detectors from their average values. The comparison between the measured and calculated values of p was good in Raffle's experiments.
3. Correction must be made for branching and internal conversion. 1·43 per cent of the transitions proceed through a low energy beta ray (0·295 MeV) and the internal conversion coefficient of the 0·411 MeV gamma ray is 4·5 per cent, i.e.

(53). A.E.R.E. Report, R 2998 (1959).

4·5 per cent of the normal transitions proceed through the emission of a 0·33 MeV electron. For detectors, Raffle used an NaI crystal (gamma rays) and a stilbene crystal (beta rays), biased so that the internal conversion electrons were not detected.

In Raffle's experiments, the flux in a beam from a thermal column was determined by the activity produced in a gold foil, and for purposes of fission cross section measurement the activity determined for the foil was used to calibrate a parallel plate chamber with B^{10} electromagnetically deposited on one of the plates. An alternative method was used by Tunnicliffe,[54] who irradiated a BF_3 proportional counter with a thermal beam, so that, knowing the sensitive volume of the counter, the pressure of the BF_3 and the absorption cross section of boron, the flux could be deduced. In neither of these experiments was a cross-calibration with an alternative method of flux determination established.

The intercomparison between gold and boron in thermal flux measurements in a moderator has been described by Larsson[55] and by de Juren and Rosenwasser.[56] Both groups were primarily concerned with absolute source strength measurements (Chapter 5), but their determination of thermal flux is relevant here. Larsson used two methods of determining the thermal neutron flux. In the first method, a BF_3 chamber, which has already been described, was used to measure the thermal neutron density. The second determination was by the use of gold foils. The contribution of resonance neutrons was determined by cadmium difference and the effects of flux perturbation and depression were allowed for by Skyrme's theory (4.5.4). The results agreed to 2 per cent, although, if the modern figure of 98·7 barns is used for the absorption cross section of gold instead of 95 barns, as used by Larsson, the discrepancy would be 5 per cent.

A similar comparison was made by de Juren and Rosenwasser,[56] using the experimental arrangement shown in Fig. 4.29. Carbon was used as a moderator in the neighbourhood

(54). Chalk River Report CRGP-458 (n.d.).
(55). *Ark. f. Fys.* **7**/25, 323 (1953).
(56). *J. Res. N.B.S.* **52**, 93 (1954); Research Paper 2477.

of the foil, so that flux depression was minimised. The thermal flux was determined by the number of counts in an aluminium parallel-plate ionisation chamber, with a thin boron film on one of the plates. The quantity of the boron was determined by chemical analysis. In a second experiment, the activity of a gold foil irradiated in the same place was determined and compared with gold foils calibrated in a standard flux at Oak Ridge. The agreement between these two determinations was 2 per cent, a figure which is reduced to 1 per cent if the modern value for the absorption cross section for gold is used.

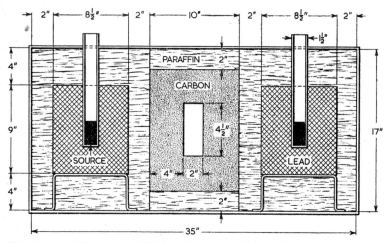

Fig. 4.29. Schematic of National Bureau of Standards thermal flux, as described by de Juren and Rosenwasser (ref. 56).

We should note that the agreement in both the above pairs of experiments is further reinforced by the fact that on these measurements are based one of the absolute methods of neutron source strength determination (Chapter 5), and in the field of absolute source strength measurement excellent agreement between a variety of independent methods of determination has been obtained. A second comparison can be obtained from absolute fission cross sections in a thermal neutron beam. These can be obtained directly by determining the number of fissions induced in a known quantity of material in a known flux, or deduced by indirect measurements. The subject is discussed at the end of Chapter 5: various recent measurements agree within ± 3 per cent.

Other methods of absolute thermal flux measurement are in principle possible. For example, manganese is an absorber whose cross section varies as $1/v$, and emits a moderately high energy beta ray as well as gamma rays. Absolute counting should therefore be possible, either by coincidence methods or by comparison with 4π beta counting of special very thin sources. Another independent method has been explored by Grimeland,[57] who irradiated NaI crystals in a thermal flux. The iodine activity (25 min) was then allowed to decay, and the sodium activity (15 hour) was counted directly. The count rate was plotted as a function of discriminator bias, and the count rate was extrapolated back to zero bias. This extrapolation constitutes one of the uncertainties involved in the method: also, the agreement between different crystals was only about 5 per cent, which represented the random as distinct from possible systematic errors.

4.5.4. Flux distortion and flux depression. In the above sections, we have postponed discussion of an important factor in any thermal flux measurement, particularly of flux measurements in a moderator. In any experiment, the ideal detector has zero perturbing effect on the quantity it detects. In the case of the determination of thermal neutron flux, for example by activation methods, this means that the foil must be infinitely thin. Apart from handling problems, however, the fluxes under study are rarely so high that very thin foils can be used, and foil thicknesses of several tens of microns, i.e. several tens of milligrams per sq. cm, are frequently employed. For such thicknesses two problems arise, both from the fact that only materials of high absorption cross section for the neutron energies under investigation are employed, and, because of this absorption neutrons of these energies will be attenuated in the foil. The first problem is flux perturbation. Consider a volume of moderator in which there is an isotropic

(57). J.E.N.E.R. Pub-12 (1956).

neutron flux, divided by an imaginary plane. Clearly the spectrum of neutrons travelling across the plane in one direction is the same as that travelling in the opposite direction. If on one side of the plane we now place an absorbing foil, then the spectrum of neutrons escaping backwards from the foil will be very different from the first case, i.e. the flux in the neighbour-hood of the foil will be considerably distorted. The effect can be alleviated in various ways: thus, the foil can be placed at the centre of a thin-walled cavity, or, in a water moderator, the detector can be a cell containing an aqueous solution of material which is to become radioactive. Although, however, the effect of flux perturbation is in this way reduced, it cannot be elimin-ated. The second problem is that of flux depression. For a foil of the thickness indicated, the attenuation of resonance or thermal neutron flux is considerable, and the mean spectrum and flux of the neutrons traversing the foil is not the same as the spectrum and flux incident at the boundary of the foil.

It is not easy to give a simple and lucid account of the experiments described in the literature, partly because the phenomena are complex and partly because the evidence presented in different papers shows considerable divergence. We give, first, the results of the calculations of the corrections for flux perturbation and depression, as they were first given by Bothe.[58] He calculated the perturbation of a spherical shell of radius R' in a medium of scattering mean free path λ_s, and diffusion length L. If C is the observed activity and C_0 the activity corresponding to an unperturbed flux, and if $R' \gg \lambda_s$, then

$$\frac{C_0 - C}{C} = \alpha\left(\frac{3}{4}\frac{R'}{\lambda_s}\frac{L}{R'+L} - \frac{1}{2}\right)$$

where α is the average probability that a neutron will be absorbed in a single traversal through the detector. When $R' \ll {}_s\lambda$, we may write

$$\frac{C_0 - C}{C} = 0\cdot34\,\frac{R'}{\lambda_s}\,\alpha.$$

For a disc-shaped foil, radius R, thickness δ, absorption

(58). *Z. Phys.* **120**, 437 (1943).

coefficient μ, in cm^{-1}, the mean absorption probability is given by

$$\alpha = 1 - e^{-\mu\delta}(1 - \mu\delta) + \mu^2\delta^2 E_i(-\mu\delta)$$

$$\approx 2\mu\delta(\mu\delta \ll 1)$$

where $E_i(-x)$ is the exponential integral, $-\int_x^\infty (e^{-t}/t)\mathrm{d}t$.

The relevance of these results, and many practical points arising in foil irradiation have been discussed by Tittle.[59-61] Tittle found his experimental results were in agreement with Bothe's calculations if he used the above formulae to calculate the perturbation of a *disc* of radius R, and if he used the transport mean free path λ_t, rather than the scattering mean path in the moderator.   An implication of these results is that flux perturbation in carbon is much less than in paraffin, because the mean free path is much greater in carbon than in paraffin. This conclusion was supported by Klema and Ritchie[62] who studied the variation of activity produced by a thermal flux in indium and gold foils as the thickness was varied.   Their results were in apparent agreement with the theories of Bothe and of Skyrme.[58],[63]   In Thompson's papers,[64] however, it appears that, in the case of indium foils irradiated in a thermal flux, the two theories give quite appreciably divergent results. Thompson's experimental results were in fair agreement with Skyrme's theory.

These and other theories[58],[63],[65-67] have been summarised by Meister.[68]   In his experimental arrangement, Meister used Ra-α-Be sources with moderators of paraffin or graphite and indium foil detectors.   The effects of flux perturbation and flux depression were separated by the device of irradiating the foil in a fairly large cavity (approximately 20 cm

(59). *Nucleonics*, 8/6, 5 (June 1951).
(60). *Nucleonics*, 9/1, 60 (Jan. 1952).
(61). *Phys. Rev.* **80**, 756 (abstract) (1950).
(62). *Phys. Rev.* **87**, 167 (abstract) (1952).
(63). Can. declassified Report MS. 91 (n.d.).
(64). A.E.R.E. RP/R. 1549 (1954); *J. Nucl. En.* **2**, 286 (1955).
(65). Corinaldesi, *Nuov. Cim.* **3**, 131 (1946).
(66). Vigon and Wirtz, *Zeit. Naturf.* **9a**. 286 (1954).
(67). Meister, *Zeit. Naturf.* **10a**, 669 (1955).
(68). *Zeit. Naturf.* **11a**, 347 (1956).

× 20 cm × 35 cm), in the case of the graphite moderator.   Since
the foil is small compared with the cavity, the neutron flux
entering the foil is in fact the neutron flux emerging from, and

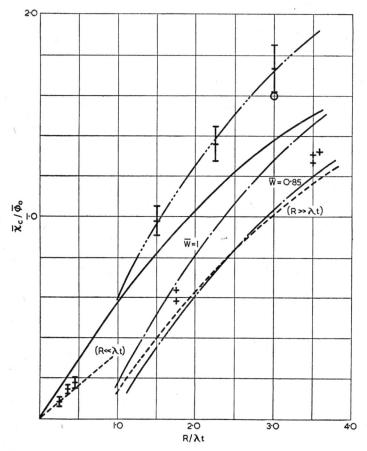

Fig. 4.30.   Meister's results on the variation of the perturbation, $\overline{X}_c$,
with radius of foil R.   Meister's experimental points are shown with
statistical errors, (the circles and crosses are those of Corinaldesi and
Bothe) while the curves correspond to the predictions of different
theories.

absorbed by, the walls of the cavity.   Since the radius of the
foils normally used is of the same order as λ_t, whereas many of
the theories are developed for the limiting cases $R \ll \lambda_t$ or $R \gg \lambda_t$,

Meister considers the variation of $\bar{\chi}_{c/\Phi_0}$ with R/λ_t, and his results are shown in Fig. 4.30. $\bar{\chi}_c$ is the perturbation, $\dfrac{C_0 - C}{C}$ above; $\Phi_0 = 0{\cdot}886\, \Phi_0(\mu_0\delta)$, where Φ_0 is the probability that a neutron of velocity 2200 m/sec will be absorbed in a single traversal of the detector: R and λ_t have meanings as above. The curves in Fig. 4.30 represent the predictions of various theories, and illustrate the divergence between them. The uppermost curve is an empirical curve fitting Meister's experimental points according to the formula

$$\bar{\chi}_c = \Phi_0(\mu\delta)\left(\frac{3}{4}\frac{L}{\lambda_t}\left(1 - e^{R/L}\right) - 0{\cdot}06\right).$$

In a later paper,[68] he outlines a theory accounting for this empirical formula.

4.6. Neutron detectors in health monitoring

Like gamma rays, neutrons constitute an appreciable health hazard. Slow neutrons are captured by elements in the body such as nitrogen and hydrogen, from which the protons and gamma rays cause damage to the tissues. Fast neutrons cause damage by recoiling protons, and since the ionisation per unit path length is about 10 to 100 times that of a Compton electron of equivalent energy, the degree of damage to the tissue is correspondingly greater. The health tolerance for slow neutrons is at present 3×10^8 n/cm²/week, and for fast (2 MeV) neutrons 6×10^6 n/cm²/week.

The accepted unit for measuring tissue dose is the roentgen equivalent physical (rep.) and is defined as the amount of radiation which is absorbed in tissue to give an energy absorption at the rate of 95 ergs per gramme. Such a unit is not directly practical. One can, however, measure ionisation produced in a hydrocarbon, in which the H:C ratio is not far different from the H:(C,N,O) in normal tissue. From this, the energy dissipated in MeV/g can be compared for the two media. With some simplifying assumptions, Hurst[69] has calculated the energy lost in the first collision in ethylene as compared with

(69). *Brit. J. Rad.* **27**/318, 353 (1954).

tissue. As Fig. 4.31 shows, the two quantities are not greatly different, and their ratio is nearly constant, independent of neutron energy. For a complete treatment, however, multiple scattering needs to be taken into account. Snyder[70] has shown that the total collision dose is larger by a factor of approximately 2 than the first collision dose.

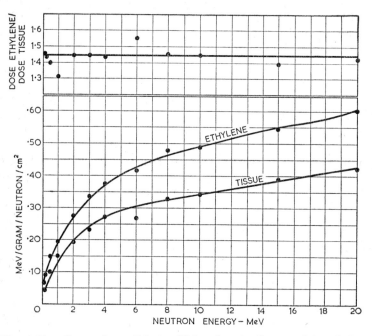

Fig. 4.31. Comparison of first collision dose in tissue and in ethylene as a function of neutron energy.

Slow neutrons. The damage to tissue is primarily from gamma rays from neutron capture, so that the weekly tolerance dose is of the same order as the number of gamma rays in a weekly tolerance. In practice, this means that the weekly tolerance of slow neutrons may be quite readily determined from a BF_3 chamber or boron-lined ionisation chamber. As we have seen also, a film impregnated with boron will give 100 tracks for

(70). *Nucleonics*, **6**/2, 46 (Feb. 1950).

an area 100 microns square, for one day's irradiation at the tolerance rate. In effect, any of the standard methods fully described before in these pages will suffice.

Fast neutrons. The problems of fast neutron health monitoring are a recapitulation of the problems of fast neutron flux measurement and spectrometry, usually in the presence of a gamma ray flux. A simple qualitative estimate can be made from a pair of chambers or proportional counters, one filled with hydrogen or methane and the other with argon, with the

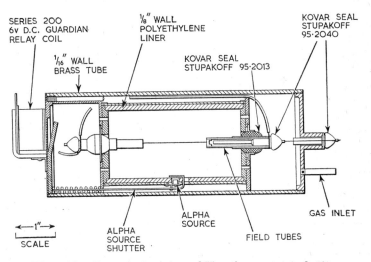

Fig. 4.32. Cross section view of Hurst's counter (ref. 69).

gains of the system adjusted so that a pure gamma ray flux gives an equal response in both counters. If the pressure is too high, the gamma ray response is high and discrimination is lost: if it is not high enough, end and wall effects on recoiling protons become excessive above about 3 MeV. This is not satisfactory, in view of the fact that first collision dose increases continuously with neutron energy. As with the fast neutron radiator spectrometer, therefore, a better solution for energetic neutrons lies in the use of film radiators. The counter developed by Hurst,[69] is filled with ethylene gas, at approximately atmospheric pressure, and the walls lined with $\frac{1}{8}$ in. thickness of polyethylene (Fig. 4.32). Field tubes ensure constant multi-plication. Gamma rays still constitute a problem, but with appropriate biasing their effect can be shown to be small. Let us consider the recoil proton energy distribution in the laboratory as a function of θ where θ is the angle between the direction of the incident neutron and the recoiling proton. We have seen that the energy of a proton recoiling at angle θ is $E_n \cos^2 \theta$. Let us assume that the bias of the counting system

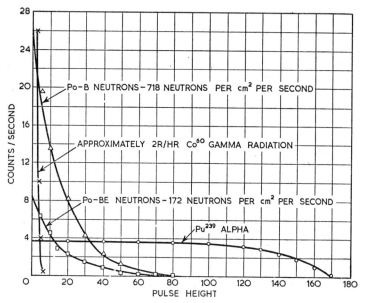

Fig. 4.33. Spectra obtained by Hurst for Po-Be neutrons, Pu-Be neutrons, Co/60 gamma rays and 5·14 MeV alphas.

is set at an energy corresponding to $B = E_n \cos^2 \theta$. The number of recoils in the cone θ_1 is $N(\theta_1) = \sin^2 \theta$, so that the number of recoils having energy less than B is $(1 - \sin^2 \theta_1) = B/E_n$. The average energy of these is $B/2$, and the average for all recoils is $E_n/2$. Therefore the energy lost under the bias varies as $(B/E_n)^2$, which is small if (B/E_n) is only moderately small. In figures, if the maximum gamma induced electron pulse is 300 keV, the counter will count neutrons of 1 MeV with only 10 per cent loss with the bias set to exclude gamma induced electrons.

The results obtained by Hurst are shown in Fig. 4.33 as integral bias curves for gamma rays, for Po-B and Po-Be sources and for Pu^{239} alpha particles. It is seen that the gamma ray contribution is negligible. With the aid of the Puα curve, one can calculate the energy dissipation in the counter per second. Alternatively, knowing the neutron source strength, and the first collision dose curve for ethylene (Fig. 4.31) one can estimate the rate of energy dissipation in the counter. The two results were in agreement. On the practical side, the counter was moderately non-directional, although one difficulty with the counter was that a sealed-off version gave values of neutron flux which were low by a factor of three. This defect was attributed to the build-up of impurities promoting electron attachment.

To determine the equivalent tissue dose, it is necessary to determine the total current due to all recoils, i.e. the area under the pulse height distributions. A simple type of pulse integrator has been described by Glass and Hurst.[71] This is a normal binary type scaling unit with 1, 2, 4, 8 count stages, but is fed not only by 5-volt pulses from a discriminator in channel 1 but by a 10-volt pulse in channel 2, a 20-volt pulse in channel 4 and a 40-volt pulse in channel 8. It can be shown that such a system integrates the pulse output from the counter, so that the output from the scaler, when fed through a ratemeter, gives the integrated dose rate.

A similar development with photographic plates has been described by Cheka[72] in describing improvements in film technique. If a film is a radiator as well as a detector, many high-energy recoil protons will penetrate the entire thickness of the film and escape. If, however, the film is contained in a suitable thickness of paper, the recoil protons emerging from the paper into the film compensate for the defect, so that the count rate in the film reproduces, over a considerable energy range, the first collision dose.

Several other types of health monitor have been described, mostly as variants of systems described in Chapters 3 and 4. Thus, de Pangher and Roesch[73] have described the operation

(71). *Rev. Sci. Inst.* **23**, 67 (1954).
(72). *Nucleonics,* **12**/6, 40 (June 1954).
(73). *Phys. Rev.* **100**, 1793 (1955).

of a long counter modified so that its response approximates to the tissue dose. The cylindrical moderator is 11 cm thick, and as the neutron energy increases, the penetration for neutrons entering at right angles to the cylinder increases, so that the response increases with increasing neutron energy.

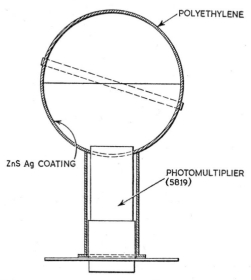

POLYETHYLENE

ZnS Ag COATING

PHOTOMULTIPLIER
(5819)

Fig. 4.34.   Sphere assembly of fast neutron scintillating survey counter of Thompson (Ref. 75).

Handloser and Higinbotham[74] have described the operation of a Hornyak button 2 in. diameter by $1\frac{1}{4}$ in. thick, which was insensitive to a gamma ray flux of 4r/hour. As reference to Fig. 3.28 of Chapter 3 shows, the response of the Hornyak button increases with increasing neutron energy, roughly in the same way that tissue dose increases with neutron energy. As regards efficiency, Handloser and Higinbotham found that a flux of 20 n/cm²/sec (the then tolerance dose) gave a count rate of 70 per min.

Two authors (Thompson[75] and Skjoldebrand[76]) have

(74). *Rev. Sci. Inst.* **25**, 98 (1954).
(75). *Nucleonics*, **12/5**, 43 (May 1954).
(76). *J. Nucl. En.* **1**, 299 (1955).

described scintillation counters suitable for fast neutron dosimetry. Thompson's counter is shown schematically in Fig. 4.34, and consisted of two hemispheres of diameter 7 in. sprayed on the inside with ZnS(Ag). A photomultiplier detected recoil protons in the ZnS. In Skjoldebrand's counter, the polythene layer was obtained by warming a glass flask to 130°C, filling with polythene powder, shaking out the powder and reheating to form a smooth film.

5

NEUTRON STANDARDS

In Chapter 4, we discussed a number of different neutron measurements, which for the most part have not been developed to a high degree of accuracy. In these measurements, recourse is often made to primary neutron standards, either in using standard cross sections or in using standardised radioactive sources to calibrate the measuring equipment. The latter, which we describe first in 5.1 and 5.2, is also of indirect interest in flux measurements. The subject of cross section standards and accuracies we consider in 5.3.

5.1. Radioactive neutron sources

The perfect neutron source standard does not exist. If it did, it would have the following properties:

(*a*) It would be accurately reproducible.

(*b*) It would have no detectable variation with time over a period of, say, ten years.

(*c*) It would have negligible mass, would give no secondary neutrons by any kind of multiplication (such as, for example, by fission in a flux of thermal neutrons) and its slow neutron capture cross section would be negligibly small.

(*d*) The neutron energy spectrum would be such that the source can be easily compared with other types. For problems in reactor measurements, a fission spectrum is of considerable advantage.

(*e*) It would have a source strength of 10^6 to 10^7 n/sec, with negligible yield of gamma rays.

(*f*) It would approximate to a point source.

While no existing neutron source fulfils all these requirements, we should mention that the criteria are nearly met by the potential use of one of the curium isotopes, Cm^{244}. The half-life for spontaneous fission varies with Z^2/A in a remarkably uniform way (Swiatecki*), and for Cm^{244} the value of Z^2/A is such that 20 mg of Cm^{244} would have a spontaneous fission neutron yield of about 10^5 neutrons per second. The fission cross section for slow neutrons is negligible, the gamma ray yield quite small and the overall half-life is twenty years.

With these criteria in mind, we consider the various types of source at present available, and their limitations.

A. Alpha-activated neutron sources. Ra-α-Be. This
is the most widely used of all neutron sources. A solution or suspension of a radium salt, together with a suspension of beryllium powder, is evaporated to dryness, and the can carefully sealed (McCallum[1]). Radium, in equilibrium with its daughter products, emits four alpha particles, of which one has an energy of about 8 MeV, which by virtue of its high penetrating power has a high neutron yield. From a curie ($3 \cdot 7 \times 10^{10}$ disintegrations per sec) one obtains 10^7 n/sec approximately. The spectrum is shown in Appendix X (a). While it is still popular and widely used, it has many disadvantages. It is subject to slow changes of source strength, due to the growth of polonium from Ra-D, according to the equation

$$Q = Q_0\{1 + 0 \cdot 17(1 - e^{-0.0315t})\}$$

where t is in years. It has also been suspected that some sources change because of the shift in physical disposition of the powders. The Ra-α-Be source has a high gamma ray output. Its neutron spectrum (which has not been well studied) has a peak at about 5 MeV, with a maximum neutron energy of 13 MeV, and it may also have some low-energy neutrons (neutron spectra, determined by photographic plates, do not detect low

(1). *Nucleonics*, **5**/1, 11 (Jan. 1949).

* *Phys. Rev.* **100**, 937 (1955).

energy neutrons). It is not easy to reproduce, in the sense that mixing a given amount of radium and a given amount of beryllium does not result in an accurately definable source strength.

A variant is radium beryllium fluoride, Ra-Be-F_4, which is a true chemical compound. Because of the relatively large amount of fluorine, the neutron yield per curie is less, but the objection of lack of reproducibility of the Ra-α-Be source is avoided. The source has not, however, been widely used.

Po-Be, Pu-Be, Am-Be. Polonium beryllium sources are often used, because gamma rays emitted are negligible, and the source size is small. They can be prepared as above, or by deposition of polonium on a very thin disc of silver or nickel pressed between two beryllium discs. The chief disadvantage is the relatively short half-life of Po (140 days). Po-B sources are also sometimes used. The spectrum of Po-α-Be is shown in Appendix X (b).

Neutron sources employing transuranic sources are coming into vogue. Pu^{239} has a half-life of 25,000 years, and when an alloy with beryllium is made, Pu-Be_{13}, the yield is about 10^6 n/sec per curie, i.e. per 13 g of Pu. The factor of 10 reduction in source strength as compared with Ra-α-Be is due to the fact that the energy of the alpha particles is only 5·35 MeV as compared with 8 for one of the alpha particles of radium. A Pu-Be source is almost gamma free. The yield for a source of usable size, however, is relatively low, and the Pu^{239} has a high thermal fission cross section (750 b.). Am^{241}-Be is a better source from both these points of view (half-life 470 years, thermal cross section 3 barns).

B. Photoneutron sources. The cross section for neutron production by gamma rays is much less than for neutron production by alpha particles, so that even with considerably more beryllium, the yield is less. The photo-source is placed at the centre of a sphere or cylinder. The spheres or cylinders used usually have heights and diameters of about 5 cm, and in sources of this size the moderation of the neutron spectrum by the beryllium is not negligible, and the spectrum may be degraded. There are several short-lived sources, such as

Na^{24}-Be, $E_n = 950$ keV; $Na^{24}D_2O$, 250 keV, half-lives 15 hours; Ga^{72}-D_2O, 200 keV, half-life 14 hours. These are sometimes useful as monoenergetic sources, although their short life makes them of interest for only special applications.

More generally used are:

Sb-Be. This is a useful and widely used source of neutrons of energy about 25 keV. It is easily and cheaply prepared by pile irradiation, and the low initial energy of the neutrons makes it an efficient source of thermal neutrons when placed in a block of paraffin. Its short half-life (60 days) makes it, however, irrelevant for the subject of neutron standards.

Ra-γ-Be. In this source, the radium is at the centre of a sphere or cylinder of beryllium. It has been extensively studied and developed by the National Bureau of Standards group in America. It is reproducible to about 1 per cent, it is constant with time and its spectrum (Appendix X (c)) is in a convenient energy range (600 keV). Its limitations, as a standard, are its high gamma activity and its relatively low neutron output (10^6 n/sec per curie of radium in a 4 cm diameter beryllium sphere, as compared with 10^7 n/sec per curie of radium for the Ra-α-Be neutron source).

Rd-Th-D_2O. The deuteron binding energy is 2·226 MeV, and there is no long-lived gamma ray of energy greater than this. Rd-Th has a daughter product, ThC″, which emits a gamma ray of energy of 2·62 MeV, so that the initial energy of the Rd-Th-D_2O neutron is almost 200 keV. The decay period of the gamma ray is determined by that of the Rd-Th, namely 1·9 years. For this reason, a Rd-Th-D_2O source, which in physical dimensions resembles the Ra-α-Be source, has limited application, although in most other respects it is attractive. Halban and his co-workers at Oxford[2] have developed such a source which is of special relevance to absolute source calibration (see 5.2.2).

C. Spontaneous fission sources. We have mentioned the potentialities of Cm^{244} as an ideal source. A standard source giving a fission spectrum is of value in some experiments concerned with reactor constants, since the neutrons under

(2). *Nucl. Inst.* **5**, 1 (1959).

study arise in fission. The spectrum of fission varies little with the excitation energy of the compound nucleus, so that the spectrum of neutrons from spontaneous fission will be nearly the same as the neutron spectrum from slow neutron capture in fissile material. Pu^{240} yields neutrons from spontaneous fission at the rate of about one per milligramme per second. Richmond[3] has developed a source which employs 187 g of Pu with a Pu^{240} content of 8 per cent and a neutron yield of 2×10^4 n/sec. The source is constant (the half-life of Pu^{240} is 6,400 years) and the gamma radiation is negligible, but the yield is low and the presence of Pu^{239} means that neutrons from Pu^{239} fission will be released if the source is placed in a thermal flux. A typical spectrum of neutrons from fission (of $U^{235}+n$) is shown in Appendix X(d).

5.2. Source calibration

5.2.1. Relative source calibrations.

A variety of methods have been developed for relative source calibrations. All these depend in one way or another on the slowing down of neutrons to thermal energies. We begin with a description of the slowing down process. The two chief moderating materials used in slowing down are water and graphite. In water, the mean free path of a 1 MeV neutron before collision is only about 2·5 cm, and in each collision with a proton the neutron loses on the average $(1/e)$ of its initial energy. In the range 0·1 eV to 10 keV, the mean free path between collisions is 0·6 cm and at thermal energies the mean free path is only 2 mm. It is clear from these figures that even from quite energetic sources, such as Ra-α-Be, the neutrons travel relatively short distances before the first collision. After one or two further collisions the distribution in velocity is isotropic, the rate of loss of energy is rapid (as compared with graphite) and the mean distance of travel is small before thermal energies are reached. The capture cross section of hydrogen is 0·3 barns, and the scattering cross section at thermal energies 50 barns, so that on the average the neutron will suffer about 160 collisions at thermal energies before capture.

(3). A.E.R.E. Report R/R. 2097 (1957).

With graphite, the picture is very different. The high energy scattering cross section of carbon is fairly constant at 4 barns, so that the mean free path of a 1 MeV neutron in graphite of density 1·6 g/cc is 3 cm, a figure which does not change radically during the slowing down of the neutron. The mean

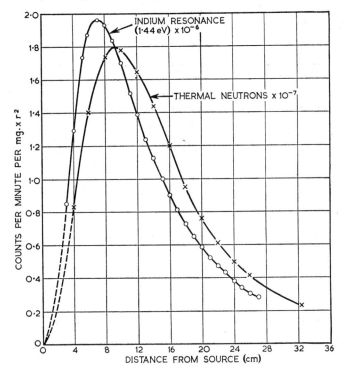

Fig. 5.1. Distribution of slow neutrons from a Ra-a-Be source in water. The ordinate is the activity A of a thin indium foil, multiplied by r^2, it represents the neutron flux in a thin shell of radius r. (Note that in Figs. 5.8 (a) and (b), A only is plotted.) The curve labelled *indium resonance* represents the activity of a cadmium-covered foil.

logarithmic energy loss is about $\frac{1}{6}$, so that it takes about 110 collisions in graphite to reduce the energy of a 1 MeV neutron to thermal energies, as compared with about 20 collisions in the case of water. When the neutrons have reached thermal energies, the capture cross section is 4 mb. so that the neutron will undergo about 1000 collisions before capture.

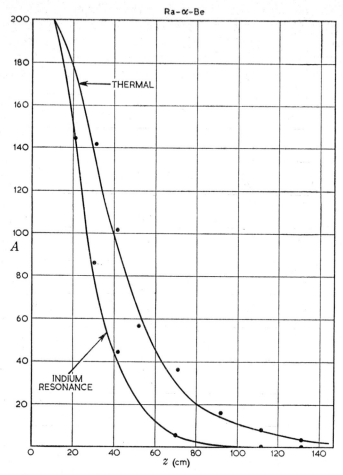

Fig. 5.2(a).   Slowing down of Ra-α-Be neutrons in graphite.

This picture of the slowing-down process is well illustrated in Figs. 5.1 and 5.2.*   The difference in scale between Figs. 5.1 and 5.2 shows the contrast between slowing down in water and graphite, while a comparison of Figs. 5.2 (a) and 5.2 (b) illustrates the difference in slowing down between Ra-α-Be neutrons

* Figs. 5.1 and 5.2 are reproduced from "The Neutron" by B. T. Feld, in *Experimental Nuclear Physics, Vol. II*, Ed. E. Segre, by courtesy of the Publishers, John Wiley & Sons Inc., New York.

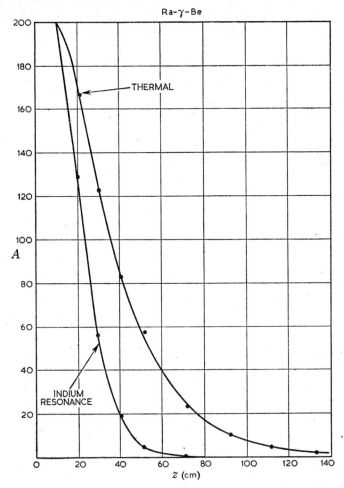

Fig. 5.2(b). Slowing down of Ra-γ-Be neutrons in graphite

(mean energy 5 MeV) and Ra-γ-Be neutrons (mean energy about 0·6 MeV.) Also shown is the distribution of In resonance neutrons which are related to the slowing-down process, and the distribution of thermal neutrons which, at the extreme right of the curves, represents the diffusion of thermal neutrons only. The difference in diffusion lengths between thermal neutrons in graphite and water is clearly illustrated.

With these considerations in mind, we shall review briefly the main methods of comparing relative strengths of neutron sources.

(a) **Determination of the integrated thermal neutron density in a water bath.** As this is discussed in detail in 5.2.2 (a), we shall only summarise here the main points. The $MnSO_4$ bath is a simple and widely used method of comparing neutron source intensities. A large tank (about 1 meter cube) is filled with a concentrated solution of $MnSO_4$, and thermal neutrons are captured by the manganese to form radioactive Mn^{56}. Although the capture cross section of manganese (14 barns) is much higher than hydrogen (0·331 barns), the ratio of hydrogen atoms to Mn atoms in a concentrated $MnSO_4$ solution is such that capture in manganese is about the same as in hydrogen. The source is placed at the centre of the tank and left there for a period comparable with the half-life of Mn^{56} decay (2·5 hours). The source is then removed and the contents of the tank thoroughly stirred. The radioactivity can be measured in the tank itself either by a thin-walled Geiger or by a crystal scintillator. If low background is required, a sample can be taken from the tank and its radioactivity measured with a Geiger counter designed for liquids, under conditions of good shielding. For the estimate of the relative neutron source strength, corrections must be made for (1) escape of neutrons from the tank, (2) absorption of thermal neutrons by the source, (3) capture of fast neutrons by oxygen $\{O^{16}(n,\alpha)C^{13}\}$ and sulphur (n,p and n,α reactions). These are discussed in 5.2.2.(a). The total thermal neutron density in the tank may also be determined by finding the activity of gold foils (or the count rate in a small BF_3 chamber), at various representative points throughout the tank, and integrating over the volume.

(b) **Graphite stacks.** For a graphite column of sufficient size (say 2 metres square by 3 metres high, and a central source) one can find a point at which the thermal density, due to thermal diffusion, is reasonably high, while the density of neutrons of energy greater than thermal is small. Inspection of Fig. 5.2 (a) shows this to be about 85 cm between source and BF_3 counter for Ra-α-Be neutrons. Measurement of the thermal neutron density at this point, for example with a BF_3 chamber, will give relative source strengths for sources with the same neutron spectra. If, however, one is comparing sources of widely differing energies, this measurement will not be very accurate. A more accurate comparison may be made by determining the activity of indium foils, screened with cadmium, at representative points throughout the stack, and integrating over the volume. The determination of the density of resonance neutrons, rather than of thermal neutrons, is preferable in this case because of the possibility of diffusion and escape of the thermal neutrons.

(c) By using a flat-response detector.

We have described in Chapter 4.2 the properties of the Hanson-McKibben "long counter" which affords a rapid means of comparing neutron source strengths. Another graphite-stack type of flat-response detector has been developed by Macklin.[4] A five-foot graphite sphere has the source at its centre and a set of eight BF_3 counters near the periphery. The response of the system is primarily determined by the balance between thermal capture (for a low energy source) and neutron escape (for a high energy source), and the response is calculated to be flat to ± 2 per cent for neutron source energies between 10 keV and 2 MeV. A similar flat-response detector has been briefly described by Dorofeev and Dobrynin.[5] This is a rectangular stack, with the source in a cavity at the centre and the BF_3 counters placed in such a position in the stack that the response is claimed to be flat to $2\frac{1}{2}$ per cent between 25 keV and 5 MeV.

5.2.2. Absolute source calibration. Many methods for absolute source strength measurements have been developed during the last five years. The main references are Littler,[6] Richmond[7] and Larsson.[8] The agreement achieved between many completely independent methods is $\pm 2\frac{1}{2}$ per cent overall, as reference to Fig. 5.4, p. 184, shows. Such agreements, like

(4). *Nucl. Inst.* **1**, 335 (1957).

(5). *J. Nucl. En.* **5**, 217 (1957).

(6). A.E.R.E. Report NP/R. 1577 (1954).

(7). *Prog. Nucl. Energy*, Ser. 1, Vol. II, p. 165, Pergamon Press, London (1958).

(8). *Ark. f. Fys.* **7**, 25, 323 (1953).

agreements on cross section values, are liable to change with time. This often arises from the very human tendency to regard apparent agreement between two quantities with a less critical eye than a palpable disagreement. In the case of absolute source strengths, however, the variety and number of source-strength measurements are such that appreciable systematic error is improbable.

The various types of measurement are as follows:

A. Thermal methods. These methods have been the subject of careful study by a number of authors. Neutrons from the source are slowed to thermal energies in a hydrogenous moderator, the thermal neutron density determined and integrated over the volume of the moderator. There are various ways of doing this, but common to them all are the corrections involved by variation of neutron energy between different sources. The spectra of Ra-α-Be, Po-α-Be, a fission source and a Ra-γ-Be source are shown in Appendix X, and it is clear that the mean energy of the Ra-α-Be and Po-α-Be neutrons is much greater than that of the other two. The first correction, as has been mentioned in 5.2.1.(a), is the loss due to neutron capture in oxygen, $O^{16}(n,\alpha)C^{13}$. This reaction has been studied from threshold at 3·5 MeV to 5 MeV by various workers.* Since the cross section varies rapidly over the range of Ra-α-Be neutrons, only an estimate can be made, but the resulting figure agrees reasonably well with the direct experimental determination made by Tavernier and de Troyer.[9] These workers compared the space integral of the thermal neutron density of two sources, Ra-α-Be and Ra-γ-Be, in a large tank filled first with distilled water and then with a medicinal paraffin oil. Since the difference in scattering between oxygen (in water) and carbon (in oil) is negligible, the only difference is that due to fast neutron capture in oxygen, which was determined as $2\frac{1}{2}$ per cent. For a concentrated $MnSO_4$ solution, there is an additional loss of 0·6 per cent due to (n,p) and (n,α) reactions in sulphur.

(9). *Bull. de l'Acad. Royale de Belgique* **40**, 150 (1954).

* Walton *et al.*, *Phys. Rev.* **107**, 1065 (1957); and Scitz and Huber, *Helv. Phys. Act.* **28**, 227 (1955).

A second correction arises when the tank is not large enough, and an appreciable fraction of the energetic neutrons escape. This escape is best determined directly by a long counter (Richmond[3]) or by placing the tank in a larger tank, and estimating the number of neutrons in the larger tank (Gailloud).[10] The escape of neutrons from a tank 75 cm diameter is 5·5 per cent for Ra-α-Be and 1·1 per cent for fission neutrons.

A third correction arises from thermal neutron absorption in the source container. To determine this, indium foils can be used to give the volume integral of thermal neutrons, and layers of silver sheet of varying thickness then wrapped round the source. The absorption of silver for thermal neutrons is known, so that extrapolating the observed absorption to zero gives the absorption of thermal neutrons by the source. Alternatively, the absorption can be minimised by supporting the source at the centre of a thin-walled aluminium sphere or cylinder, 5 to 10 cm in diameter.

We now consider the various methods of source strength determination:

(a) By MnSO$_4$ bath techniques. When fast neutrons are slowed down in a concentrated solution of MnSO$_4$, about half the neutrons are absorbed in the manganese. Let us assume initially that all the neutrons are absorbed by the manganese. Then when saturation is reached, the number of neutrons emitted by the source equals the number of Mn^{56} nuclei decaying. Now the source can be removed, the Mn^{56} allowed to decay completely, and an amount of pile-produced Mn^{56} added to give a comparable and accurately determined activity. The amount of Mn^{56} added can be determined to 1 to 2 per cent by taking aliquots and counting by 4π beta counting. Knowing the rate of decay from the 4π beta counting, we can determine the number of neutrons emitted by the source.

The ratio of the number of neutrons captured by the manganese to the number captured by the hydrogen remains to be determined. This can be estimated from cross section data. Alternatively, the MnSO$_4$ concentration can be varied, and the

(10). *Ann. de Phys.* (13me Serie) 1, 808 (1956).

results extrapolated to infinite concentration. The difficulty here is that the lower concentrations of $MnSO_4$ give rather low count rates, and the errors involved in extrapolation are considerable.

(*b*) *By determination of the thermal neutron density in a water bath with detectors such as boron or gold.* In these determinations, the accuracy in the long run depends on the knowledge of the thermal cross section of the detector relative to hydrogen. For, neglecting any possibility of capture other than by thermal neutrons in hydrogen, we can say that the number of neutrons being emitted by the source is equal to the number being captured, viz.:

$$Q = 4\pi N \int_0^\infty \phi(r)\, \overline{\sigma_H} \cdot r^2 dr \tag{5.1}$$

where Q is the source strength,

      $\phi(r)$ is the flux of thermal neutrons at radius r,

      $\bar{\sigma}_H$ is the mean absorption cross section of hydrogen for thermal neutrons,

and N is the number of hydrogen atoms per cm^3.

If we have a detector of N' atoms/cm^3, volume V, thermal cross section $\overline{\sigma_a'}$, then the number of radioactive atoms produced per second in flux $\phi(r)$ is

$$R'(r) = N'V\phi(r)\, \overline{\sigma_a'}$$

or

$$\phi(r) = \frac{R'(r)}{N'V\sigma_a'}$$

Therefore

$$Q = \frac{4\pi N}{N'V} \frac{\overline{\sigma_H}}{\overline{\sigma_a'}} \int_0^\infty R'(r)r^2 dr. \tag{5.2}$$

In this expression, one needs to know $R'(r)$, in such a way as to give an accurate expression for ϕ. Several workers[8],[9] have described the absolute calibration of neutron sources using gold indicators. The flux at a number of points throughout the volume of the tank is determined by irradiating gold foils and determining their radioactivity by a coincidence method. From the activity of the foils the flux can be calculated, making allowance for flux perturbation and flux depression as described in Chapter 4.4. The source strength is then determined according to equation 5.2. A critical factor is σ_H/σ_{Au}, but, as we shall describe in (5.3.2 (b)), this quantity is now known to an accuracy of at least 2 per cent.

A variant of this method has been described by Larsson.[8] One can use in the tank, instead of pure water, a solution of boric acid, and instead of a gold detector, a small BF_3 ionisation chamber. If the boric acid concentration is very strong, then capture of neutrons by water is negligible, and the cross section factor is eliminated from equation 5.2. This situation is hypothetical, since then the count rate in the BF_3 chamber would be very small, and in any case the solubility of boric acid in water is low. The absorption in water therefore is not negligible, and we must rewrite equation 5.2 as

$$Q = 4\pi \cdot \frac{N_B}{V N_B'}\left(1 + \frac{\sigma_H \cdot N_H}{\sigma_B \cdot N_B}\right)\int_0^\infty R'(r)r^2 \mathrm{d}r \qquad (5.3)$$

where N_B, N_B' are the number of boron atoms per cm^3 in the solution and the chamber respectively, and V is the active volume of the chamber. The ratio $\frac{\sigma_B}{\sigma_H}$ however, was experimentally determined by Larsson by determining the quantity,

$$S = \int_0^\infty R'(r)r^2 \mathrm{d}r \qquad (5.4)$$

for pure water and for boric acid solution. Then from two equations of type 5.3 above, we can derive

$$\frac{\sigma_B}{\sigma_H} = \frac{N_H}{N_B}\cdot\left(\frac{S_H}{S_{H+B}} - 1\right) \qquad (5.5)$$

The value obtained by Larsson for the ratio σ_H/σ_B was in good agreement with recent values.

(c) *The "negative source" technique.* A variant of the moderator technique has been used in Russia (Spivak *et al.*[11]). The source (Ra-α-Be) was placed in the centre of a large graphite stack, and the thermal neutron density obtained in a

(11). *J. Nucl. En.* **6**, 243 (1958).

large number of BF_3 chambers.   The source was then removed, the stack centre was irradiated by a beam from the thermal column of a reactor, and the thermal flux as measured by the BF_3 chambers was observed.   A gold foil was then placed at the centre of the stack, and the absorption of thermal neutrons in the gold endowed it with the properties of a negative source, whose effect on the BF_3 counters was determined.   The activity of the gold was determined by coincidence counting, so that the BF_3 chambers were in effect calibrated by the effect on their reading of a negative source of known value.   From this calibration, the strength of the Ra-α-Be source was determined.

B. Calibration methods involving fast neutrons.   A number of quite different methods of source strength determinations have been developed which do not depend on the slowing down of fast neutrons :

(a) *The T(d,n)α reaction.*   We have referred before (Chapter 4.2.(a)) to the ease with which flux measurements can be made with this reaction, by counting the number of alpha particles produced.   Larsson[8] has used this fact in an extensive series of comparison measurements.   He compared, first of all, the flux from a T(d,n)α source, as determined by alpha particle measurement, with the flux determined by a homogeneous ion chamber measurement, and obtained agreement to 3 per cent. He also confirmed the angular distribution of the neutrons and obtained a correction for the D-D neutrons produced by deuterium occluded in the target.   He then used a large tank, 2 m in diameter and 2 m high, with a (T,d) source at the centre, to compare the integrated flux (determined by BF_3 proportional counters) in water and in paraffin oil.   In water, the loss due to $O^{16}(n,\alpha)C^{13}$ and other reactions at 14 MeV neutron energy is quite large, while in carbon there are no such sources of loss.   Larsson showed that with primary neutrons of 14 MeV, the loss of neutrons in water was more than 20 per cent. Finally, he used the T(d,n) source in oil, with BF_3 chambers as detectors, as a means of calibrating his Ra-Be source.   The agreement between this measurement, and two other measurements using BF_3 chambers (boric acid solution) and water (gold foils) was 1 per cent.

(b) *The "Oxford source"*.   An entirely different approach to the problem has been made by Halban and his co-workers at Oxford.[6]   The gamma rays from RdTh (5.1) liberate photo-neutrons from deuterium of energy 200 keV, and if we knew the gamma source strength accurately, and the cross section for photodisintegration accurately, we could determine the neutron

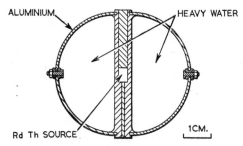

Fig. 5.3.   Source developed by Marin (ref. 2).

source strength accurately.   Neither quantity is, however, accurately known, and Halban's method avoids the necessity of knowing either.   A RdTh source is placed at the centre of a thin aluminium sphere 1 in. in radius (Fig. 5.3) which is equipped with small electrodes.   The chambers are first filled with deuterium gas.   Now the reaction involved is

$$D + \gamma \rightarrow p + n - 2 \cdot 226 \text{ MeV}$$

so that to each photoneutron there must correspond a photo-proton.   By using the electrodes as an ion chamber, one can count the photoprotons produced.   The gas is then replaced by heavy water, increasing the neutron source strength by a factor of about 1000.   Knowing the ratio of the number of deuterium atoms in the gas to the number in the liquid, one can determine the final source strength.   Various corrections, such as the neutron yield from the RdTh alphas on oxygen impurities, and the attenuation of 2·62 MeV gamma rays in D_2O, need to be made.   The overall accuracy is estimated as 3 per cent.

A variant of the method is under development at Harwell by Sowerby and Colvin.   The photoprotons from deuterium are counted in a high pressure deuterium chamber, situated in a graphite stack with a considerable number of BF_3 counters embedded in it. The coincidence rate between the chambers and the BF_3 counters enables one to determine the efficiency of the stack for neutron detection, as a function of neutron energy. This experimental arrangement should permit the direct determination of any neutron source.

(c) *The measurements by W. D. Allen and Ferguson* (Ch. 4.2.(e)) of fast neutron flux provide another independent check of neutron source strengths, and have already been described. To recapitulate, a long counter was calibrated for neutrons of 200 keV energy by (1) a RdTh-D_2O source from Oxford, (2) a flux of neutrons from the Li(p,n) reaction calibrated by a hydrogen-filled proportional counter. The agreement was 1 to 2 per cent. Similarly, the strength of the Harwell Ra-α-Be source, as determined indirectly from $MnSO_4$ bath measurements and from proportional counter flux measurements at 1 MeV, agreed within 3 per cent with a recent $MnSo_4$ bath determination by Richmond.

C. Measurement by the determination of rate of helium production. A third independent method of neutron source strength determination has long been worked on, but not yet perfected. Consider the reaction

$$Be + \gamma \rightarrow 2He^4 + n$$

If 10^5 neutrons are liberated per second, and the irradiation lasts say 100 days, then 2.10^{12} helium atoms are liberated in the beryllium. Chemical treatment now liberates the helium, which can be readily measured by methods of microanalysis. The method is well suited to the determination of the strength of Ra-γ-Be sources, but has not so far given results of accuracy comparable with the foregoing.

Several other methods of source strength measurement have been described, but we limit our discussion to those which have been the subject of international comparison.

5.2.3. Intercomparison of source strength measurements. The present (1958) status of source strength measurement can be seen from the following summary:

1. Comparison by Richmond at Harwell. Richmond[3] determined the strength of a number of sources, relative to a Pu^{240} spontaneous fission source, by the manganese bath technique, using both relative and absolute calibration methods. His results are shown in Table 5.1. The reader is referred to Richmond's paper for details of method and comments on the sources compared. It is seen that the agreement between three different measurements of the Oxford source is ± 1 per cent, and that of the seven sources measured, five agreed within $\pm 2\frac{1}{2}$ per cent while two Ra-α-Be sources, calibrated several years previously, showed agreement within 7 per cent.

Table 5.1. Values of Richmond's spontaneous Fission Neutron Source, as Compared with the Oxford Source by 3 methods and as Compared with 6 other International Sources

Source	Strength at given date (n/sec)	Strength of spontaneous fission source. Q (n/sec $\times 10^4$)	$Q/Q(Oxford)$
Oxford (RdTh-D$_2$O)	(1) $(6\cdot17 \pm 2\frac{1}{2}\%) \times 10^4$ (Marin *et al.*)	$2\cdot01_8$	
	(2) $(6\cdot29 \pm 3\%) \times 10^4$ (Allen & Ferguson)	$2\cdot01_8$ $2\cdot03_8$	
	(3) $(6\cdot20 \pm 3\%) \times 10^4$ (Richmond & Gardner) 25/1/1955	$2\cdot02_8$	
	Weighted mean $(6\cdot18 \pm 1\cdot6\%) \times 10^4$	$2\cdot02_1$	$1\cdot000$
N.B.S. (Secondary (Ra-γ-Be)	$(1\cdot86 \pm 3\%) \times 10^6$ 1955	$2\cdot04_3$	$1\cdot011$
Basel (B2) (Ra-α-Be)	$(1.515 \pm 2\cdot8\%) \times 10^6$ April 1955	$1\cdot98_3$	$0\cdot982$
Harwell (Ra-α-Be)	$(9\cdot66 \pm 4\cdot5\%) \times 10^6$ March 1951	$2\cdot15_9$	$1\cdot069$
Los Alamos 44 (Ra-α-Be)	$(6\cdot07 \pm 5\%) \times 10^6$ August 1944	$2\cdot07_5$	$1\cdot027$
A.N.L. 38 (Ra-α-Be)	$(5\cdot5 \pm 7\%) \times 10^6$ October 1944	$2\cdot14_3$	$1\cdot061$
U.M. (Ra-α-Be)	$(7\cdot87_5 \pm 2\cdot0\%) \times 10^6$ December 1952	$2\cdot02_6$	$1\cdot003$

2. Comparison by Larsson in Sweden. Larsson[9] has compared a number of Ra-α-Be sources, and also the N.B.S. standard source, in a water bath using the volume integral of the counts recorded by BF_3 proportional counters. The results are exhibited in Fig. 5.4.

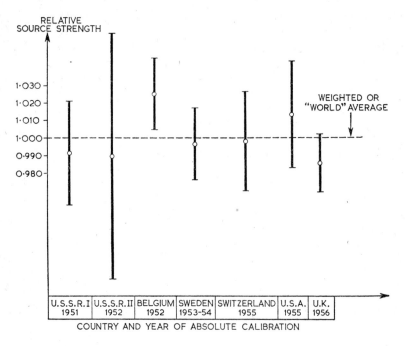

Fig. 5.4.   Result of intercomparison of seven sources by Larsson (ref. 12).

We may summarise these results by saying that many independent measurements have now been made, by many methods, which agree within $\pm 2\frac{1}{2}$ per cent, and which have an R.M.S. spread of about 1 per cent. Considering the number of different methods used in these determinations, this accuracy is high.

(12). *J. Nucl. En.* **6**, 322 (1957).

5.3. Fundamental neutron cross sections

Neutron measurements, especially those of flux and of cross sections relative to a fundamental cross section, depend for their accuracy on the precision of the fundamental cross section. We shall therefore make a short survey of the methods of deriving these cross sections, and of their probable accuracy. Such a survey is of necessity a function of time: what is written now is appreciably different from what might have been written five years ago, and may be different from what will be written in five years' time. However, most standards approach their final value asymptotically in time, and it is unlikely that any change of more than 2 to 3 per cent in fundamental cross sections will take place in future. It is important to recall, however, that the cross section of normal boron for neutrons of 2200 m/sec velocity was for many years after the war taken as 707 barns, and cross section data taken relative to this value are now subject to correction. Similarly, the absorption cross section of gold was taken as 93 barns, and cross section values measured relative to this are also subject to correction.

5.3.1. Neutron-proton cross sections.

The neutron-proton interaction is of fundamental interest in nuclear physics, and a good account of the theoretical aspect has been given by Squires.[13] Several physical properties, such as the binding energy of the deuteron, can be accurately determined experimentally and their values intercompared by theory. Two of these quantities are the n,p scattering cross section and the capture cross section of hydrogen for thermal neutrons, and these we shall discuss here.

(a) **The n,p scattering cross section.** As described in Chapter 2, the measurement of the n,p scattering cross section is simple and straightforward. A hydrocarbon (usually of accurately known chemical composition) and pure graphite are the substances used. The transmission of each is determined for the neutrons under study, and the total cross section for the compound and for carbon is deduced. The scattering cross

(13). *Prog. Nucl. Phys.* Vol. 2, p. 89, Ed. O. R. Frisch, Pergamon Press, London (1952).

13—N.D.

section for hydrogen is obtained by subtraction. With a strong source and an efficient detector, the accuracy of the transmission experiment can be quite high. In an accurate experiment, the main problem is the estimation of small corrections and the exact determination of the number of hydrogen and carbon atoms concerned in the scattering. The results are shown in Appendix I (a), together with the semi-empirical formula of Gammel, which summarises the experimental results.

We can summarise very briefly here, too, the theoretical means of intercomparison of these measurements with other results. There are four constants which characterise the n,p interaction. They are the scattering lengths (a_t, a_s) and the effective ranges (r_t and r_s). All four occur in the formula for (n,p) scattering, although the value of the cross section is insensitive to the value of r_s. The other quantities which are characterised by some of these constants are as follows:

(1) At low neutron energies, the (n,p) scattering cross section is characterised only by a_t and a_s. This cross section has been determined by Melkonian at a neutron energy of 20 eV with an accuracy of $\frac{1}{2}$ per cent.

(2) The binding energy of the deuteron involves the constants r_t and a_t, and has been determined by three different methods to an accuracy of $1\frac{1}{2}$ parts in 10^3.

(3) The coherent (n,p) scattering amplitude has been determined to an accuracy of $\frac{1}{2}$ per cent by determining the angle of total reflection of slow neutrons from a liquid hydrocarbon mirror. This quantity also involves the constants a_t and a_s.

It will be seen that these experiments all determine the constants a_t, a_s and r_t with good accuracy. With these values, accurate determinations of (n,p) scattering cross sections at one or two specific neutron energies then give values for r_s, which are in agreement with the value determined from the capture cross section of neutrons by hydrogen. The four constants then give a theoretical figure for the (n,p) scattering cross section which is in good agreement with a curve drawn through the experimental points. The accuracy is of the order of 1 per cent.

(b) **Capture cross section of thermal neutrons by hydrogen,** σ_{cap}. The value of this cross section, which we have called σ_{cap}, is of interest in this discussion because it enters into neutron source strength measurements. It has been determined by experiments which give the ratio of the capture cross sections for thermal neutrons of boron and hydrogen. The accuracy of σ_{cap} therefore depends on the accuracy of the boron absorption cross section. Alternatively, σ_{cap} may be determined by using a pulsed source of neutrons, for example from the D-D reaction, and observing the rate of decay of neutron amplitude. Since, when neutrons are captured, one has a 2·226 MeV gamma ray according to the reaction

$$n + p \rightarrow D + 2\text{·}226 \text{ MeV},$$

the rate of decay is relatively easy to detect in a scintillation counter and measure accurately. The problem is to estimate accurately the corrections, such as for example those due to neutron diffusion and escape, in the pipe carrying the beam. A recent measurement is by Meads et al.,[14] in whose paper a full discussion is given of the experimental method and the corrections applied. The final value obtained by Meads *et al.* is 0·335 barns at 2200 m/sec, which is 1 per cent higher than the mean of three other recent measurements. A value of 0·332 barns is probably accurate to 1 per cent.

5.3.2. Other thermal cross sections. (a) Boron. It is
unfortunate, from the point of view of accurate neutron measurement, that the material most widely used should have an appreciable variation in its isotopic composition. Thus, in any comparison between British and American results, it is necessary to bear in mind that pile oscillator measurements on both sides of the Atlantic have shown a variation of 1·4 per cent in absorption cross section between the stocks from which samples for test are drawn. It is therefore not possible to speak with high accuracy of the "cross section of boron for neutrons of 2200 m/sec velocity". However, errors arising from this are not likely to be greater than ± 1 per cent and are, at most, ± 2 per cent.

(14). *Proc. Phys. Soc.* **A-69**, 469 (1956).

Over and above this, however, there has been a marked change in the accepted cross section value for boron in the last few years. A study of the determination and evaluation of the fundamental neutron cross sections, up to 1955, was presented by Harvey[15] at the 1955 Geneva Conference. Early measurements indicated a mean value of 710 barns, a value 6 per cent different from the present accepted value (755 barns for American boron). The variation in isotopic composition (± 2 per cent at most) and the contribution due to scattering (4 barns) are too small to account for the discrepancy, which was probably due to errors in determining chemical composition. Recent measurements have taken a variety of forms. At Argonne and Brookhaven, transmission measurements have been made on B_2O_3 dissolved in D_2O. A second independent method is that of the determination of the neutron lifetime in borax solution. It is identical to the determination of σ_{cap} described above, except that borax solutions of varying concentrations are employed instead of water. The lifetime τ in the solution may then be written

$$\tau = A + N_B'v\sigma_B$$

where A is a constant, v is 2200 m/sec and N_B' is the number of boron atoms per cm^3, with a small correction for the change in concentration of protons on the addition of borax. To determine σ_{cap} accurately, an accurate determination of A is necessary. For an accurate determination of σ_B, however, this is not so, and all one needs to know is the variation of τ with N_B'. The method is therefore capable of considerable accuracy. A third set of transmission measurements have been made by Egelstaff[16] on solutions of B_2O_3 in NaOD and D_2O, and on cells containing borax powder. As with the Argonne and Brookhaven measurements, the transmission was observed as a function of neutron energy, and the 2200 m/sec value determined. The results of Egelstaff's paper, compared with those of other workers, are shown in Table 5.2. The present value is 755 barns for "American boron" and 765 barns for "British boron", with an accuracy of 1 per cent.

(15). International Conference on the Peaceful Uses of Atomic Energy, Vol. IV, Paper P/382, p. 147 (1955).
(16). *J. Nucl. En.* **5**, 41 (1957).

Table 5.2.   Comparison of Results for Boron and Gold as
Tabulated by Egelstaff

(a) Boron

Author	*Method*	*Observed cross section* (barns)	*Ratio to Harwell boric acid*	*Predicted cross section for Harwell boric acid*
Carter *et al.* (1953)	Total cross section of B_2O_3	749 ± 4	$0 \cdot 986 \pm 0 \cdot 003$	760 ± 5
Ringo (Hamermesh *et al.*, 1953)	Total cross section of B_2O_3	755 ± 3	$0 \cdot 986 \pm 0 \cdot 003$	766 ± 4
Von Dardel and Sjöstrand (1954)	Neutron life-time in borax solution	763 ± 3	$0 \cdot 983 \pm 0 \cdot 003$	776 ± 4
Meads and Collie (1956)	Neutron life-time in borax solution	761 ± 2	$1 \cdot 002 \pm 0 \cdot 002$	760 ± 3
Egelstaff (1957)	Total cross section of B_2O_3	—	—	771 ± 5

(b) Gold)

Author	*Value for absorption cross section at 2200 m/sec of gold* (barns)
Carter *et al.* (1953)	$98 \cdot 7 \pm 0 \cdot 6$
Gould *et al.* (1955)	$99 \cdot 0 \pm 0 \cdot 2$
Egelstaff (1954)	$97 \cdot 7 \pm 0 \cdot 9$

(b) Gold.   As we have remarked earlier, gold has nearly all
the properties desirable in a material with which neutron
standards are to be established.   It is monoisotopic, it has a
decay scheme with a predominant beta-gamma cascade of
convenient energy, and so on.   Like the boron cross section,
the absorption cross section of gold has undergone a variation
with time: it was once 93 barns, but is now 98·7 barns.   The

reason for this discrepancy is that in transmission measurements, the total cross section is measured and, unlike boron, scattering is by no means negligible. In the earlier estimations, too great a correction (11 barns) was made for scattering in gold. The scattering is not easy to measure with thermal neutrons, but can be estimated from measurements with very slow neutrons. At long neutron wavelengths, the coherent scattering disappears, leaving only other scattering terms which are small compared with the absorption cross section. The absorption cross section can be obtained from the fact that it varies with velocity almost as $1/v$ and is independent of temperature. Gold does not obey strictly the $1/v$ law, and a correction of 1 per cent has to be made to the low-energy neutron value to obtain the 2200 m/sec value. The final value for the absorption cross section at 2200 m/sec, 98·7 barns, is probably correct to at least 1 per cent.

(c) U^{235}. The fission cross section of U^{235} is not so often taken as a reference standard as those above, but its importance is obvious. There are two methods of determining the fission cross section of U^{235} at 2200 m/sec. The first depends on indirect measurements in reactors, which result in a determination of α, the ratio of capture to fission cross sections. Since the total cross section (capture plus fission plus a small scattering cross section) can be accurately determined, the fission cross section can be deduced. Since the Geneva Conference, comparisons between British, American and Russian data have shown good agreement, with a figure for the fission cross section of 585 barns. Other methods are more direct, and are typified by the determination of the number of fissions from a sample of known thermal flux. Earlier results (555 barns and 638 barns) show marked divergencies from the value deduced from indirect measurements, but even in more recent measurements (575 ± 5 barns and 606 ± 6 barns) some discrepancies still persist. Thus, while 585 barns may be taken as the average figure, it is clear that the degree of agreement in the fission cross section of U^{235} is not quite so good as in the other measurements we have discussed.

In conclusion, then, we may say that most of the fundamental cross sections are now known with an accuracy of about 1 per cent.

APPENDICES

Appendix I(a)

The (n,p) cross section as a function of neutron energy. The theoretical analysis has been described by Gammel* and an empirical expression based on effective range theory has been derived which is a close fit to the experimental points. This is

$$\tau_n(E) = \frac{3\pi}{1 \cdot 206E + (-1 \cdot 86 + 0 \cdot 09415E + 0 \cdot 0001306E^2)^2}$$

$$+ \frac{\pi}{1 \cdot 206E + (0 \cdot 4223 + 0 \cdot 13E)^2}$$

The fit is accurate to a few parts in 10^3 over the range thermal energies to 42 MeV. The extreme departure occurs at 25 MeV, where the calculated value is 0·381 barn, compared with an experimental value of 0·39 ± 0·03 barn.

* See Bibliography for Chapter 5.3.1.

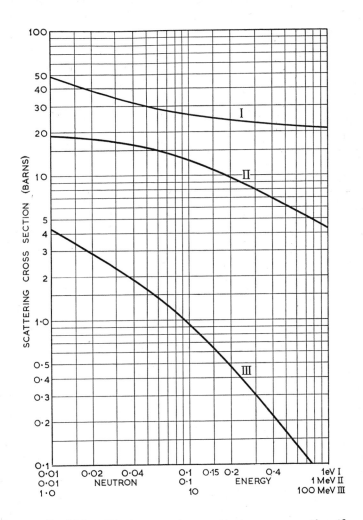

Appendix I(a). Neutron-proton scattering cross section (from BNL 325)

    Curve I   0·01 to 1 eV
    Curve II   0·01 to 1 MeV
    Curve III   1 to 100 MeV

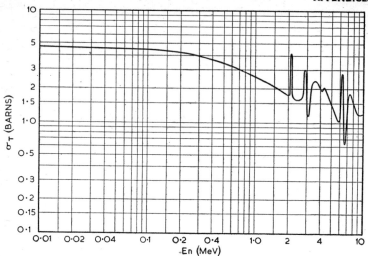

Appendix I(b). Total cross section of carbon (from BNL 325). (Thermal cross section value 4.8b)

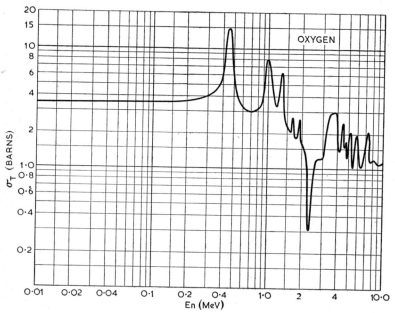

Appendix I(c). Variation of the total cross section of oxygen with neutron energy (from BNL 325). (The thermal value is 4.2b)

Appendix II(a). Ranges of protons and alphas in air (Bethe and Ashkin)

Reproduced from *Experimental Nuclear Physics, Vol I*, Ed: E. Segre (1953), by courtesy of the Publishers, John Wiley & Sons Inc., New York

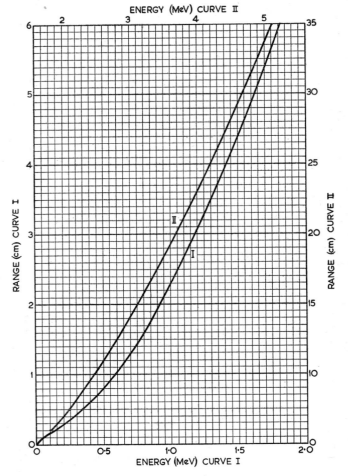

1. Range of protons in air (15°C, 760 m/m). (Ref. 2.4)

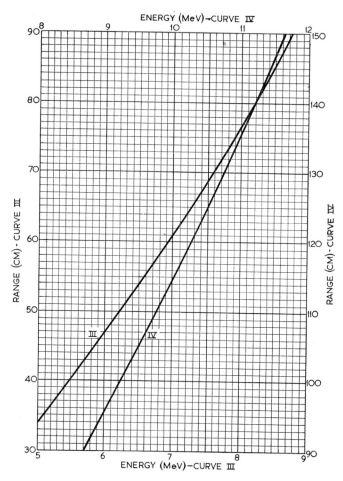

2. Range energy relation for protons in air (15°C, 760 m/m).
(Ref. 2.4)

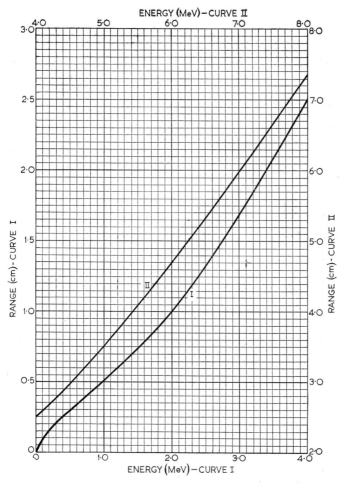

3. Range energy relation for alpha particles in air (15°C, 760 m/m).
(Ref. 2.4)

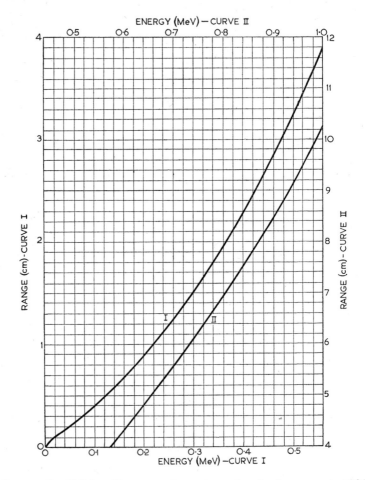

Appendix II(b). Ranges of protons in hydrogen at 15°C 760 m/m. (Ref. 2.4)

Reproduced from *Experimental Nuclear Physics, Vol. I,* Ed: E. Segre (1953), by courtesy of the Publishers, John Wiley & Sons Inc., New York

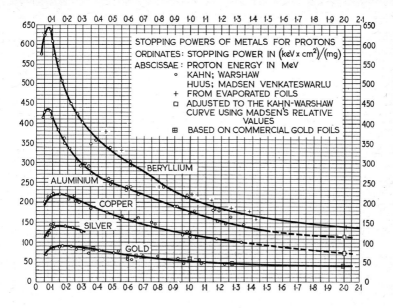

STOPPING POWERS OF METALS FOR PROTONS
ORDINATES: STOPPING POWER IN $(keV \times cm^2)/(mg)$
ABSCISSAE: PROTON ENERGY IN MeV
  ∘ KAHN; WARSHAW
  HUUS; MADSEN VENKATESWARLU
  + FROM EVAPORATED FOILS
  □ ADJUSTED TO THE KAHN-WARSHAW
    CURVE USING MADSEN'S RELATIVE
    VALUES
  ⊞ BASED ON COMMERCIAL GOLD FOILS

BERYLLIUM
ALUMINIUM
COPPER
SILVER
GOLD

Appendix II(c)

Data from Allison and Warshaw* on the variation of $\dfrac{\mathrm{d}E}{\mathrm{d}x}$ with E_p for various materials. In $\dfrac{\mathrm{d}E}{\mathrm{d}x}$, E is in keV and x is in mg/cm². The range for a proton of incident energy E_keV in any material is

$$R = \int_0^E \frac{\mathrm{d}x}{\mathrm{d}E}\,\mathrm{d}E \;\; \mathrm{mg/cm^2}$$

and must be determined from the graph by numerical integration. It is useful to remember that 1 cm thickness of air corresponds to 1·3 mg/cm².

* See ref. 2.5.

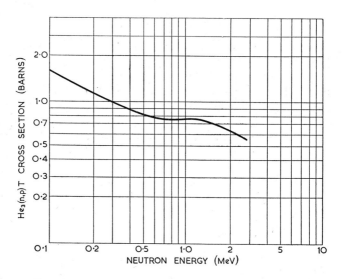

Appendix III. Variation with neutron energy of the cross section $He_3(n,p)T$ in the region 0·1 to 3 MeV (from BNL 325)

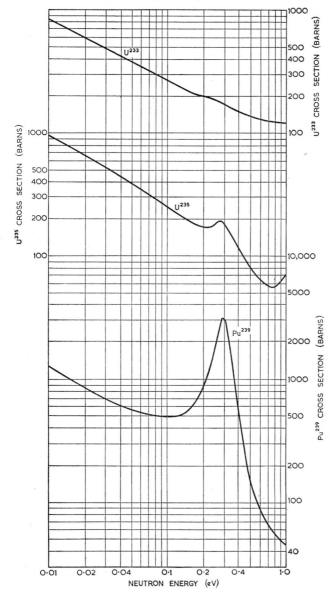

Appendix IV(a).   Variation with neutron energy of the fission cross sections of U²³³, U²³⁵ and Pu²³⁹ in the range 0·01 to 1 eV (from BNL 325)

14—N.D.

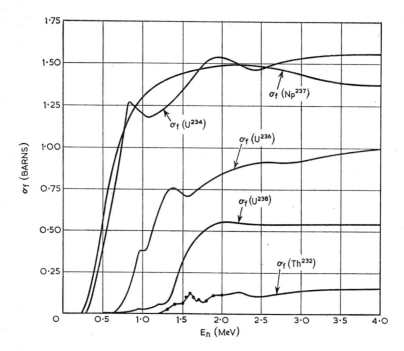

Appendix IV(b).   Variation with neutron energy of the fission
cross section of Th²³², U²³⁴, U²³⁶, U²³⁸ and Np²³⁷ in the
range 0 to 4 MeV.   (*Reprinted with permission from article
by W. D. Allen and R. L. Henkel, in "Progress in Nuclear
Energy", Series 1, Vol. II (1957), Pergamon Press Ltd.*)

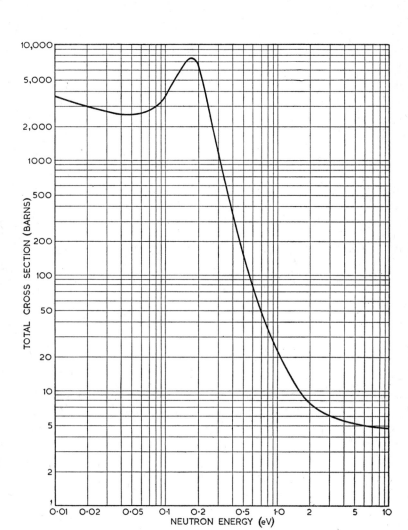

Appendix V(a). Total cross section of cadmium as a function of neutron energy in the thermal region (BNL 325)

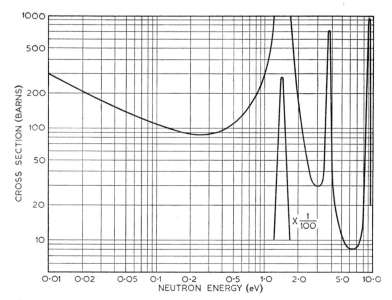

Appendix V(b). Total cross section of indium as a function of neutron energy in the thermal region (BNL 325)

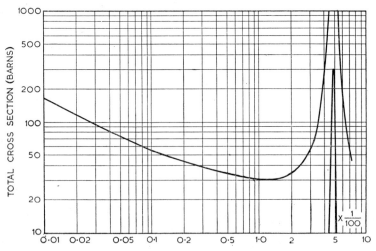

Appendix V(c). Total cross section of gold as a function of neutron energy in the thermal region (BNL 325)

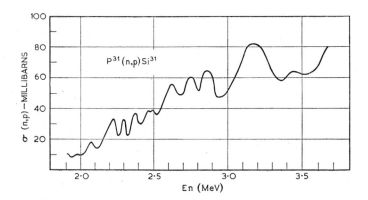

Appendix VI(a). The variation of the P(n,p) cross section as a function of neutron energy (from BNL 325)

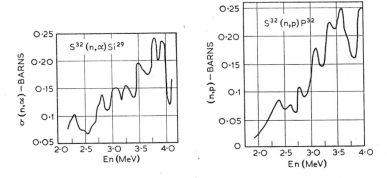

Appendix VI(b). The variation with neutron energy of the S(n,p) and S(n,α) cross sections (from BNL 325)

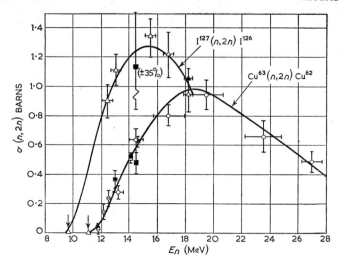

Appendix VII(a). Variation with neutron energy of the I^{127} (n,2n)I^{126} and Cu^{63}(n,2n) reactions. (From Brolley and Fowler (ref. 2.22))

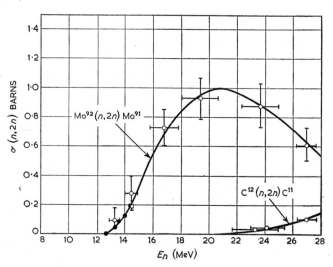

Appendix VII(b). Variation with neutron energy of the Mo^{92}(n,2n)Mo^{91} and C^{12}(n,2n)C^{11} reactions (ref. 2.22)

Appendix VIII. Drift velocity of electrons in various gases in centimetres per microsecond, as a function of X/p (volts per cm per m/m Hg). (W. N. English and G. C. Hanna, *Can. J. Phys.* **31**, 768 (1953))

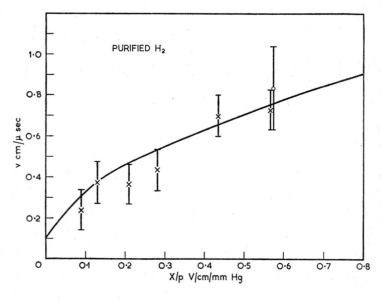

VIII(A). Hydrogen

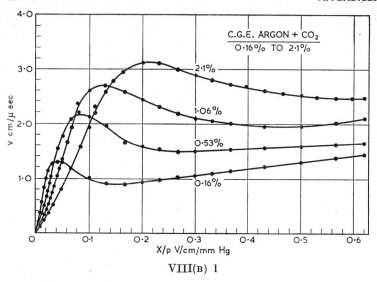

VIII(B) 1

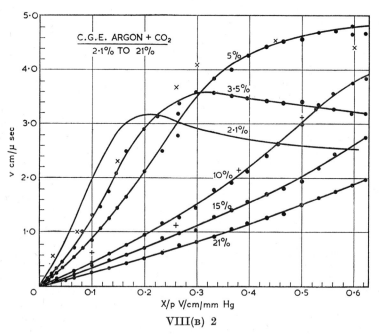

VIII(B) 2

Electron drift velocities: Argon-Co_2 mixtures

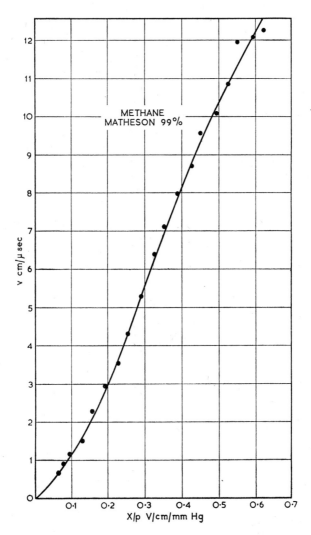

VIII(c).   Electron drift velocity: Methane

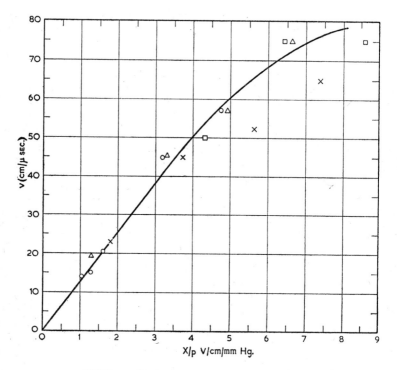

VIII(D).   Drift velocity of electrons in BF₃

(Reproduced from "Ionization Chambers and Counters" by Rossi and Staub (1949), by courtesy of the publishers, United States Atomic Energy Commission)

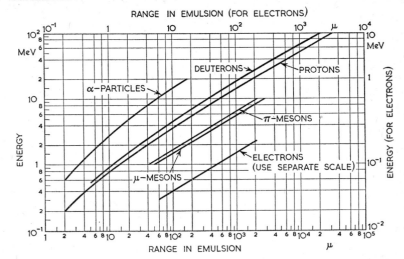

Appendix IX(a). Variation of range in photographic emulsion of various particles as a function of energy. (Rotblat, ref. 3.81)

Appendix IX(b).

Percentage straggling in range as a function of energy. (This determines the upper limit to the resolution when photographic plates are used in fast neutron spectrometry). (Rotblat, ref. 3.81)

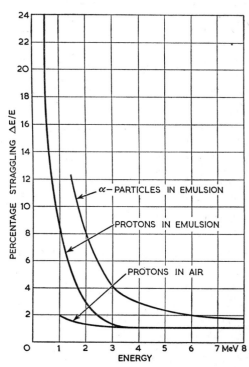

Appendix X. The spectrum of three radioactive sources and
the spectrum of neutrons from the slow neutron fission of
U²³⁵

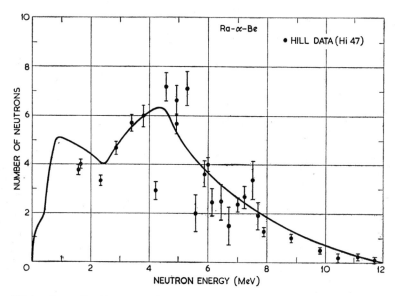

X(A). Ra-α-Be (data on this spectrum appear to be few). (D. C. Hill
AECD 1945 (1947)—see also A. O. Hanson *Radioactive Neutron Sources*,
from *Fast Neutron Physics* (1960), Ed. J. B. Marion and J. L. Fowler,
Interscience)

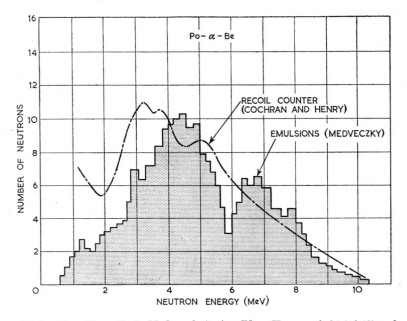

X(B).   Po-α-Be.   (L. L. Medveczky), *Act. Phys. Hungar.* **6**, 26 (1956) and
R. C. Cochran and K. M. Henry, *Rev. Sci. Inst.* **26**, 757 (1955)

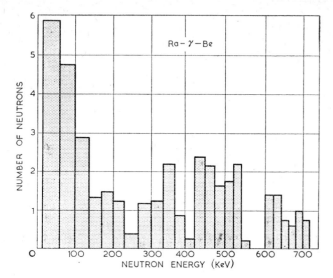

X(c). Ra-γ-Be. (C. Eggler and D. J. Hughes U.S.A.E.C. Report
ANL 4476 (1950))

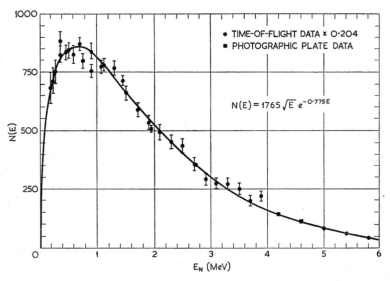

X(D). The fission spectrum of U[235] (Cranberg *et al.*, *Phys. Rev.* 103,
662 (1956))

Appendix XI

Decay schemes of isotopes commonly produced in neutron detection by radiative capture.

Sources: Hollander, Perlman, Seaborg, *Rev. Mod. Phys.* **25**, 469 (1953); Neutron Cross Sections, BNL 325.

Energies. All energies are quoted in MeV. Total decay energy is the difference between the initial state of radioactive isotope and the final state of daughter nucleus. Beta and gamma ray energies are obtained by subtracting the energies of the appropriate levels.

e.g. Na^{24} emits a beta ray of maximum energy 1·39 MeV ($=5·53-4·14$) and gamma rays of 1·38 MeV and 2·76 ($=4·14-1·38$).

Activation cross sections are quoted in barns, and refer to a neutron velocity of 2200 m/sec.

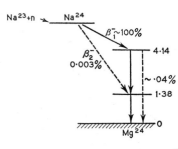

XI(A)

Decay scheme of Na^{24}   *Decay scheme of Co^{60}, Co^{60m}*

Half-life, 15 h
Total decay energy, 5·53 MeV
Activation cross section, 0·505
    barns

Half-lives:
  Co^{60m} 10·4 min
  Co^{60} 5·3 y

Total decay energy for Co^{60m},
  2·89 MeV

Activation cross sections:
  Co^{60m}, 16 ± 36 barns
  Co^{60}, 20 ± 36 barns

Total activation of 5·3y + 10·4 mm.
  $36 \pm 1·56$ barns

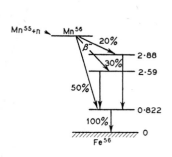

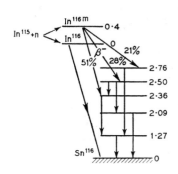

XI(B)

Decay scheme of Mn^{56}	Decay scheme of In^{116m} and In^{116}
Half-life, 2·58 h	Half-lives: In^{116}, 13 sec, In^{116m}, 54 min
Total decay energy, 3·63 MeV	Total decay energy of In^{116m}, 3·36 MeV
Activation cross section, 13·4 ± 0·36 barns	Activation cross sections: In^{116m}, 145 ± 156 barns In^{116}, 52 ± 66 barns

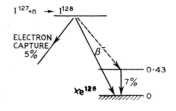

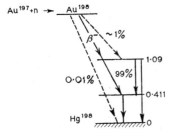

XI(c)

Decay scheme of I^{128}	Decay scheme of Au^{198}
Half-life, 25 min	Half-life, 2·7 days
Total decay energy, 2·0 MeV	Total decay energy, 1·374 MeV
Activation cross section, 5·5 ± 0·5 barns	Activation cross section, 98·5 barns

Appendix XII

In the text, we refer without comment or definition to a number of terms in common use in neutron physics. With some of the terms, e.g. the relation of the mean cross section of a $1/v$ detector in a thermal neutron beam to the 2200 m/sec value, a brief further discussion, rather on the lines of Chapter 1.2, may be of some use. We append, therefore, comment and definition of some of the terms we have employed, viz.:

> Cross section.
> Differential and integral spectra.
> Efficiency.
> Endoergic and exoergic.
> Flux.
> Statistics.

Cross section. This is the subject of an entire book, by Hughes.* A cross section is an area. Just as atomic cross sections (10^{-16} sq. cm) are of the order of the square of the atomic radius (10^{-8} cm), but vary widely with the type of reaction and with the energy of interacting particles, so nuclear cross sections (10^{-24} sq. cm) are of the order of the square of the nuclear radius (10^{-12} cm) but vary widely with the type of reaction and with the energy of interacting particles. The unit of 10^{-24} sq. cm is called the *barn*.

The total cross section is a measure of the probability that an incident neutron will interact with the nucleus, and its measurement is described in Chapter 4.1. There may be many ways in which the interaction may proceed. The neutron may be re-emitted with energy corresponding to the simple kinematics of Chapter 2.1; this process is *elastic scattering*. The neutron may be re-emitted with energy different from elastic scattering (*inelastic scattering*); it may be absorbed, with the binding energy liberated by emission of gamma rays (*radiative capture*); it may induce fission, and so on. The probability of these separate

---

* See Bibliography, ref. 0.4.

15—N.D

events is represented by partial cross sections, whose sum is the probability of interaction as a whole, i.e.

$$\sigma_{total} = \sigma_{capture} + \sigma_{fission} + \sigma_{elastic} + \text{etc.}$$

Cross sections are usually defined for a specific energy, e.g. 1 MeV. For slow neutrons, the energy usually specified is 0·0253 eV, which is the most probable energy of a Maxwellian distribution corresponding to a temperature of $20°C = 293°K$. A neutron energy of 0·0253 eV corresponds to a neutron velocity of 2200 metres/sec.

The answer to the question "what is the effective cross section of a thin $1/v$ absorber in a thermal beam of neutrons, given the 2200 m/sec value?" depends on the circumstances. One such answer is required in the example of counter efficiency given below.

Consider a thin absorber placed in a beam of thermal neutrons. We wish to determine the total cross section, using a detector which is energy independent (i.e. whose response meters the neutron flux). Now, the neutron flux (see below) is $\int \rho v \, dv$, where ρ, the density of neutrons in a Maxwellian distribution varies with neutron velocity v as $v^2 e^{-v^2/v_0^2}$ (v_0 is 2200 m/sec). To each velocity v there corresponds a cross section $\sigma_0 \cdot \dfrac{v_0}{v}$, since the absorber has a cross section which varies as $1/v$ and is σ_0 at velocity v_0. The total flux is $\int \rho v \, dv = \int_0^\infty v(v^2 e^{-v^2/v_0^2}) dv$, and the total absorption $\int \rho v \, dv \sigma = \sigma_0 v_0 \int_0^\infty v^2 e^{-v^2/v_0^2} dv$. The effective cross section is therefore

$$\sigma_0 v_0 \cdot \frac{\displaystyle\int_0^\infty v^2 e^{-v^2/v_0^2} \, dv}{\displaystyle\int_0^\infty v^3 e^{-v^2/v_0^2} \, dv}$$

$$= \sigma_0 v_0 \cdot \frac{\sqrt{\pi}}{2 v_0} = \frac{\sigma_0}{1\cdot128}.$$

In these circumstances, therefore, the observed cross section is some 13 per cent *below* the 2200 m/sec value. In the case quoted by Hughes in *Neutron Cross Sections* Chapter 6 the detector, instead of being energy independent, has itself a response which varies as $1/v$. In this case, the quantity detected (Chapter 4.5.1) is neutron *density* not *flux*, and considerations similar to the above give the effective cross section as

$$\frac{\int \rho dv \cdot \sigma}{\int \rho dv} = \sigma_0 v_0 \cdot \frac{\int_0^\infty v e^{-v^2/v_0^2} \, dv}{\int v^2 e^{-v^2/v_0^2} \, dv}$$

Since it can be shown by simple partial integration that

$$\int_0^\infty v^3 e^{-v^2/v_0^2} \, dv = \int_0^\infty v e^{-v^2/v_0^2} \, dv,$$

we find the effective cross section for a thin $1/v$ absorber, $1/v$ detector is

$$\sigma_0 v_0 \cdot \frac{2}{v_0 \sqrt{\pi}} = \sigma_0. \, 1{\cdot}128,$$

so that the effective cross section is 13 per cent *above* the 2200 m/sec value.

There are some important absorbers whose slow neutron response, in the thermal region, varies approximately but not exactly as $1/v$. These include the thermally fissile elements, U^{233}, U^{235} and Pu^{239}. For these elements, further corrections, in addition to the factors discussed above, are required to give the effective cross section in a thermal beam from the 2200 m/sec value. For U^{233} and U^{235}, this factor is $0{\cdot}98$; for Pu^{239}, it is $1{\cdot}08$.*

Differential and integral spectra. To illustrate these definitions, we consider the spectra:

(a) Of protons from elastic scattering of neutrons of 1 MeV energy by protons.

(b) Of protons from capture of thermal neutrons by He^3.

(c) As in (b), but with a background of pulses from gamma-induced electrons.

All spectra are idealised, i.e. the counters are considered perfect, with very high resolution and without end and wall effects. The spectrum of (a) is a plateau continuous from 0 to

* These factors are more extensively discussed by Westcott (TNCE, CAN 7) and by Campbell and Freemantle (Harwell report RP/R 2031).

E_{max}, while (b) is a sharp line at 765 keV and (c) is a sharp line with a "background" of low energy pulses. They are shown in Fig. XII.1 and are called *differential pulse spectra*. They are the spectra obtained by injecting the pulses from the output of

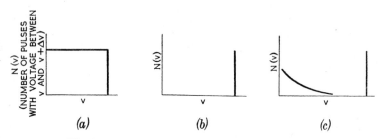

Fig. XII.1. Schematic differential spectra from:

(a) proton recoil at 1 MeV
(b) He³ counter with thermal neutrons
(c) as in (b) but with background of gamma-induced electrons.

the amplifier into a pulse height analyser. However, if a pulse height analyser is not available, one injects the pulses into a discriminator, which selects and feeds into a register all pulses above a certain bias level. If the number of pulses above this level is plotted as a function of bias voltage, then the spectra of

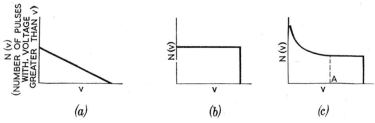

Fig. XII.2. Schematic integral spectra of the cases shown in Appendix XI.1.

Fig. XII.1 will become those of Fig. XII.2, and are called *integral spectra*. Inspection of Fig. XII.2 (a) shows why systems employing a biased detector for neutron detection by proton recoil are sensitive to bias. Fig. XII.2 (c) shows what is meant by "biasing out unwanted pulses": with the bias level set at A, all $He^3(n,p)T$ pulses are recorded, while all gamma ray pulses are eliminated.

Mathematically, the processes of integration and differentiation are complementary, but in the physical examples quoted above, they are far from complementary. For example, Fig. XII.2(b) is an integral bias curve, from which Fig. XII.1(b) can be obtained by differentiation. If this is done by taking differences between successive experimental points, the values of these differences are often comparable with the statistical errors on the original points of the integral curve, and the errors on the difference curve are large compared with the errors involved in obtaining a differential curve with a pulse height analyser.

The same point may be illustrated in another way. The spectra of fast neutrons have been determined by direct methods using proton recoil (Chapter 4.3.1). Each neutron energy will give, under ideal conditions, a plateau, and the neutron spectrum is therefore obtained by differentiating again this curve (itself a differential pulse height distribution). If one is analysing a spectrum containing only two neutron energy groups, well separated in energy and equal in intensity, then some results can be obtained by this process of double differentiation. If the spectra are complex, however, then the difficulties are very great, and true meters of neutron energy spectrum, such as the He^3 spectrometer or neutron time-of-flight, are essential.

Efficiency. It is not always possible to define accurately the efficiency of a counter. If a neutron beam is unidirectional, and the counter has an accurately defined area at right angles to the beam, then the efficiency is the ratio of the total number of counts to the total incident flux over the area of the counter. In other cases (e.g. the long counter) precise definition is not possible, but the ratio of total counts to total incident flux remains a qualitative index of efficiency.

For many simple counters, the efficiency can be readily estimated. Thus, if one has a $B^{10}F_3$ chamber filled with 76 cm of gas at $0°C$, and the mean depth in the direction of an incident beam of thermal neutrons is 1 cm, the efficiency is

Number of atoms × cross section per atom

$$= \frac{1 \times 6 \times 10^{23}}{22,400} \times \frac{4010}{1·128} \times 10^{-24}$$

$$\approx 9\tfrac{1}{2} \text{ per cent,}$$

where one is neglecting the attenuation and hardening of the beam in the counter. A similar calculation for a hydrogen-filled proportional counter at atmospheric pressure 10 cm long in the direction of incidence of 1 MeV neutrons, shows that its efficiency is between 0·1 per cent and 1 per cent. The exact value will depend on the bias and on the correction required for end and wall effects.

Endoergic, Exoergic. These terms are borrowed from the chemical terms *endothermic* and *exothermic*. An endothermic reaction is one in which heat is absorbed, an exothermic reaction one in which heat is evolved. When we say "heat is evolved", we mean that the kinetic energy of the final products is greater than the kinetic energy of the initial materials. Similarly an endoergic nuclear reaction is one in which the kinetic energy of the constituent particles is reduced as a result of the reaction, e.g.

$$T + p \rightarrow \text{He}^3 + n - 0·765 \text{ MeV,}$$

while in an exoergic nuclear reaction the kinetic energy of the constituent particles is increased, e.g.

$$D + D \rightarrow \text{He}^3 + n + 3·28 \text{ MeV.}$$

Flux. In the case of a unidirectional beam of monoenergetic neutrons, the flux corresponds to current density, i.e. the number of neutrons crossing unit area (1 sq. cm) per second normal to the incident direction. If the number of neutrons per cubic centimetre is ρ, and their velocity is v cm/sec, the flux is ρv neutrons/cm^2 sec.

If the neutron distribution is neither unidirectional nor monoenergetic (e.g. neutron distribution in a reactor) the flux is still defined as $\int \rho v \, dv$ neutrons/cm^2 sec. This can perhaps be understood by a different approach. Consider an absorber of cross section σ, with n atoms per c.c. Then the flux should be so defined that the absorption rate is flux $\times n\sigma$ per c.c. Now, to each neutron velocity v there corresponds a lifetime τ which will depend on the mean free path l of the neutron in the absorber: $\tau = l/v$. The mean free path for each velocity is equal to $1/n\sigma$, so that $\tau = 1/n\sigma v$. But the absorption rate is proportional to the neutron density divided by the mean life, i.e. to

$$\int \frac{\rho}{\tau} \, dv \;=\; \int \rho dv \cdot nv\sigma \;=\; \int \rho v \, dv \cdot n\sigma.$$

Comparing this with our statement above, we see that the quantity corresponding to flux is

$$\int \rho v \, dv.$$

Statistics. This subject is discussed in many books on nuclear physics (e.g. Evans).* We shall therefore restrict ourselves to only three comments:

1. The principle of all these calculations is that one defines p as the probability that an event will occur and $(1-p)$ as the probability that it will not occur. For example, in tossing a penny, the chance of throwing a head is $p = \frac{1}{2}$; in throwing dice, the chance of throwing a deuce is $p = \frac{1}{6}$. Bernoulli, early in the eighteenth century, showed that in a random group of z independent trials, the probability P_x that the event will occur x times is represented by that term in the binomial expansion in which p is raised to the xth power, viz.

$$P_x = \frac{z!}{x!(z-x)!} \, p^x (1-p)^{(z-x)} \qquad (1)$$

Now in this example, p and x are integers, while most physical events represent continuous processes. To proceed from the discrete to the continuous, we let the probability of an event become very small, while the number of trials z becomes very

---

* See Bibliography, 1.2.

large, in such a way that $m = pz$ is constant. Then it can be shown that expression (1) becomes

$$dP_x = \frac{1}{\sigma\sqrt{2\pi}}\, e^{-\frac{(x-m)^2}{2\sigma^2}}\, dx \tag{2}$$

where dPx is the probability that the result of a trial lies between x and $(x + dx)$. Clearly the most probable result is $x = m$: while the root mean square deviation, i.e. the value of $(x - m)^2$ is σ, which for most practical purposes is $\sqrt{m}$. Expression (2) is referred to as a *Gaussian distribution*.

2. In tossing pennies or thowing dice, the result of a given number of trials is calculable. The object of a penny-tossing experiment is simply to confirm the distribution of the observed results from the calculated mean. In an experiment, the result is unknown, and one measurement will not in general repeat the previous measurement. The "real value" remains hypothetical, and becomes more and more clearly defined only as more and more results accumulate. The object of analysis such as the foregoing is to enable one to ascribe limits within which, given the observed results, the actual value must lie.

3. In expression (2), the standard deviation σ is $\sqrt{m}$, so that the *relative* standard deviation is $\dfrac{\sqrt{m}}{m} = \dfrac{1}{\sqrt{m}}$. This expression is widely used as a figure of merit to indicate the relative spread or scatter of results due to random processes. Thus, if the number of counts in a certain interval is 100, the "statistical error" is $\dfrac{10}{100} = 10$ per cent; if the number is 10,000 the error is 1 per cent, and so on.

By way of example, consider the examples of Chapter 3. In 3.1, we observed that the mean number of ion pairs produced by the capture of a neutron in BF_3 was 75,000. The standard deviation is $(75,000)^{\frac{1}{2}}$ or 273, so that the relative standard deviation is $\dfrac{273}{75,000} \simeq 0.36$ per cent. In section 3.3.1 we saw that the number of photoelectrons injected into the photomultiplier was 2000, for which the relative standard deviation is $\dfrac{45}{2000} \simeq 2.2$ per cent.

It is worth emphasising that there is an appreciable chance that the individual value of x will fall outside the standard deviation, $\sqrt{m}$. Let us define P_u as the total probability that individual values of x will fall further from the mean by an amount u, i.e. $P_u = 2\int_{m+u}^{\infty} \mathrm{d}P_x$. Then for $u = \sigma$, $P_u = 0.32$, i.e. there is a 32 per cent chance that the result of an experiment will lie further from the mean than a standard deviation. For $u = 2\sigma$, $P_u = 5$ per cent; for $u = 3\sigma$, $P_u = 0.3$ per cent and thereafter rapidly declines.

REFERENCE INDEX
AND
BIBLIOGRAPHY

GENERAL REFERENCES

0.1. BARSCHALL, H. H., "The Detection of Neutrons", *Encyclopaedia of Physics*, Vol. XLV p. 437, Springer-Verlag, Berlin (1958).
0.2. ROSSI, B. B. and STAUB, H. H., *Ionization Chambers and Counters*, McGraw-Hill Book Co., New York (1949).
0.3. FELD, B. T., "The Neutron", *Experimental Nuclear Physics*, Vol. II, Ed. E. Segre, John Wiley & Sons, New York (1953).
0.4. *Fast Neutron Physics*, Ed.: J. L. Marion and J. B. Fowler, Interscience Publishing Co., New York (1960).
0.5. HUGHES, D. J., *Pile Neutron Research*, Addison-Wesley Publishing Co., Cambridge, Mass., U.S.A. (1953).

1. INTRODUCTION
1.1. Historical

(1) BOTHE, W. and BECKER, H. *Zeit. für Phys.* **66**, 289 (1930).
(2) CURIE, I. and JOLIOT, F. *Comptes Rendus*, **194**, 273 (1932).
(3) CHADWICK, J. *Proc. Roy. Soc.* **A-136**, 692 (1932).
(4) FEATHER, N. *Proc. Roy. Soc.* **A-136**, 709 (1932).
(5) SZILARD, L. and CHALMERS, T.A. *Nature*, **134**, 494 (1934).
(6) CHADWICK, J. and GOLDHABER, M. *Nature*, **134**, 237 (1934).
(7) FERMI, E. and RASETTI, F. *Nuov. Cim.* **12**, 201 (1935).
(8) MOON, P. B. and TILLMAN, J. R. *Proc. Roy. Soc.* **A-153**, 475 (1936).
(9) DUNNING, J. R., PEGRAM, G. B., FINK, G. A. and MITCHELL, D. P. *Phys. Rev.* **48**, 265 (1935).
(10) AMALDI, E. and FERMI, E. *Phys. Rev.* **50**, 899 (1936).
(11) SZILARD, L. *Nature*, **136**, 950 (1935).

Summary accounts are given by:

CHADWICK, J. *Proc. Roy. Soc.* **A-142**, 1 (1933).
DARROW, K. K. *Rev. Sci. Inst.* **4**, 58 (1933).
MOON, P. B. *Repts. Prog. Phys.* Vol. IV, 198 (1937).

1.2. Elementary principles of neutron detection

Of the wealth of books on nuclear physics now available, the following are recommended:

CORK, J. M. *Radioactivity and Nuclear Physics*, Van Nostrand, New York (1950) (2nd Ed.).

HALLIDAY, D. *Introductory Nuclear Physics* (2nd Ed.). John Wiley & Sons, New York (1955).

EVANS, R. D. *The Atomic Nucleus*, McGraw-Hill Book Co., New York (1955).

1.3.1. The neutron energy range 10 keV to 20 MeV

(12) HANSON, A. O., TASCHEK, R. F. and WILLIAMS, J. H. *Rev. Mod. Phys.* **21**, 635 (1949). (Monoergic Sources.) FOWLER, J. L. and BROLLEY, J. E. *Rev. Mod. Phys.* **28**, 103 (1956) (10 to 30 MeV).

(13) NOBLES, R. *Rev. Sci. Inst.* **28**, 962 (1957) (gas targets with double windows for high currents).

1.3.2. Slow neutrons

BECK, C. K. *Nuclear Reactors for Research*, Macmillan, London (1957).

GLASSTONE, S. *Principles of Reactor Engineering*, Van Nostrand, New York (1955).

Ibid. Source Book of Atomic Energy, Macmillan, London (1951).

Nuclear Reactor Experiments, Chapter 7, Ed. J. B. HOAG, Van Nostrand, New York (1958).

HUGHES, D. J. General ref. 0.5.

1.3.3. Radioactive neutron sources

See Chapter 5.

2. REACTIONS USED IN NEUTRON DETECTION

General

Neutron cross sections, BNL 325, 2nd Ed. D. J. HUGHES and R. B. SCHWARTZ (1st July 1958).

HUGHES, D. J. *Neutron Cross sections*, Pergamon Press, London and New York (1957).

2.1.1. Kinematics

(1) BARSCHALL, H. H. and KANNER, M. H. *Phys. Rev.* **58**, 590 (1940).

(2) BARSCHALL, H. H. and WALT, M. *Phys. Rev.* **93**, 1062 (1954).

BARSCHALL, H. H. and POWELL, J. L. *Phys. Rev.* **96**, 713 (1954).

BLUMBERG, L. and SCHLESINGER, S. I. U.S.A.E.C. Report LADC 2121 (1955).

(n,p) angular distribution

CAPLEHORN, W. F. and RUNDLE, G. P. *Proc. Phys. Soc.* **A-64**, 546 (1951).

A review of higher energy (n,p) scattering is given by BROLLEY, J. E. and FOWLER, J. L. *Rev. Mod. Phys.* **28**, 103 (1956).

(n,d) scattering

ADAIR, R. K., OKAZAKI, A. and WALT, M. *Phys. Rev.* **89**, 1165 (1953).

ALLEN, W. D., FERGUSON, A. T. G. and ROBERTS, J. *Proc. Phys. Soc.* **A-68**, 650 (1955).

ALLRED, J. C., ARMSTRONG, A. H. and ROSEN, L. *Phys. Rev.* **91**, 90 (1953).

TUNNICLIFFE, P. R. *Phys. Rev.* **89**, 1247 (1953).

(n,He) scattering

ADAIR, R. K. *Phys. Rev.* **86**, 155 (1952).

SEAGRAVE, J. D. *Phys. Rev.* **92**, 1222 (1953).

2.1.2. Cross section values

BNL 325.

See also Chapter 5.2.

2.1.3. Range-energy relation

(3) BETHE, H. and LIVINGSTONE, M. S. *Rev. Mod. Phys.* **9**, 245 (1937).

(4) BETHE, H. and ASHKIN, J. *Experimental Nuclear Physics*, Vol. 1. Ed. E. Segre. John Wiley & Son, New York (1953).

(5) ALLISON, S. K. and WARSHAW, S. D. *Rev. Mod. Phys.* **25**, 779 (1953).

2.2. $B^{10}(n,\alpha)$, Li^7 reaction

Cross-section values

BNL 325

See also Chapter 5.2

Lifetimes of Li^{7*}

(6) BUNBURY, D. St. P., DEVONS, S., MANNING, G. and TOWLE, J. H. *Proc. Phys. Soc.* **A-69**, 165 (1956).

BELL, R. E. and ELLIOT, L. G. *Phys. Rev.* **74**, 1869 (1948).

Branching ratio at high neutron energy
(7) BICHSEL, H., HALG, H., HUBER, P. and STEBLER, A.
    Phys. Rev. **81**, 456 (1951).
(8) PETREE, B., JOHNSON, C. H. and MILLER, D. W. *Phys.
    Rev.* **83**, 1148 (1951).
Other reactions at higher energy
(9) FRYE, G. M. and GAMMEL, J. H. *Phys. Rev.* **103**, 328
    (1956).
    JAMES, D. B., KUBELKA, W., HEIBERG, S. A. and
    WARREN, J. B. *Can. J. Phys.* **33**, 219 (1955).

2.3 Exoergic reactions
$He^3(n,p)T$

BATCHELOR, R., AVES, R. and SKYRME, T. H. R. *Rev. Sci.
    Inst.* **26**, 1037 (1955).
$Li^6(n,\alpha)T$
Thermal Properties BNL 325
Cross sections, intermediate energies:
(10) BAME, S. J. and CUBITT, R. L. *Phys. Rev.* **114**, 1580
    (1959).
(11) MURRAY, R. B. and SCHMITT, H. W. *Phys. Rev. Letters*
    3, 360 (1959).
Total cross section, 265 *keV level*
    JOHNSON, C. H., WILLARD, H. B. and BAIR, J. H. *Phys.
    Rev.* **96**, 985 (1954).
Angular distribution, 1 *to* 1·1 *MeV:*
    WEDDELL, J. B. and ROBERTS, J. H. *Phys. Rev.* **89**, 891
    (abstract only) (1953).
Reactions at 14 *MeV:*
    FRYE, G. M. *Phys. Rev.* **93**, 1086 (1954).

2.3.2. Fission

Thermal cross section values
    SANDERS, J. E. and HARVEY, J. A. *Progress in Nuclear
    Energy*, Series 1, Vol. I, Pergamon Press, London (1956).
Fast fission cross section values
    ALLEN, W. D. and HENKEL, R. L. *Progress in Nuclear
    Energy*, Series 1, Vol. II, pp. 1–50, Pergamon Press, London
    (1957).
    (See also BNL 325).
Alpha pile-up calculation
    GILLESPIE, A. B. *Signal Noise and Resolution in Nuclear
    Counter Amplifiers*, Pergamon Press, London (1953).
    See also general ref. 0.2.

2.3.3. Radiative capture

Decay schemes
STROMINGER, D., HOLLANDER, J. M. and SEABORG, G. T.
    Rev. Mod. Phys. **30**, 2, part 2 (April 1958).
Cross sections
BNL 325
Gamma rays from thermal neutron capture
(12) MITTELMAN, P. S. and LIEDTKE, R. A. *Nucleonics*
    13/5, 50 (1955). (A practical summary of an ex-
    tensive subject.)
Use of copper wire as pile flux monitor
BOGAARDT, M., HALG, W. and PELSER, J. J.E.N.E.R. 21
    (1953).
COHEN, R. and BARLOUTAUD, R. *Comptes Rendus*, **238**,
    2413 (1954).

2.3.4. The Szilard-Chalmers reaction

(13) SZILARD, L. and CHALMERS, T. A. *Nature*, **134**, 462
    (1934).
(14) McKAY, H. A. C. *Prog. Nucl. Phys.* I Ed. O. R.
    Frisch, Pergamon Press, London (1950).
(15) EDGE, R. D. *Aus. J. Phys.* **9**, 429 (1956).
COLLIE, C. H. and SHAW, P. F. D. *J. de Chim. Phys.* **48**,
    198 (1951).

2.4. Endoergic reactions and threshold detectors

General
BROLLEY, J. E. and FOWLER, J. L. *Rev. Mod. Phys.* **28**, 103
    (1956).
COHEN, B. L. *Nucleonics*, 8/2, 29 (Feb. 1951).
KIEHN, R. M. *Nuclear Shielding Study No.* 8, M.I.T. Labora-
    tory for Nuclear Science and Engineering Technical
    Report No. 40 (1950).
TASCHEK, R. F. MDDC 360 (1946).

Inelastic scattering, In115 and Au197:
EBEL, A. A. and GOODMAN, C. *Phys. Rev.* **93**, 197 (1954).
MARTIN, H. C., DIVEN, B. C. and TASCHEK, R. F. *Phys. Rev.*
    93, 199 (1954).
Threshold detectors
(16) O^{16} (*n,p*) MARTIN, H. C. *Phys. Rev.* **93**, 498 (1954).
(17) Al^{27} (*n,p*) BNL 325.
(18) P^{31} (*n,p*) RICAMO, R. *Nuov. Cim.* **8**, 383 (1951).
(19) S^{32} (*n,p*) *Ibid.*

(20) S^{32} (n,p) HURLIMAN, T. and HUBER, P. *Helv. Phys. Act.* **28**, 33 (1955).

(21) Cl^{35} (n,α) ADLER, H., HUBER, P. and HÄLG, W. *Helv. Phys. Act.* **26**, 349 (1953).

(22) C^{12} $(n,2n)$ BROLLEY, J. E., FOWLER, J. L. and SCHLACKS. *Phys. Rev.* **88**, 618 (1952).

(23) SHARPE, J. and STAFFORD, G. H. *Proc. Phys. Soc.* **A-64**, 211 (1951).

(24) Mo^{92} $(n,2n)$ ref. 2.22.

(25) Ni^{58} $(n,2n)$ MARTIN, H. C. and DIVEN, B. C. *Phys. Rev.* **86**, 565 (1952).

(26) Cu^{63} $(n,2n)$ *Ibid.*

(27) Tl^{208} $(n,2n)$ *Ibid.*

(28) I^{127} $(n,2n)$ MARTIN, H. C. and TASCHEK, R. F. *Phys. Rev.* **89**, 1302 (1953).

Bi fission at energies above 50 MeV

   KELLY, E. L. and WIEGAND, C. *Phys. Rev.* **73**, 1135 (1948).

Sphere experiments using threshold detectors

   GITTINGS, H. T., BARSCHALL, H. H. and EVERHART, G. G. *Phys. Rev.* **75**, 1610 (1949).

(29) HURST, G. S., HARTER, J. A., HENSLEY, P. N., MILLS, W. A., SLATER, M. and REINHARDT, P. W. *Rev. Sci. Inst.* **27**, 153 (1956).

(30) PHILLIPS, D. D., DAVIS, R. W. and GRAVES, E. T. *Phys. Rev.* **88**, 600 (1952).

3. THE CHIEF INSTRUMENTS OF NEUTRON DETECTION

General

(1) ROSSI, B. B. and STAUB, H. H. *Ionization Chambers and Counters*, N.N.E.S. Div. V, Vol. 2. McGraw-Hill, New York (1949).

(2) STAUB, H. H. *Experimental Nuclear Physics*, Vol. I(a) Detection Methods. Ed.: E. Segre. John Wiley & Son, New York (1953).

(3) WILKINSON, D. H. *Ionization Chambers and Counters*, The University Press, Cambridge (1950).

Encyclopaedia of Physics, Vol. XLV, Nuclear Instrumentation II, Springer-Verlag, Berlin (1958).

PRICE, W. T. *Nuclear Radiation Detection.* McGraw-Hill, New York (1958).

3.1.1.(a). The behaviour of free ions and electrons in gases

> ENGLISH, W. N. and HANNA, G. C.   *Can. J. Phys.* **31**, 768 (1953).
> HEALEY, R. H. and REED, J. W.   *The Behaviour of Slow Electrons in Gases*, Amalgamated Wireless Ltd., Sydney (1941).

3.1.1.(b). Saturation

> (4) FACCHINI, U. and MALVICINI, A.   *Nucleonics*, **13**/4, 36 (April 1955).
> (5) MCCREARY, H. S. and BAYARD, R. T.   *Rev. Sci. Inst.* **25**, 161 (1954).
> (6) WEILL, J.   *Nucleonics*, **15**/8, 45 (August 1957).
> (This paper summarises several French developments in instrumentation.)
> LAPSLEY, A. C.   *Rev. Sci. Inst.* **24**, 602 (1953).

3.1.2. The induction effect

(b) The Frisch grid

> (7) FRISCH, O. R.   British Atomic Energy Report BR 49 (n.d.).
> (8) BUNEMANN, O., CRANSHAW, T. E. and HARVEY, J. A. *Can. J. Res.* A. **27**, 191 (1949).
> (9) RAFFLE, J. F.   Private communication, and to be published.
> (The Frisch grid is very widely used in alpha counting, for which purpose its use is fully described in Rossi and Staub (ref. 1 above).

(c) The cylindrical ion chamber

> (10) LARSSON, K. E. and TAYLOR, C.   *Ark f. Fys.* **3**, 9, 131 (1952).

3.1.3. Practical ion chambers

(a) Boron-lined counters

> (11) LOWDE, R. D.   *Rev. Sci. Inst.* **21**, 835 (1950).
> (12) JAQUES, T. A., BALLINGER, H. A. and WADE, R. *Proc. I.E.E.* **100** (1), 110 (1953).
> (13) TAYLOR, D. and SHARPE, J.   *Proc. I.E.E.* **98** (II), 174 (1951).
> (14) DUCHENE, J., LAVERGNE, J. and WEILL, J.   *J. Nucl. En.* **4**, 1, 26 (1957).
> ABSON, W. and WADE, E.   *Proc. I.E.E.* **103B**, 590 (1956).

B_4C *layers*
>   LABEYRIE, J., LALLEMONT, C. and WEILL, J. *J. Phys. Rad.* **12**, 32A (1951).

(b) **Fission counters**

(15) HOLMES, J. E. R., McVICAR, D. D., SHEPHERD, L. R. and SMITH, R. D. *J. Nucl. En.* **1**, 117 (1954).
(16) ALLEN, W. D. and FERGUSON, A. T. G. *J. Nucl. En.* **2**, 38 (1955).
(17) ERICKSEN, G. F., KAUFMAN, S. G. and PAHIS, L. E. *I.R.E. Trans. on Nucl. Science*, NS-3, **3**, 8 (1956).
(18) AVES, R., BARNES, D. and MCKENZIE, R. B. *J. Nucl. En.* **1**, 110 (1954).
(19) ABSON, W., SALMON, P. G. and PYRAH, S. *Proc. I.E.E.* **105B**, **22**, 349 (1958).
>   HART, R. R., UCRL 2996 (1955).
>   KAUFMAN, S. C. and PAHIS, L. E. *Nucleonics*, **16**/3, 90 (1958).
>   TRICE, J. B. *Nucleonics*, **16**/7, 84 (1958).

(c) **Deposition techniques**

Boron
(20) SMITH, M. L. "Enrichment of Stable Isotopes by Electro-magnetic Separation", p. 162. *Prog. Nucl. Phys.* Vol. 6, Ed. O. R. Frisch. Pergamon Press, London (1957).
(21) SAFFORD, G. J. *Rev. Sci. Inst.* **27**, 972 (1956).
(22) HILL, H. A. *Rev. Sci. Inst.* **27**, 1086 (abstract) (1956).
(23) BARNES, D., MACKENZIE, R. B. and AVES, R. A.E.R.E. Report R/M 125 (June 1957).

Fissile material:

Electrodeposition
(24) HUFFORD, D. L. and SCOTT, B. F. *N.N.E.S.* Div. IV, Vol. IVB, Pt. II, p. 1167, McGraw-Hill: also MDDC 1515.
(25) FLEMING, E. H., Jr. AECD, 3395 (1952).
>   FLEMING, E. H., GHIORSO, A. and CUNNINGHAM, B. B. *Phys. Rev.* **88**, 642 (1952).
>   LAMPHERE, R. W. and GREENE, R. E. *Phys. Rev.* **100**, 763 (1955).

Painting
(26) GLOVER, K. M. and BORRELL, P. A.E.R.E. Report C/R 1359 (1954).
>   GRAVES, R. and FROMAN, D. K. "Miscellaneous Physical and Chemical Techniques of the Los Alamos Project". *N.N.E.S.* Vol. V-3, McGraw-Hill, New York (1952).

Evaporation
(27) MILSTED, J. A.E.R.E. Report C/R 1379 (1954).
(28) STRONG, J. *Procedures in Experimental Physics*, Prentice Hall (1946).

3.2. Proportional counters

General

In addition to the general references of 3.1, there are the following:
CURRAN, S. C. *Encyclopaedia of Physics*, Vol. XLV, p. 174, Springer-Verlag, Berlin (1958).
KORFF, S. A. *Electron and Nuclear Counters*, 2nd ed. Van Nostrand, New York (1955).
KORFF, S. A. I. *Nucleonics*, **6**/6, 5 (June 1950).
KORFF, S. A. II. *Nucleonics*, **7**/5, 46 (Nov. 1950).
KORFF, S. A. III. *Nucleonics*, **8**/1, 38 (Jan. 1951).
WEST, D. *Prog. Nucl. Phys.* Vol. 3, p. 18, Ed. O. R. Frisch, Pergamon Press, London (1953).

Geiger counters

(29) KORFF, S. A. *Encyclopaedia of Physics*, Vol. XLV, p. 52, Springer-Verlag, Berlin (1958).
See also refs. (1) to (3).

Proportional counters

(30) FRISCH, O. R. Quoted by West, D. *Prog. Nucl. Phys.* Vol. 3. Ed. O. R. Frisch, Pergamon Press, London (1953).
(31) COCKCROFT, A. L. and CURRAN, S. C. *Rev. Sci. Inst.* **22**, 37 (1951).
(32) ALLEN, R. C. Los Alamos Report LADC 2442 (unpublished) (1955, decl. 1956).
Ibid. Phys. Rev. **105**, 1796 (1957).
(33) SKYRME, T. H. R., TUNNICLIFFE, P. R. and WARD, A. G. *Rev. Sci. Inst.* **23**, 204 (1952).
LEVINTOV, I. I., MILLER, A. V. and SHAMSHEV, V. N. *Nucl. Phys.* **3**, 221 (1957). (He⁴ polarisation analyser.)
ROHR, R. C., ROHRER, E. R. and MACKLIN, R. L. *Rev. Sci. Inst.* **23**, 595 (1952).

BF₃ Counters

(34) FOWLER, I. L. and TUNNICLIFFE, P. R. *Rev. Sci. Inst.* **21**, 734 (1950).
(35) LOCKWOOD, J. A., WOODS, F. R. and BENNETT, E. F. *Rev. Sci. Inst.* **25**, 446 (1954).
(36) SOBERMANN, R. K., KORFF, S. A., FRIEDLAND, S. S. and KATZENSTEIN, H. S. *Rev.Sci.Inst.***24**,1058 (1953).

(37) ABSON, W., SALMON, P. G. and PYRAH, S. A.E.R.E.
Report EL/R. 2280 (1957).
Ibid. Proc. I.E.E. **105B**, 22, 357 (1958).

(38) SCHULTZ, M. and CONNOR, J. C. *Nucleonics*, **12**/2, 8
(1954).
BEAUVAL, J. J., DOUSSON, S. and PRUGNE, P. *Le Vide*,
Vol. 12, No. 69, p. 208 (1957).
BRACCI, A., FACCHINI, U., GERMAGNOLI, E. and ZIMMER, E.
Nuov. Cim. **7**, 512 (1950).

Time delays

(39) NICHOLSON, K. P. A.E.R.E. Report N/R. 1639 (1955).
Ibid. Proc. Phys. Soc. **A-69**, 413 (1956).
SIMPSON, O. D. *Phys. Rev.* **95**, 600 (A) (1954).

Diborane

ORIENT, O. J. and VIZSOLYI, E. I. *Nuov. Cim.* **5**, 6,
1722 (1957).

3.3. Scintillation counters
General

(40) BIRKS, J. B. *Scintillation Counters.* Pergamon Press,
London (1953).

(41) CURRAN, S. C. *Luminescence and the Scintillation
Counter.* Butterworth, London (1953).

(42) BROOKS, F. D. "Organic Scintillators". *Prog. Nucl.
Phys.*, Vol. 5, p. 252. Ed. O. R. Frisch. Pergamon
Press, London (1956).

(43) MOTT, W. E. and SUTTON, R. B. "Scintillation and
Cerenkov Counters", *Encyclopaedia of Physics*, Vol.
XLV, p. 86, Springer-Verlag, Berlin (1958).
Ref. 54 below.

3.3.1. Principles of scintillation detection
Wavelength shifters

(44) HAYES, F. N. OTT, D. G. and KERR, V. N. *Nucleonics*, **14**/1, p. 42 (January 1956).

(45) AVIVI, P. and WEINREB, A. *Rev. Sci. Inst.* **28**, 427
(1957).

Breakdowns

(46) STUMP, R. and TALLEY, H. E. *Rev. Sci. Inst.* **25**,
1132 (1954).

Luminescence process

(47) BIRKS, J. B. and BLACK, F. A. *Proc. Phys. Soc.* **A-64**,
511 (1951).

(48) BIRKS, J. B. *Proc. Phys. Soc.* **A-64**, 874 (1951).

(49) BELL, C. F. Jr. and HAYES, P. N. eds. *Liquid*

Scintillation Counting, Pergamon Press (1958). See in particular article by Brooks, F. D. "Scintillation Counters with Pulse Shape Selection", p. 268.

(50) Wright, G. T. *Proc. Phys. Soc.* **B-69**, 358 (1956).

The use of pulse shape to discriminate between gamma ray pulses and neutron pulses in organic scintillators is further discussed by:

Brooks, F. D. *Nucl. Inst.* **4**, 151 (1959).

Owen, R. B. A.E.R.E. Report EL/R 2712.

Ibid. *I.R.E. Trans. Nucl. Sci.* NS-5, **3**, 198 (1958).

Ibid. *Nucleonics* **17**/9, 92 (September 1959).

3.3.2. Organic scintillators

(a) Slow neutron detectors, with borazole, etc.

(51) Hoorn, J. I. and Dohne, C. F. *Rev. Sci. Inst.* **25**, 922, (1954).

(52) Muelhause, C. O. and Thomas, G. E. *Nucleonics*, **11**/1, p. 44 (Jan. 1953).

(53) Bollinger, L. M. and Thomas, G. E. *Rev. Sci. Inst.* **28**, 489 (1957).

(54) Bollinger, L. M. Geneva Conference on the Peaceful Applications of Atomic Energy, Vol. IV, Paper P/580, p. 47 (1955).

Kallmann, H. and Brucker, G. S. *Phys. Rev.* **108**, 1122 (1957).

Muelhause, C. O. and Thomas, G. E. *Phys. Rev.* **85**, 926 (1952).

Thielens, G. *App. Sci. Res. B.* **7**, 87 (1958).

(b) Fast Neutron detectors

(55) Poole, M. J. *Proc. Phys. Soc.* **A-65**, 453 (1952). *Phil. Mag. Series 7*, **43**, 1060 (1952).

(56) Berlman, I. B. and Marinelli, L. D. *Rev. Sci. Inst.* **27**, 858, (1956).

(57) Allen, R. A., Beghian, L. E. and Calvert, J. M. *Proc. Phys. Soc.* **A-65**, 295 (1952).

(58) Taylor, H. L., Lonsjo, O. and Bonner, T. W. *Phys. Rev.* **100**, 174 (1955).

Segel, R. E. Schwartz, C. D. and Owen, G. E. *Rev. Sci. Inst.* **25**, 140 (1954).

Hardy, J. E. *Rev. Sci. Inst.* **29**, 705 (1958).

Sandwich scintillators

Wilkinson, D. H. *Rev. Sci. Inst.* **23**, 414 (1952).

Williamson, C. F. and Hudspeth, E. L. *Bull. Am. Phys. Soc.* **11**, 2, 101 (1957).

(c) Large liquid scintillators

(59) REINES, F., COWAN, C. L., HARRISON, F. B. and CARTER, D. S. *Rev. Sci. Inst.* **25**, 1061 (1954). ANDREWS, P. T. *Rev. Sci. Inst.* **28**, 56 (1957). DIVEN, B. C., MARTIN, H. C., TASCHEK, R. F. and TERRELL, J. *Phys. Rev.* **101**, 1012 (1956). HARDY, J. E. *Rev. Sci. Inst.* **29**, 705 (1958).

Wavelength shifters
See refs. 44 and 45 above.

High energy neutrons
(60) THRESHER, J. J., VAN ZYL, C. P., VOSS, R. G. P. and WILSON, R. *Rev. Sci. Inst.* **26**, 1186 (1955).
(61) CHRISTIE, E. R., FELD, B. T., ODIAN, A. C., STEIN, P. C. and WATTENBERG, A. *Rev. Sci. Inst.* **27**, 127 (1956).

A new form of plastic scintillator, the directional counter, has been developed. See for example: REYNOLDS, G. T. *Nucleonics* **16**/6, 60 (June 1958). STETSON, R. F. BERKO, S. *Nucl. Inst.* **6**, 94 (1959).

3.3.3. Inorganic scintillators

(a) ZnS

(62) KOONTZ, P. G., KEEPIN, G. R. and ASHLEY, J. E. *Rev. Sci. Inst.* **26**, 352 (1955).
(63) GUNST, S. B., CONNOR, J. C. and BAYARD, R. T. *Rev. Sci. Inst.* **26**, 894 (1955).
(64) BAILEY, G. M. and PRESCOTT, J. R. *Aus. Jour. Phys.* **11**, 135 (1958).
(65) HORNYAK, W. F. *Rev. Sci. Inst.* **23**, 264 (1952).
(66) SEAGONDOLLAR, L. W., ESCH, K. A. and CARTWRIGHT, L. M. *Rev. Sci. Inst.* **25**, 689 (1954).
(67) KEEPIN, G. R. *Rev. Sci. Inst.* **25**, 30 (1954). SKARSVAG, K. J.E.N.E.R. 39 (1955). BROWN, B. and HOOPER, E. B. *Nucleonics*, **16**/4, 96 (April 1958).

(b) LiI

(68) HOFSTADTER, R., McINTYRE, J. A., RODERICK, H. and WEST, H. L. *Phys. Rev.* **82**, 749 (1951).
(69) SCHENCK, J. *Nucleonics*, **10**/8, 54 (August 1952).
(70) SCHENCK, J. and HEATH, R. L. *Phys. Rev.* **85**, 923 (1952).
(71) SCHENCK, J. *Nature*, **171**, 518 (1953).
(72) NICHOLSON, K. P. and SNELLING, G. F. A.E.R.E. Report EL/R. 1350; *Brit. J. Appl. Phys.* **6**, pp. 104–6 (1955).

BERNSTEIN, W. and SCHARDT, A. W. *Phys. Rev.* **85**, 919 (1952).

MURRAY, R. B. *Bull. Am. Phys. Soc.* II, **2** (5) 267 (1957). *Nucl. Inst.* **2**, 237 (1958).

NICHOLSON, K. P., and PATTENDEN, N. J. A.E.R.E. Report NP/M. 73 (1955).

(c) **Gamma rays in neutron detection**

(73) DUCKWORTH, J. C., MERRISON, A. W. and WHITTAKER, A. *Nature*, **165**, 69 (1950).

(74) RAE, E. R. and BOWEY, E. *Proc. Phys. Soc.* A-66, 1073 (1953).

(75) ALBERT, R. D. and GAERTTNER, E. R. *Rev. Sci. Inst.* **26**, 572 (1955).

(d) **Other Inorganic Scintillators**

(76) HARDING, G. *Nature*, **167**, 437 (1951).

(77) BROWN, B. *Rev. Sci. Inst.* **26**, 970 (1955).

BROWN, B. and HOOPER, E. B. *Nucleonics*, **16**/4, 96 (1958).

3.3.4. Miscellaneous scintillation techniques

(78) ERICKSEN, G. F. and KAUFMAN, S. G. *Rev. Sci. Inst.* **27**, 107 (1956).

DAUM, L. *I.R.E. Trans. Nucl. Science*, NS-5, **2**, 30 (1958).

An interesting development is described by:

VON ARDENNE, M. *Atomkern Energie* **1**, 121 (1956) (this is a scintillation image converter, in which the electrons from the photocathode are accelerated through 25 keV, so that 40 thermal neutrons give the light flash of apparent brilliance of 2 Lamberts).

Gas scintillation counters

(79) NOBLES, R. A. *Rev. Sci. Inst.* **27**, 280 (1956).

BOICOURT, G. P. and BROLLEY, J. E. *Rev. Sci. Inst.* **25**, 1218 (1954).

EGGLER, C. and HUDDLESTONE, C. M. *Phys. Rev.* **95**, 600 (abstract) (1954).

PALEVSKY, H., ZIMMERMAN, R. L. and LARSSON, K. E. *Rev. Sci. Inst.* **27**, 323 (1956).

SAYERS, A. and WU, C. S. *Rev. Sci. Inst.* **28**, 758 (1957).

3.4.1. Photographic plates

General

(80) POWELL, C. F., FOWLER, P. H. and PERKINS, D. H. Study of *Elementary Particles by Photographic Methods*. Pergamon Press, London (1959).

(81) ROTBLAT, J. *Progress in Nuclear Physics* (ed. O. R. Frisch), Vol. 1, p. 37, Butterworth–Springer (1950).

(82) BEISER, A. *Rev. Mod. Phys.* 24, 273 (1952).

(83) ROSEN, L. *Nucleonics*, 11/7, 32 (1953).

(84) ROSEN, L. *Nucleonics*, 11/8, 38 (1953).

(85) ROSEN, L. International Conference on the Peaceful Uses of Atomic Energy, Vol. IV, Paper P/582, p. 97 (1955).

GOLDSCHMIDT-CLERMONT, Y. *Annual Reviews of Nuclear Science*, 3, 141 (1953).

VOYVODIC, L. *Prog. Cosmic Ray Physics*, 2, 219 (1954) Interscience Publishers Inc.

WHITE, R. S. *Fast Neutron Physics*, p. 297. Ed. J. B. Marion and J. L. Fowler. Interscience Publishers Inc. (1960).

(a) Slow neutrons

(86) CUER, P., MORAND, M., KING, T. and LOCQUENEUX, R. *Comptes Rendus*, 228, 6, 557 (1949).

(87) KAPLAN, N. and YAGODA, H. *Rev. Sci. Inst.* 23, 155 (1952).

(88) TITTERTON, E. W. and HALL, M. E. *Brit. J. Rad.* 23, 465 (1950).

(89) BAKER, A. R. *J. Sci. Inst.* 31, 187 (1954).

BLAU, M., RUDERMAN, I. W. and CZECHOWSKY, J. *Rev. Sci. Inst.* 21, 232 (1950).

(d,n) studies

(90) GIBSON, W. M. and THOMAS, E. E. *Proc. Roy. Soc.* A-210, 543 (1952).

(91) JOHNSON, V. R. *Phys. Rev.* 86, 302 (1952).

(92) EVANS, W. H., GREEN, T. S. and MIDDLETON, R. *Proc. Phys. Soc.* A-66, 108 (1953).

(93) GIBSON, W. M. *Phil. Mag.* 44, 297 (1953).

(b) Fast neutrons: internal radiators

14 MeV inelastic scattering

(94) STELSON, P. H. and GOODMAN, C. *Phys. Rev.* 82, 69 (1951).

(95) WHITMORE, B. G. and DENNIS, G. E. *Phys. Rev.* 84, 296 (1951).

(96) WHITMORE, B. G. *Phys. Rev.* 92, 654 (1953).

(97) GRAVES, E. R. and ROSEN, L. *Phys. Rev.* 89, 343 (1953).

2 to 5 MeV inelastic scattering

(98) JENNINGS, B., WEDDELL, J., ALEXEFF, I. and HELLENS, R. L. *Phys. Rev.* 98, 582 (1955).

(99) STELSON, P. H. and PRESTON, W. M. *Phys. Rev.* **86**, 132 (1952).

(100) SNOWDON, S. C., ROTHMAN, M. A., KENT, D. W. and WHITEHEAD, W. D. *Rev. Sci. Inst.* **24**, 876 (1953).

Fast neutrons: spectrum studies using internal radiators or Li loaded emulsions

(101) NERESON, N. and REINES, F. LA 1192 (1950) (decl. 1957).

(102) KEEPIN, G. R. and ROBERTS, J. H. *Rev. Sci. Inst.* **21**, 163 (1950).

BATTY, C. J. *Nucl. Inst.* **1**, 138 (1957) (loading with water).

NERESON, N., and REINES, F. *Rev. Sci. Inst.* **21**, 534 (1950).

ROBERTS, J. H., SOLANO, W. O., WOOD, D. E. and BILLINGTON, H. R. *Rev. Sci. Inst.* **24**, 920 (1953).

ROBERTS, J. H. *Rev. Sci. Inst.* **28**, 677 (1957).

ROBERTS, J. H. *Fast Neutron Flux Measurement* (unpublished) (1958). Northwestern University, Evanston, Illinois.

ROBERTS, J. H. and KINNEY, F. E. *Rev. Sci. Inst.* **28**, 610 (1957).

(c) External radiators

(103) ALLRED, J. C., ARMSTRONG, A. H. and ROSEN, L. *Phys. Rev.* **91**, 90 (1953).

(104) ALLAN, D. L. *Proc. Phys. Soc.* **A-68**, 925 (1955). *Ibid. Proc. Phys. Soc.* **A-70**, 195 (1957).

AHN, S. H. and ROBERTS, J. H. *Phys. Rev.* **108**, 110 (1957).

ALLRED, J. C., ROSEN, L., PHILLIPS, A. N. and TALLMADGE, F. K. *Rev. Sci. Inst.* **21**, 225 (1950).

3.4.2. Neutron radiography

(105) THEWLIS, J. *Brit. J. App. Phys.* **7**, 345 (1956).

3.5 Other methods

(a) Cloud chambers

(106) BONNER, T. W., FERRELL, R. A. and RINEHART, M. C. *Phys. Rev.* **87**, 1032 (1952).

(107) A.N.L. TID-7506—Part 1, July 1956.

(108) CONNOR, J. P. *Phys. Rev.* **89**, 712 (1953).

(109) ROSE, B., TAYLOR, A. E. and WOOD, E. *Nature*, 181, 1630 (1958).
RANDLE, T. C., SKYRME, D. M., SNOWDEN, M., TAYLOR, A. E., URIDGE, R. and WOOD, E. *Proc. Phys. Soc.* A-69, 760 (1956).

Bubble chambers
General.
DODD, C. *Prog. Nucl. Phys.* 5, 142 (1956).
FRETTER, W. B. *Ann. Rev. Nucl. Sc.* 5, 145 (1955).
GLASER, D. A. *Encyclopaedia of Physics*, Vol. 45, p. 314. Berlin: Springer (1958).
Range 5 to 30 MeV.
ADELSON, H. E., BOSTICK, H. A., MOYER, B. J. and WADDELL, C. N. *Rev. Sci. Inst.* 31, 1 (1960).

(b) Neutron thermopiles

(110) JAQUES, T. A. A.E.R.E. Report EL/M. 45 (1950, decl. 1956) and 46 (1950 decl. 1957). See also ref. 3.12.
(111) LEONARD, R. R. U.S. Report AECD 3325 (1951, decl. 1952).
(112) WEAVER, C. V., SMITH, C. K. and CHASTAIN, J. W. *Elec. Eng.* 76, 8, 665 (1957). Also *Trans. A.I.E.E. Comm. & Elec.* 76, 573 (1957).
(113) GRAY, T. S., GRIM, W. M., REPLOGIE, F. S. and SPENCER, R. H. *Elec. Eng.* 76, 8, 678 (1957). Also *Trans. A.I.E.E. Comm. & Elec.* 76, 368 (1957).
(114) LAPSLEY, A. C. Argonne National Laboratory Report 4869 (1952).
LAPSLEY, A. C. *Nucleonics* 16/2, 106 (February 1958).

(c) Miscellaneous

Gas evolution
(115) HART, E. J. and GORDON, S. *Nucleonics*, 12/4, 40 (April 1954)
(116) HARTECK, P. and DONDES, S. *Nucleonics*, 14/3, 66 (March 1956).
Spark counters, boron lined
(117) SAVEL, P. *Comptes Rendus*, 234, 2596 (1952).
(118) SWETNICK, M. J. and ANTON, N. G. *Nucleonics*, 15/6, 93 (June 1957).

16*

(119) LAISK, E. *Nucleonics*, **16**/7, 95 (July 1958).
      SAHA, N. K. and WATH, N. *Nucleonics* **15**/69, 4 (1957).
Semiconductor variation
(120) CASSEN, B., CROUCH, T. and GASS, H. *Nucleonics*, **13**/3, 58 (March 1955).
Palladium film dosimeter (resistance change)
(121) CHILDERS, H. M. *Rev. Sci. Inst.* **29**, 1008 (1958).

4. APPLICATIONS OF NEUTRON DETECTION

4.1. Measurement of relative intensity

(1) GRAVES, E. R. and DAVIS, R. W. *Phys. Rev.* **97**, 1205 (1955).
(2) See under 4.3(c).
(3) BARSCHALL, H. H. and WALT, M. M. *Phys. Rev.* **93**, 1062 (1954).
(4) WILLARD, H. B., BAIR, J. K. and KINGTON, J. D. *Phys. Rev.* **98**, 669 (1955).
(5) ALLEN, R. C. quoted by R. F. TASCHEK, Paper P/573, Geneva Conference on the Peaceful Uses of Atomic Energy (1955), Vol. IV, p. 62. See also *Phys. Rev.* **95**, 637 (A) (1954).
(6) HUGHES, D. J. *Pile Neutron Research*, p. 123, Addison-Wesley Publishing Co., Cambridge, Mass., U.S.A. (1953).
(7) LANGSDORF, A. S., HIBDON, C. T. and HOLLAND, R. E. *Phys. Rev.* **85**, 595 (1952).
    HIBDON, C. T. *Phys. Rev.* **108**, 414 (1957).
    GIBBONS, J. H. *Phys. Rev.* **102**, 1574 (1956).

Shielding
(8) BETHE, H. A. Los Alamos Report LA 1428 (1952).
(9) PRICE, B. T., HORTON, C. C. and SPINNEY, K. T. *Radiation Shielding*, Pergamon Press, London (1957).
(10) ROSEN, L. Paper P/582, Geneva Conference on the Peaceful Uses of Atomic Energy (1955), Vol. IV, p. 97.
     LANGSDORF, A. S. *Fast Neutron Physics*, Eds. J. B. Marion and J. L. Fowler, Interscience Publishers, New York (1960).

The inverse problem of shielding, viz, the estimate of the probability of capture of a neutron from a central neutron source in a large liquid scintillator has been calculated by Monte Carlo methods by DIVEN, B. C., MARTIN, H. C., TASCHEK, R. F. and TERRELL, J. *Phys. Rev.* **101**, 1012 (1956).

4.2. Fast neutron flux

General

(11) BARSCHALL, H. H., ROSEN, L., TASCHEK, R. F. and WILLIAMS, J. H. *Rev. Mod. Phys.* **24**, 1 (1952).

ALLEN, K. W., LIVESEY, D. L. and WILKINSON, D. H. *Proc. Camb. Phil. Soc.* **46**, 339 (1950).

BARSCHALL, H. H. and BETHE, H. A. *Rev. Sci. Inst.* **18**, 147 (1947).

BARSCHALL, H. H. *Rev. Mod. Phys.* **24**, 120 (1952).

PERRY, J. E. in *Fast Neutron Physics.* Ed. J. B. MARION and J. L. FOWLER, Interscience Publishers, New York (1960).

(a) *Associated particle techniques*

(12) FRANZEN, W., HUBER, P. and SCHELLENBERG, L. *Helv. Phys. Act.* **28**, 328 (1955).

SEAGRAVE, J. D. Los Alamos Report LA 2162, unpublished (1957).

OKHUYSEN, P. L., BENNETT, E. W., ASHE, J. B. and MILLETT, W. E. *Rev. Sci. Inst.* **29**, 982 (1958).

BENVENISTE, J., MITCHELL, A. C., SCHRADER, C. D. and ZENGER, J. H. U.C.R.L. 5619 (1959).

See also ref. 4.55.

(b) *Hydrogen-filled proportional counter*

(13) ALLEN, W. D. and FERGUSON, A. T. G. *Proc. Phys. Soc.* **A-70**, 639 (1957).

See also ref. 3.33.

(c) *Thin film radiator*

(14) DIVEN, B. C. *Phys. Rev.* **105**, 1350 (1957).

See also ref. 0.2.

(d) *Thick film radiator*

(15) KINSEY, B. B., COHEN, S. G. and DAINTY, J. *Proc. Camb. Phil. Soc.* **44**, 96 (1948).

(16) GOSSICK, B. R. *Rev. Sci. Inst.* **26**, 754 (1955).

(17) COCHRAN, R. G. and HENRY, K. M. *Rev. Sci. Inst.* **26**, 757 (1955).

(18) JOHNSON, C. H. and TRAILL, C. C. *Rev. Sci. Inst.* **27**, 468 (1956).

(19) BAME, S. J., HADDAD, E., PERRY, J. E. and SMITH, R. K. *Rev. Sci. Inst.* **28**, 997 (1957). A simplified counter is described by the same authors in *Rev. Sci. Inst.* **29**, 652 (1958).

(*e*) *Long counter*
(20) HANSON, A. O. and McKIBBEN, J. L.   *Phys. Rev.* **72**, 673 (1947).
(21) PERRY, J. E.   Private communication (1958).
(22) ALLEN, W. D.   A.E.R.E. Report NP/R. 1667.   Also ref. 4.13.
ALLEN, W. D.   "Flat Response Detectors", *Fast Neutron Physics*, Ed: J. B. Marion and J. L. Fowler, Interscience Publishers (1960).
McTAGGART, M. H., A.W.R.E. Report NR/A1/59, Aldermaston (1959).

(*f*) *Homogeneous ion chamber*
(23) BRETSCHER, E. and FRENCH, A. P.   British declassified report BR-386 (1944).
(24) LARSSON, K. E.   *Ark. f. Fys.* **9**, 293 (1955).
GRAY, L. H.   *Proc. Camb. Phil. Soc.* **40**, 72 (1944).
For flux measurement with an organic scintillator, see also ref. 3.55.

4.3. Neutron Spectrometry

CRANBERG, L., DAY, R. B., ROSEN, L., TASCHER, R. F. and WALT, M.   "Techniques for Measuring Elastic and Non-elastic Cross Sections," *Prog. Nucl. En.* Series I, Vol. 1, p. 107, Pergamon Press, London (1956).

(*a*) *Direct methods using proton recoils*
(25) ELIOT, E. A., HICKS, D. BEGHIAN, L. E. and HALBAN, H.   *Phys. Rev.* **94**, 144 (1954).
(26) SEGEL, R. E., SWARTZ, C. D. and OWEN, G. E.   *Rev. Sci. Inst.* **25**, 140 (1954).
(27) STELSON, P. H. and PRESTON, W. M.   *Phys. Rev.* **86**, 132 (1952).
(28) PERLOW, G. J.   *Rev. Sci. Inst.* **27**, 460 (1956).
(29) GILES, R.   *Rev. Sci. Inst.* **24**, 986 (1953).
ALLEN, R. C.   See ref. 4.5.
BENENSON, R. E. and SHURMAN, M. B.   *Rev. Sci. Inst.* **29**, 1 (1958).

(*b*) *He³ spectrometer*
(2) BATCHELOR, R.   *Proc. Phys. Soc.* **A-69**, 214 (1956).
(30) BATCHELOR, R., AVES, R. and SKYRME, T. H. R.   *Rev. Sci. Inst.* **26**, 1037 (1955).

(*c*) *Other telescope techniques*
(31) NERESON, N. and DARDEN, S.   *Phys. Rev.* **89**, 775 (1953).
(32) HOLT, J. R. and LITHERLAND, A. E.   *Rev. Sci. Inst.* **25**, 298 (1954).

(33) RIBE, F. L. and SEAGRAVE, J. D.   *Phys. Rev.* **94**, 934 (1954).

(34) MOZLEY, R. F. and SHOEMAKER, F. C.   *Rev. Sci. Inst.* **23**, 569 (1952).

(35) CALVERT, J. M., JAFFE, A. A. and MASLIN, E. E.   *Proc. Phys. Soc.* **A-68**, 1008 (1955).

(36) CHAGNON, P. R., OWEN, G. E. and MADANSKY, L. *Rev. Sci. Inst.* **26**, 1165 (1955).

(37) DRAPER, J. E.   *Rev. Sci. Inst.* **25**, 558 (1954).

(38) BEGHIAN, L. E., ALLEN, R. A., CALVERT, J. M. and HALBAN, H.   *Phys. Rev.* **86**, 1044 (1952).

(39) PATRO, A. P.   *Ind. J. Phys.* **30**, 99 (1956).
     RIBE, F. L.   *Phys. Rev.* **106**, 767 (1957).
     WORTH, D. C.   *Phys. Rev.* **78**, 378 (1950).
     Also relevant to these references are the references of section 4.2(*d*)

(40) KINSEY, B. B., *Can. Jour. Phys.*, to be published.

(41) FERGUSON, A. T. G. and PAUL, E. B., *Nucl. Phys.* **12**, 426 (1959).

4.4. Time-of-flight spectrometry

See ref. 0.5.

(*a*) *Thermal neutron range*

EGELSTAFF, P. A.   *J. Nucl. En.* **1**, 57 (1954).
The slow neutron field was covered by several papers given at the Geneva Conference on the Peaceful Uses of Atomic Energy (1955) Vol. IV:
HAVENS, W. W. (P/574); EGELSTAFF, P. A. (P/767); WIBLIN, E. R. (P/421);   HUGHES, D. J. (P/576).

(*b*) *Range 1eV to 10 keV*

NICHOLSON, K. P. and HALL, J. W.   A.E.R.E. N/M. 76 (1956).
BOLLINGER, L. M., THOMAS, G. E., and PALMER, R. R. *Phys. Rev.* **91**, 452 (abstract) (1953).
PALEVSKY, H., SJOSTRAND, N. G. and HUGHES, D. J. *Phys. Rev.* **91**, 451 (abstract) (1953).
EGELSTAFF, P. A.   *Nucl. Inst.* **1**, 197 (1957) (glass scintillators).

(*c*) *Range 1 to 100 MeV: millimicrosecond time-of-flight*

(42) NIELSON, G. C. and JAMES, D. B.   *Rev. Sci. Inst.* **26**, 1018 (1955).
     See also GREEN, R. E. and BELL, R. E.   *Nucl. Inst.* **3**, 127 (1958).

(43) O'NEILL, G. K.   *Phys. Rev.* **95**, 1235 (1954).

(44) MALMFORS, K. G., KJELLMANN, J. and NILSSON, A. *Nucl. Inst.* **1**, 186 (1957).

(45) BLOOM, S. D., GLASOE, G. N., MUEHLHAUSE, C. O. and WEGNER, H. E.   *Phys. Rev.* **103**, 720 (1956).

(46) CRANBERG, L. and LEVIN, J. S.   *Phys. Rev.* **103**, 343 (1956).

(47) WEBER, W., JOHNSTONE, C. W. and CRANBERG, L.   *Rev. Sci. Inst.* **27**, 166 (1956).

(48) CRANBERG, L., BEAUCHAMP, R. K. and LEVIN, J. S.   *Rev. Sci. Inst.* **28**, 89 (1957).

CHASE, R. L. and HIGINBOTHAM, W. A.   *Rev. Sci. Inst.* **28**, 448 (1957).

CRANBERG, L. and LEVIN, J. S.   *Phys. Rev.* **100**, 434 (1955).

DRAPER, J. E.   *Rev. Sci. Inst.* **29**, 137 (1958).

GARG, J. B.   *Nucl. Inst.* **6**, 72 (1959).

GRISMORE, R. and PARKINSON, W. C.   *Rev. Sci. Inst.* **28**, 245 (1957).

LEPRI, F., MEZZETTI, L. and STOPPINI, G.   *Rev. Sci. Inst.* **26**, 936 (1955).

O'NEILL, G. K.   *Rev. Sci. Inst.* **26**, 285 (1955) (chronotron principle).

High energy (30 to 120 MeV) neutrons

(49) SCANLON, J. P., STAFFORD, G. H., THRESHER, J. J. and BOWEN, P. H.   *Rev. Sci. Inst.* **28**, 749 (1957).

4.5. Slow neutron flux measurement

4.5.1. General

(50) MARTIN, D. H.   *Nucleonics*, **13**/3, 52 (March 1955).

(51) ROBERTS, L. D., HILL, J. E. and McCAMMON, G.   *Phys. Rev.* **80**, 6 (1950).

Nuclear Reactor Experiments.   Ed. J. B. Hoag.   Van Nostrand, New York (1958).

4.5.2. Relative measurements

BEVAN, G., MUMMERY, P. W., SALMON, A. J. and THOMPSON, M. W.   A.E.R.E. Report R/R. 2602 (decl. 1958).

Reactor Physics Constants.   Argonne National Laboratory report ANL 5800 Chap. 8 (1958).

4.5.3. Absolute measurements

(52) DUNWORTH, J. V.   *Rev. Sci. Inst.* **11**, 167 (1940).

(53) RAFFLE, J. F.   A.E.R.E. Report R2998 (1959).

(54) TUNNICLIFFE, P. R.   Chalk River Report CRGP-458 (n.d.).

(55) LARSSON, K. E. *Ark. f. Fys.* **7**/25, 323 (1953).
(56) deJUREN, J. and ROSENWASSER, H. *J. Res. N.B.S.* **52**, 93 (1954). Research Paper 2477.
(57) GRIMELAND, B. J.E.N.E.R. Pub-12 (1956).
COHEN, R. *Ann. de Phys.* **7**, 185 (1952).
GREENFIELD, M. A., KOONTZ, R. L., JARRETT, A. A. and TAYLOR, J. C. *Nucleonics*, **15**/3, 57 (March 1957).

4.5.4. Flux distortion and flux depression

(59) TITTLE, C. W. *Nucleonics*, **8**/6, 5 (June 1951).
(60) *Ibid.* *Nucleonics*, **9**/1, 60 (Jan. 1951).
(61) *Ibid.* *Phys. Rev.* **80**, 756 (abstract) (1950).
(62) KLEMA, E. D. and RITCHIE, R. H. *Phys. Rev.* **87**, 167 (abstract) (1952).
(64) THOMPSON, M. E. A.E.R.E. RP/R. 1549 (1954).
Ibid. *J. Nuc. En.* **2**, 286 (1955).
GALLACHER, T. L. *Nuc. Sci. Eng.* **3**, 110 (1958).
See also ref. 67 below.

Theories

(58) BOTHE, W. *Z. Phys.* **120**, 437 (1943).
(63) SKYRME, T. H. R. Can. declassified report MS. 91 (n.d.).
(65) CORINALDESI, E. *Nuov. Cim.* **3**, 131 (1946).
(66) VIGON, M. A. and WIRTZ, K. *Zeit. Naturf.* **9a**, 286 (1954).
(67) MEISTER, H. *Zeit. Naturf.* **10a**, 669 (1955).
(68) *Ibid.* *Zeit. Naturf.* **11a**, 347 (1956).
GRAVES, G. A. LA 1964 (1955).

4.5. Neutron detectors in health monitoring

General

MOYER, B. J. *Nucleonics*, **10**/4, 14 (April 1952).
Nucleonics, **10**/5, 14 (May 1952).
HURST, G. S. *Fast Neutron Physics*, Section IVG, Ed. J. L. Fowler and J. B. Marion. Interscience Publishers, New York (1960).
LEA, D. E. *Action of Radiation on Living Cells*, Cambridge University Press (1955).
HANDLOSER, J. S. *Health Physics Instrumentation*, Pergamon Press, London (1959).

Proportional counters and associated electronics

(69) HURST, G. S. *Brit. J. Rad.* **27**/318, 353 (1954).
(71) GLASS, F. M. and HURST, G. S. *Rev. Sci. Inst.* **23**, 67 (1952).

HURST, G. S.   Oak Ridge Report O.R.N.L. 589.
HURST, G. S. and WAGNER, E. B.   *Rev. Sci. Inst.* **29**, 153 (1958).
HURST, G. S. and RITCHIE, R. H.   *Radiology,* **60**, 864 (1953).
KARP, I. L.   *Rev. Sci. Inst.* **28**, 902 (1957).
O'BRIEN, K. and McLAUGHLIN, J. E.   *Nucleonics,* **15**/1, 64 (Jan. 1957).
PERKINS, J. F.   *Rev. Sci. Inst.* **26**, 88 (1955).
ROSSI, H. H., HURST, G. S., MILLS, W. A. and HUNGERFORD, H. E. Jr.   *Nucleonics,* **13**/4, 46 (April 1955).
SLATER, M., BUNYARD, G. B. and RANDOLPH, M. L.   *Rev. Sci. Inst.* **29**, 601 (1958).
See also GRAY, L. H. ref. under 4.2(f).

Scintillation counters
(74) HANDLOSER, J. S. and HIGINBOTHAM, W. A.   *Rev. Sci. Inst.* **25**, 98 (1954).
(75) THOMPSON, B. W.   *Nucleonics,* **12**/5, 43 (May 1954).
(76) SKJOLDEBRAND, R.   *J. Nuc. En.* **1**, 299 (1955).

Other counters
(73) DE PANGHER, J. and ROESCH, W. C.   *Phys. Rev.* **100**, 1793 (1955).
    Ref. 2.29 also describes measurement by threshold detectors.   See also refs. 3.120 and 3.121.

Films
(72) CHEKA, S.   *Nucleonics,* **12**/6, 40 (June 1954).

Tissue dose calculations
(70) SNYDER, W. S.   *Nucleonics,* **6**/2, 46 (Feb. 1950).
    SNYDER, W. S.   *Wash-95* (1952).   Quoted by Cheka ref. 72 (above).
    SNYDER, W. S. and NEUFELD, J.   *Brit. J. Rad.* **28**, 342 (1955).
    Ibid.   Brit. J. Rad., Supplement 6 (1955).
    Ibid.   O.R.N.L. 1872 (1955).
    TAIT, J. H.   *Brit. J. Rad.* **23**, 282 (1950).

5. NEUTRON STANDARDS

5.1. Radioactive neutron sources

General
(1) McCALLUM, K. J.   *Nucleonics,* **5**/1, 11 (Jan. 1949).
    ANDERSON, H. L. and FELD, B. T.   *Rev. Sci. Inst.* **18**, 186 (1947).

HANSON, A. O. in *Fast Neutron Physics*, Ed. J. B. Marion and J. L. Fowler, Interscience Publishers, New York (1960).

Photoneutron sources

WATTENBERG, A. *Phys. Rev.* **71**, 497 (1947).

Fission and fission sources

CRANE, W. W. T., HIGGINS, G. H. and BOWMAN, W. R. *Phys. Rev.* **101**, 1804 (1956).
See also ref. 5.7.

Spectrum measurement
Ra-Be(α,n)

EGGLER, C. and HUGHES, D. H. U.S.A.E.C. Report ANL 4476 (1950, decl. 1957).

Fission

CRANBERG, L., FRYE, G., NERESON, N., and ROSEN, L. *Phys. Rev.* **103**, 662 (1956).
HILL, D. C. *Phys. Rev.* **87**, 1034 (1952).
WATT, B. E. *Phys. Rev.* **87**, 1037 (1952).

α-Be sources: calculation

HESS, W. N. *Ann. Phys.* **6**, 115 (1959).

Ra-α-Be

HILL, D. C. AECD 1545 (1947).
SCHMIDT-ROHR, U. *Zeit. Naturf.* **8a**, 470 (1953).

Po-α-Be

ADER, M. *Comptes Rendus* **239**, 1290 (1954).
CURTIS, C. D. Report ORO 158 (1956).
ELLIOTT, J. O., McGARRY, W. I. and FAUST, W. R. *Phys. Rev.* **93**, 1348 (1954).

Actinide-α sources

RUNNALLS, O. J. C. and BOUCHER, R. R. *Can. J. Phys.* **34**, 949 (1955).
STEWART, L. *Phys. Rev.* **98**, 740 (1955).

Rd-Th-D$_2$O

(2) MARIN, P. *Nucl. Inst.* **5**, 1 (1959).

5.2. Source calibration

(6) LITTLER, D. J. A.E.R.E. Report NP/R. 1577 (1954).
(7) RICHMOND, R. *Prog. Nucl. Energy*, Ser. 1, Vol. II, p. 165, Pergamon Press, London (1958).
HUGHES, D. J. *Nucleonics*, **12**/12, 26 (Dec. 1954).
WATTENBERG, A. *Standardization of Neutron Measurements*, Annual Reviews of Nuclear Science, Vol. 3, p. 119 (1953).

5.2.1. Relative calibration

(4) MACKLIN, R. L.   *Nucl. Inst.* **1**, 335 (1957).
(5) DOROFEEV, G. A. and DOBRYNIN, Y. P.   *J. Nucl. En.*
     5, 217 (1957).
     LUDEMANN, C. A., LEVESQUE, R. J. A. and MARION,
     J. B.   *Bull. Am. Phys. Soc.* II, **5**, 16 (1960).
     See also refs. 5.6 and 5.7.

5.2.2. Source calibration, absolute

(3) RICHMOND, R. and GARDNER, B. J.   A.E.R.E. Report
     R/R. 2097 (1957).
(8) LARSSON, K. E.   *Ark. f. Fys.* **7**, 25, 323 (1953).
(9) TAVERNIER, G. C. and de TROYER, A.   *Bull. de
     l'Acad. Royale de Belgique* **40**, 150 (1954).
(10) GAILLOUD, M.   *Ann. de Phys.* (13me Serie) **1**, 808
      (1956).
(11) EROZOLIMSKY, B. G. and SPIVAK, P. E.   *J. Nucl. En.*
      6, 243 (1958).
(12) LARSSON, K. E.   *J. Nucl. En.* **6**, 322 (1958).
      BEZOTOSNII, V. M. and ZAMYATNIN, Y. S.   *J. Nucl. En.*
      6, 237 (1958).
      LILLIE, A. B.   *Phys. Rev.* **87**, 716 (1952).
A method of source calibration using a reactor has been
described by:
      LITTLER, D. J.   *Proc. Phys. Soc.* **A-64**, 638 (1951).
      See also refs. 4.55 and 4.56.

5.3. Fundamental cross sections

5.3.1. Neutron-proton cross sections

(13) SQUIRES, G. L.   *Prog. Nucl. Phys.* Vol. 2, p. 89, ed.
      O.R. Frisch, Pergamon Press, London (1952).
      GAMMEL, J. L.   Quoted by B. C. DIVEN in International
      Conference on Peaceful Uses of Atomic Energy,
      Vol. IV, Paper P/594, p. 251 (1955).
      See also *Fast Neutron Physics*, Ed. J. B. MARION
      and J. L. FOWLER.   Interscience Publishers, New
      York (1960).

(n,p) capture cross section
(14) MEADS, R. E., ENGLAND, C. J., COLLIE, C. H. and
      WEEKS, G. C.   *Proc. Phys. Soc.* **A-69**, 469 (1956).

von DARDEL, G. and SJÖSTRAND, N. G. *Phys. Rev.* **96**, 1245 (1954).
HAMERMESH, B., RINGO, G. R. and WEXLER, S. *Phys. Rev.* **90**, 603 (1953).
HARRIS, S. P., MUELHAUSE, C. O., ROSE, D., SCHROEDER, H. P., THOMAS, G. E. and WEXLER, S. *Phys. Rev.* **91**, 125 (1953).

5.3.2. Other thermal cross sections

(15) HARVEY, J. A. International Conference on Peaceful Uses of Atomic Energy, Vol. IV, Paper P/382, p. 147 (1955).
(16) EGELSTAFF, P. A. *J. Nucl. En.* **5**, 41 (1957).
CARTER, R. S., PALEVSKY, H., MYERS, V. W. and HUGHES, D. J. *Phys. Rev.* **92**, 716 (1953).
GREEN, A., LITTLER, D. J., LOCKETT, E. E., SMALL, V. G., SPURWAY, A. H. and BOWELL, E. *J. Nucl. En.* **1**, 144 (1954).
MEADS, R. E., COLLIE, C. H. and LOCKETT, E. E. *Proc. Phys. Soc.* **A-69**, 464 (1956).
The results available up to July, 1958 have been surveyed by HUGHES, D. J., Geneva Conference on the Peaceful Uses of Atomic Energy 1958, Paper P/2483, which, with other papers from the same Conference, has been reprinted in *Progress in Nuclear Energy*, Series I, Vol. 3, Pergamon Press, London (1958).

INDEX

Absolute determination of thermal flux, 151
— — by determination of radioactive intensity in Au, 151, 152
— — — absolute yield of $B^{10}(n,\alpha)Li^7$, 153, 154
— — of fast neutron flux, 113 ff
— source calibration, 175 ff
fast neutron methods, 180–2
thermal methods, 176–80
Absorption, neutron, 7
Accelerators, as continuous neutron sources, 12–13, 114
—, as pulsed neutron sources, 94–5, 138, 141, 145, 187
Activators, in inorganic scintillators, 78
—, in LiI (LiI(Sn), LiI(Eu)), 93
Agitation energy of electrons in gases, 43
Alpha-activated neutron sources, 167–9
Alpha build-up in fission counters, 31
Alpha particles, interaction with matter, 8
Am-Be source, 168
Amplification process, in proportional counters, 64
Antimony-beryllium source, 16, 169
Associated particle method, fast neutron flux measurement, 114
Attenuation of neutrons in detection shields, 111
Available neutron fluxes from various reactors, 14

$B^{10}(n,\alpha)Li^7$, cross section, 26, 187–8
—, lifetime, 24
—, reaction, 4, 24
Ball-type scintillator, 85
Barn, definition of, 212
BBO, 87
Beta counting, shielded back-to-back, 150
BF_3 ionisation chamber, 54, 55

BF$_3$ proportional counter, 16, 66
construction of, 68
differential bias curves, 69
integral bias curves, 70
life of, 70
soaking of, 67
temperature effects in, 67
time delay in, 71
Binding energy, 5
Bioplastic, 93
Birks, explanation of response to organic scintillators, 80
Boron deposition:
by evaporation, 61
diborane, cracking, 61
electron bombardment, 61
Boron-lined ionisation chambers, 55
Breakdown in chambers, precautions against, 47
Bubble chamber, 55

Cadmium absorption:
as detector shield, 110
cross section, 34, 203
in early experiments, 3
in resonance energy range, 146
Cadmium ratios, 146
Calomel, 111
Capture cross section of thermal neutrons by hydrogen, 187
Carbon total cross section, 194
Cavities, as used in source measurements, 177
—, as used in thermal flux measurements, 158
Ceresin wax, 48
Cleaning counters, technical details, 48–9
Cloud chambers, 8, 103
Cobalt, decay scheme, 215
—, thermal absorption, 34, 215
Cockcroft Walton generators, 12
Coincidence techniques:
absolute $\beta\gamma$ counting, 151

Coincidence techniques—*continued*
  in fast neutron spectrometry, 128, 131, 133, 134
  in liquid scintillators, 86–7
Collimation, 110
Compton scattering of electrons, 11
Concrete, attenuation of neutrons in, 111
Counters, boron-lined, 55
Counting of beta rays by Geigers, 148
Cross section:
  $B^{10}(n,\alpha)$, 26, 185, 187
  cadmium (slow), 34, 203
  carbon, total, fast, 194
  definition, 217
  fissile nuclides, fast, 29, 30, 202
  fissile nuclides, thermal, 29, 201
  fundamental, measurement of, 185 ff
  gold, (thermal), 34, 189, 204
  $He^3(n,p)$, 27, 200
  indium, slow, 34, 204
  iodine, 35
  manganese, 33, 35
  (n,p) fast, 22, 185, 193
  (n,p) thermal capture, 179, 187
  oxygen $(n,\alpha)C^{13}$, 174
  oxygen, total, fast, 194
  of various $(n,2n)$ reactions, 39
  of various $(n,p,$ and $n,\alpha)$ reactions, 39
  phosphorus, (n,p) fast, 205
  relation of 2200 m/sec to thermal value, 218
  sodium, 33, 35
  sulphur (n,p, n,α) fast, 205
  U^{235}, thermal, 190
Cylindrical ion chamber, 53
Cylindrical fission chamber, 60

D-D reaction, 12, 13, 115
Decay, radioactive, correction for in foil measurements, 147
Decay schemes of isotopes used in neutron detection by radiative capture, 215, 216
Density, neutron, measurement of, 147
Deposition, boron, 61
—, fissile material, 61
—, hydrogenous material, 62

Detection by gamma ray emission, 33, 94
  in boron, 94
  in samarium, 95
Differential spectrum, definition, 219
Direct fast neutron spectrometry, using proton recoils, 126
Drift velocity of electrons in various gases, 207–10

Early experiments in neutron detection, 2
Effective threshold of nuclear reactions, 37
Efficiency of neutron detectors, 72
  definition, 221
Elastic scattering, 6, 17, 217
Electron velocity as function of X/p, 43
  in argon-CO_2, 208
  in BF_3, 210
  in hydrogen, 207
  in methane, 209
Electrons, capture by oxygen or water vapour, 44
—, fast, effect of passage through matter, 9–10
Elementary principles of neutron detection, 5 ff.
End and wall effects in proportional counters, 66, 116
Endoergic reactions, 36 ff
  definition of, 222
Energy bands of inorganic scintillators, 77
Epithermal neutrons, 14
Excitons, 77
Exoergic reactions, 26 ff
  definition of, 222
External radiators, with nuclear emulsions, 100

Fast chopper, 138
Fast neutron detectors, 83, 91
Fast neutron dosimetry, 161 ff
Fast neutron flux, measurements of, 113 ff
Fast neutron source calibration methods, 180

Fast neutron survey counter, 164

Fast neutron threshold spectrometer, 135

Fast neutrons, health hazards from, 161

— —, photographic plates for, 98

Field tubes, in proportional counters, 65, 115

Film, means of deposition, 62

Film radiator, 120

Fission, 29 ff
  spectrum of neutrons from, 214
  thresholds of fast neutrons in Th^{232}, etc., 30, 202

Fission chamber, 57 ff
  as monitor, 109
  Aves, 59
  Bright, 58
  cylindrical, 60
  parallel-plate, 60
  spiral, 58

Fission cross section of thermally fissile nuclides, 201

Fission fragments, interaction with matter, 10

— —, range, 10, 31

Fissile material, methods of deposition, 61–2

Fissile nuclides, nuclear properties of, 29–30

Flat-response detector, 123, 175

Flux, definition of, 222

Flux depression, 155

Flux distortion, 155

Flux perturbation, 155
  Bothe's experiments in, 156
  Meister's experiments in, 157

Foil irradiation, 157

Free ions in gases, behaviour of, 42

Fundamental neutron cross sections, 185

Gamma ray compensated ion chambers, 15, 46, 56

Gamma ray emission, detection by, 33, 94

Gamma rays, interaction with matter, 10

— —, use in neutron detection, 94

Gamma rays, means of minimising of sensitivity of organic scintillators, 83

Gas-filled proportional counter, 62 ff, 116

Gas-scintillators in fission counters, 96

Geiger counter, 64, 148

Geiger counter monitoring, 149

Geiger discharge, 63

Glycerol tristearate, 62, 118

Gold, as detector by radiative capture, 34

—, cross section in thermal beam, 189

—, cross section variation with (slow) neutron energy, 204

Gold foils, in absolute thermal flux measurement, 152

Graphite stacks, 151, 154, 171, 174, 175, 182

Gridded ion chamber, spectrum of pulses from, 52

Guard tubes in counters, 47, 68

Hanson and *McKibben*'s long counter, 123

Harwell electron linear accelerator, 138

He^3 spectrometer, 130

He^3(n,p)T, cross section, 27, 200

—, reaction, 27

Health monitoring, 159 ff

Helium-filled detector, 22

Helium production, rate of, for source calibration, 182

High voltage, leakages and breakdowns, 46

— —, precautions against, 47

Homogeneous ionisation chamber, 125, 161

Hornyak detector, 91, 109

Hydrocarbons, gaseous sources and storage of, 49

Hydrogen as counter gas, 49

Hydrogen-filled proportional counter, 115

Indium, as detector in radiative capture, 34

—, as vacuum seal in counters, 49

Indium, decay scheme, 216
—, variation of cross section with (slow) neutron energy, 204
—, use of foils, 151
Induction effect, 50
  methods of reducing, 51–4
Inelastic neutron spectra, study of 127–31, 143
Interaction of foils in anisotropic flux, 151
Interactions of neutrons with nuclei, elements of, 6 ff
Inorganic scintillators, in neutron detection, 76–8, 88 ff
  LiI, 93
  miscellaneous, 95
  ZnS, 88
Integral spectra, definition, 219
Integrated thermal neutron density, determinations of, 174, 178–9
Iodine, as slow neutron detector, 34
—, decay scheme, 216
Ionisation chamber, boron-lined, 55
  compensated, 46, 56
  cylindrical, 53, 54, 56, 59
  homogeneous, 125, 161
  parallel plate, 41, 56, 60
  schematic of, 42
Iron, use as fast neutron shield, 112
Isotopes, definition of, 6
— used for radioactive capture, 35

K.A.P.L. betatron spectrometer, 138
KI scintillator, 95
Kinematics, of (n,p) and allied reactions, 17

Langsdorf's counter, 109, 110
Large liquid scintillators, 85
Larsson's comparison of source strengths, 184
Leakage, schematic of, in ion chambers, 47
Li, loading in photographic plates, 98, 100
$Li^6(n,\alpha)T$ reaction, 28
LiI scintillation detectors for thermal neutrons, 93

Liquid drop model, 5
Long counter, 109, 123
Low geometry counter, 120
Luminescence, process, 76 ff
  of solid inorganic phosphors, 76
  of organic scintillators, 78
  reduction of, due to quenching, 80

Manganese as radioactive detector, 33
  in the Szilard-Chalmers process, 36
Measurement of fast neutron flux, 113 ff
Measurement of relative intensity, general, 107
Measurements by activation, 15, 145 ff
Mechanical choppers first use as spectrometer, 4
Mechanical fast chopper, 138
Mechanical slow chopper, 137
Millimicrosecond time-of-flight, 136, 139
Miscellaneous scintillation techniques, 95
$MnSO_4$ bath techniques of absolute source calibration, 177
Monitors, neutron, 109
Monoenergetic fast neutron sources, 12
Multiplication in proportional counters, 64
  uniformity, 65

(n,α) reactions, 38
(n,d), (n,He) scattering, 21–2
(n,n′) reaction, 37
(n,2n) reaction, 39, 206
(n,p) reactions, 17
$N^{14}(n,p)C^{14}$ reaction, 24
National Bureau of Standards thermal flux, 154
Negative ion formation, 45
"Negative source" technique of absolute source calibration, 179
Neutron absorption, 7
Neutron cross sections, fundamental, 185

Neutron cross sections, of nuclides in neutron detectors, Chapter 2 and pp. 193–4, 200–6
Neutron detectors:
in detection of slow neutrons:
in experiments using pulsed beams of neutrons, En ⩽ 10 keV:
BF₃ proportional counter, 66 ff
gamma rays from neutron capture, 94
LiI crystals, 93
liquid scintillators, 85
time of flight, general, 136 ff
ZnS.B₂O₃ button, 89
in reactors:
boron-lined ionisation chambers, 55
gamma-ray compensated, 46, 56
fission chambers, 59 ff
neutron thermopiles, 105 ff
radioactive indicators, 33, 34
threshold detectors, 36
in stacks of graphite or other moderators:
BF₃ proportional counters, 66 ff
flux measurements, relative, 147
— —, absolute, 151
radioactive detectors, 33, 34
in fast neutron experiments:
determination of non-elastic cross sections:
threshold detectors, 40
ball counters, 85
directional counters:
counter telescopes, 131–6
proportional counters, 62 ff 115–7, 130
shielded counters, 109
fast neutron spectrometry:
coincidence techniques, 128–130, 131–6
He³ spectrometer, 130–1
millimicrosecond time-of-flight, 139–145
organic scintillators, 83–4, 126–7
photographic plates, 98–101, 127–8

flux measurements:
associated particle method, 144–5
homogeneous ion chambers, 125–6
long counters, 123–5
proportional counters, 115–7
thick and thin film radiators, 118–23
high efficiency detectors:
large liquid scintillator, 85
organic scintillator, using gamma ray discrimination, 83
shielded detector, 110, 135, 142
monitors, or flat response detectors:
long counters, 123
graphite stacks, 174
ZnS-lucite buttons, 91
in miscellaneous experiments:
in high intensity bursts, 39
neutron radiography, 102–3
source strength measurements:
absolute, 175–83
flat response detectors, 175
MnSO₄ baths, 174
relative, 170–5
special problems using cloud chambers, 103–6
very weak fluxes:
Li- or B-loaded emulsions, 98
Szilard-Chalmers reaction, 35
Neutron, discovery of, 2
Neutron-induced reactions, 26 ff
Neutron monitors, 109
Neutron-proton cross sections, scattering, 21–3, 185, 193
— — —, capture, 187
Neutron-proton scattering, kinematics, 17
— —, angular distribution, 21
Neutron radiography, 102
Neutron sources, range 10 keV–20 MeV, 11
— —, radioactive, 166 ff
— —, slow neutrons, 13
— —, spectra, 212–14
Neutron spectrometry, fast, 126 ff

Neutron spectrometry, millimicro-
second time-of-flight, 139
— —, slow neutrons, 137
Neutron standards, 166–90
Neutron thermopiles, 105
Neutron width, variation with energy
and nuclide, 33
Noble gases, purification of, 49
Noise pulses in photomultipliers, 75
Non-directional survey monitors, 164
Non-elastic scattering, 40, 85
Nuclear emulsions, 96 ff
in fast neutron detection, 98–101,
128
in slow neutron detection, 98
loading with B and Li, 98

O-ring seals, 49
Organic scintillators, 78
advantages of, 79
in fast neutron detection, 83–88
in slow neutron detection, 82
large liquid, 85
means of discriminating against
gamma rays, 83–4
Outgassing of counters, 48
"Oxford source" method of source
strength determination, 187
Oxygen, total cross section, 194
—, $O^{16}(n,\alpha)C^{13}$ reaction, 174

Pair production, 11
Paraffin wax, use of in neutron
shields, 111
Parallel-plate fission chamber, 60
Parallel-plate gamma-ray com-
pensated chamber, 56
Parallel-plate ion chamber, 41
Particle detection, 8
Perturbation of neutron flux by foil,
155, 157
Phosphorus (n,p) threshold detection,
38, 39, 205
Photoelectric effect, 10
Photographic plates, 96; *see also*
Nuclear emulsions
Photomultiplier, 73
electrode systems of, 76
negative resistance characteristics,
75

noise pulses in, 75
system, efficiencies of, 74
Photoneutron sources, 168
Po-Be source, 168
spectrum, 213
Polystyrene insulators, 47, 95
POPOP, 87
Positive ion, 8, 42
Proportional counter, 62
advantages of, 64
BF_3, 66 ff
gas-filled, 116
hydrogen-filled, 115
practical considerations, 66
schematic of, 65
telescopes, 120
Protons, range of, in air, 195
—, range of, in hydrogen, 198
Protons and alpha particles interaction with matter, 8
Pu^{239}, relevant nuclear properties, 29
—, variation of fission cross section
with (slow) neutron energy, 201
Pu-Be source, 168
Pulse integrator, 163
Purification of counter gases, 49

Quartz insulators, 47
Quenching centres, in phosphors, 80
Quenching of Geiger discharge, 63

Ra-α-Be source, 4, 16, 124, 167
spectrum, 212
Radiation widths, variation with
neutron energy and nuclide
mass, 33
Radiative capture, 32
isotopes used for, in neutron detection, 35
decay schemes, 215, 216
Radiators, thin film, 118
—, thick film, 120
Radioactive decay, corrections in
activation measurements, 147
Radioactive intensity, absolute determination of, 151
Radioactive neutron sources, 16,
166 ff
Ra-γ-Be source, 169
spectrum, 213

Ramsauer effect, 43
Range, definition of, 10
Range in air, typical values of, 9
Range-energy relation, 23
    for alpha particles in air, 197
    for fast charged particles in nuclear emulsion, 211
    for protons in air, 197, in hydrogen, 198
    of fission fragments, 10, 31
Rd-Th-D_2O source, 169, 181
Reactions:
    $B^{10}(n,\alpha)Li^7$, 4, 24
    charged particles, 26
    endoergic, 36
    exoergic, 26
    $He^3(n,p)T$, 27
    $Li^6(n,\alpha)T$, 28
    (n,α), 38
    (n,n'), 37
    $(n,2n)$, 39
    (n,p), 17, 38, 39
    neutron-induced, 26
    used in neutron detection, 17–40
Reactors as neutron sources, 13
Reciprocity theorem, 110
Recombination, high count rate, 45
—, high pressure, 45
Recovery time, in Geiger counters, 63, 149
Reines and *Cowan*'s liquid scintillator, 85
Relative intensity, measurement of, 107
Relative long counter efficiency, 124
Relative source calibrations, 170
Resonance neutrons, 14
Richmond's comparison of source strengths, 183
Rubber seals, 49

Saturation, in ionisation chambers, 44
Sb-Be source, **16**, 169
Scattering, 6
Scattering (n,α), 21
Scattering, non-elastic, 40, 85
Scintillation counter, 72 ff
Scintillation detection, principles of, 73
Scintillation techniques, miscellaneous, 95

Scintillators, fast neutron, 83
—, inorganic, 88
—, large liquid, 85
—, LiI, 93
—, organic, 78
—, slow neutron, 82
—, ZnS, 88
—, $ZnS-B_2O_3$, 89
Seals, glass-to-metal, 47
—, indium, 49
—, O-ring, 49
Series capacitor, choice of, 48
Shielded proportional counter, 109
Shielding of detectors, 107, 110
Shrinkage, in nuclear emulsions, 97
Slow chopper, 137
Slow neutron detection, 15
Slow neutron flux measurements, 145
Slow neutrons, 13
—, health hazards from, 160
—, photographic plates for, 98
Slowing down of neutrons in water and graphite, 171, 173
Sodium capture cross section in absolute slow neutron flux measurement, 155
Solid inorganic phosphors, 76
Source calibration, 170 ff
Source strength measurements, inter-comparison of, 182
Sources, neutron, 11, 166
Spectrum of neutron sources:
    fission, 214
    from high intensity neutron burst, 39
    from reactors, 15
    Po-α-Be, 213
    Ra-α-Be, 212
    Ra-γ-Be, 214
Sphere transmission experiments, 108
Spontaneous fission sources, 169
    Pu^{240}, 183

Statistics, notes on, 223
— of multiplication on proportional counters, 64
— of pulses, from scintillator systems, 74
Stopping power, 24: of various metals, 199

Sulphur (n,p) (n,α) reaction, 38, 205
Szilard-Chalmers process, 35

T + D reaction, 12, 114
   method of absolute source cali-
      bration, 180
T(p,n) reaction, 13
Techniques in counter construction,
   47–9
Teflon insulators, 48
Telescopes, proportional counter, 121
—, general techniques, 131
Thallium as an activator, 93
Thermal column, 15
Thermal cross sections, 187
   boron, 187
   gold, 189
   U^{235}, 190
Thermal emission at cathode of
   photomultiplier, 75
Thermal methods of absolute source
   calibration, 176
   with boron or gold detectors, 178
Thermal neutron flux, relative meas-
   urement, 147
— — —, absolute measurement, 151
Thermal neutron sources from
   reactors, 14
Thermally fissile nuclides, properties
   of, 29, 201
Thermopiles, neutron, 105
—, various types of, 106
Thick film radiator, 121

Thin film radiator, 118
Threshold detectors, 30, 36, 39
Threshold, effective, 37
Time-of-flight spectrometry, 136
Tissue dose, 159
Total cross section:
— measurements of, 107
— of carbon and oxygen, 194
— of hydrogen, 193

U^{233}, relevant nuclear properties,
   29
—, variation of fission cross section
   with (slow) neutron energy, 201
U^{235}, fission cross section in thermal
   beam, 190
—, relevant nuclear properties, 29
—, variation of fission cross section
   with (slow) neutron energy, 201

Van de Graaff machines, 13

Wavelength shifters, 75, 87

ZnS scintillator, 88
   conversion efficiency, 74
   response time, 88
ZnS.B$_2$O$_3$ glass, 16, 89
ZnS-lucite (*Hornyak* detector), 91

Date